ALEXANDRU NICA

Theory and practice of lubrication systems

ALEXANDRU NICA

Doctor of Technical Sciences
Head of Hydrodynamic Lubrication Laboratory
Institute of Fluid Mechanics
Bucharest

THEORY AND PRACTICE
OF LUBRICATION SYSTEMS

PUBLISHING HOUSE OF THE
RUMANIAN ACADEMY
Bucharest, Str. Gutenberg 3 bis
Rumania

SCIENTIFIC PUBLICATIONS
(GREAT BRITAIN) LIMITED
Broseley, Shropshire,
England

Distributed exclusively in the U.S.A. by
SCHOLIUM INTERNATIONAL INC.
130-30 31st AVE.
FLUSHING, N. Y. 11354

This book is the English revised version of *Sisteme de lubrificație* published by
Editura Academiei Republicii Socialiste România, Bucharest, 1967

Translated and revised by

ALEXANDRU NICA

and

P. A. J. SCOTT

Doctor of Technical Sciences
Manager, Hydrostatic Bearings Section
Glacier Research and Development Organisation
Great Britain

Foreword

Lubrication is an indispensable item for any machine or mechanical device with moving parts, and is subject to the attention of all technologists, to a variable degree, from the design department to the shop floor.

The extent and diversity of its application makes lubrication one of the most complex problems in technology. For many years the lack of theoretical data and generalisation has been overcome by rule of thumb methods, sometimes at the price of costly machine failure. Moreover, the use of purely empirical data is a brake to the development of new types of machines, with the increased speeds and loads demanded by rapid technological progress. In spite of its importance, lubrication was for a long time considered a secondary aspect of machine design, and was only paid superficial attention.

The tremendous technical development achieved in recent years has brought with it significant changes in the field of lubrication (more correctly tribology, if we wish to include the many aspects of friction and wear) which is now an independent science, and to a large extent further technological progress depends on the results it yields.

Scientific and technical literature has been brought up to date in the past decade or so, with various works in this field, so that lubrication now has a real place among the sciences, and is capable of yielding new ideas and solutions, with valuable implications in physics, mechanics, chemistry, rheology, metallurgy, elasticity and so on.

The present work forms part of a series of Rumanian books devoted to various aspects of tribology, and it contains an overall view of some recent results regarding the design methods and supply systems in lubrication science. The author's long experience in this field is manifest in many chapters of the book, and the diversity of the various sources of information used is specially noted.

Particular emphasis is placed on the new problems met with in modern technology : lubrication at high temperatures, in high vaccum, in irradiated media, solid lubricants, new antifriction materials, electrostatic and magnetic bearings, etc. At the same time it should be mentioned that the approach afforded to the design of systems for fluid or semifluid lubricant supply includes both the detailed description of the physical mechanism of lubrication and the theoretical models which reproduce it, as well as practical design data which covers the majority of engineering applications.

This work thus derives its value not only from the information it includes, but also from the manner in which this information is presented to explain lubrication system design in depth.

It is to be hoped that the present book will stimulate the interest of those people involved in the solution of lubrication problems, be they from research laboratories and design offices, or from industry and workshops. The efforts of Scientific Publications (G.B.) Ltd and of Editura Academiei Republicii Socialiste România in producing the English version of this book must be recognised, and we hope that the interest of the readers will be their just award.

Prof. N. TIPEI

Corresponding Member of the Rumanian Academy,
Head of Lubrication Division
Institute of Fluid Mechanics,
Bucharest, RUMANIA.

Contents

Chapter IV

AUXILIARY COMPONENTS OF LUBRICATION SYSTEMS

Chapter V

INFLUENCE OF BEARING CHARACTERISTICS ON THEIR LUBRICANT SUPPLY SYSTEMS

Chapter VI

LUBRICANTS, MATERIALS AND PARTICULAR ANTIFRICTION METHODS

Chapter VII

SPECIAL LUBRICATION SYSTEMS

Nomenclature

A	— area of contact
A_r	— area of contact (real)
A	— area of piston face
A	— heat exchange area
$\mathcal{A}$	— coefficient in the expression of oil flow (axial bearings)
A_{11}, A_{12}	— coefficients in the oil flow formulae
$\overset{\circ}{A}$	— Ångström
B	— induced magnetic field
B_0	— external magnetic field
$C_{q_{i,e,s}} = \dfrac{Q_{i,e,s}}{V\,c\,b}$	— dimensionless flow coefficients
$\overline{C}_{q_{i,e,s}} = \dfrac{Q_{i,e,s}}{V\,h_2\,b}$	— dimensionless flow coefficients related to the minimum thickness
$C_{q_s}^{*} = \dfrac{e_{q_s}}{2k_b}$	— modified dimensionless flow coefficient excluding the influence of oil supply geometry
e_{q_s}	— dimensionless total side flow coefficient
D	— inner diameter of vane pump housing
E	— longitudinal modulus of elasticity
F	— friction force
F_a	— force necessary to overcome the interlocking of surface asperities
F_f	— force necessary to shear metallic junctions
F_p	— force required to drag or to deform the asperities of the softer metal
G	— transverse modulus of elasticity
H	— magnetic field
H	— material hardness
H	— rate of heat transfer
I	— total electric current
J	— electric current density
K	— constant
$K = \dfrac{2k}{\pi^n g}$	— parameter influencing the flow of fluids through pipes
L	— pipe length

M	— friction torque
$\mathbf{M} = \sqrt{\dfrac{Gh^2 B_0^2}{\mu}}$	— Hartmann number
N	— normal force
$\mathbf{N_u}$	— Nusselt number
$\mathbf{P_r}$	— Prandtl number
Q	— flow rate
Q	— heat
Q	— quantity of wear debris
Q_e	— flow rate at exit from load carrying zone $(h = h_2)$
Q_i	— flow rate at entry to load-carrying zone $(h = h_1)$
Q_0	— flow rate for zero Hartmann numbers
Q_s	— side flow
Q_v	— volume rate of flow for greases
$\mathbf{R}$	— Roentgen
$\mathbf{R_e}$	— Reynolds number
S	— Sommerfeld number
T_1	— oil temperature at entry to cooler
T_2	— oil temperature at exit from cooler
V	— peripheral bearing velocity.
V	— velocity of a moving surface
W	— load
a	— constant in the Powell-Eyring model of grease flow
a	— dimension of MHD bearings
$a_1, \overline{a}$	— coefficients in the expression of oil flow (journal bearings)
b	— bearing width
b	— constant in the Powell-Eyring model of grease flow
b	— dimension of MHD bearings
b	— width of the groove in the softer material
b_i	— width of the supply hole
c	— radial clearance
c	— ratio of the unsheared central plug of grease to the radius of the pipe
c	— specific heat
d	— bearing diameter
d	— pitch diameter
d_i	— supply hole diameter
e	— dimension of centrifugal filters
e	— eccentricity
f	— coefficient of friction
$f = \tau_r \cdot c$	— parameter influencing grease flow
g	— gravitational acceleration
h	— dimension of centrifugal filters

h	— oil film thickness
h	— tooth height (gear pumps)
$h_{1,2}$	— maximum and minimum film thickness
$h_{1,2}$	— head of lubricant
$h_m = \dfrac{1}{2}(h_1 + h_2)$	— mean film thickness (axial bearings)
$\bar{h}$	— total film thickness (roller bearings)
$i = \dfrac{h_1 - h_2}{L}$	— hydraulic slope
i	— number of pistons (piston pumps)
k	— heat transfer coefficient
$k = \dfrac{b_i}{b}$	— ratio of the oil hole and bearing widths
k_r	— coefficient of energy loss in pipes
l	— bearing length (developed)
l	— dimension of centrifugal filters
l	— groove length
l	— tooth width (gear pumps)
$l_{1,2}$	— dimensions of externally pressurized bearings
$l_{1,2}$	— molecular distances
m	— mobility (greases)
m	— pitch (gear pumps)
n	— exponent
n	— normal to the moving surface
n	— number of foreign particles in oils
n	— number of rings (ring-fed bearings)
n	— ratio of oil to coolant contact areas
n	— speed (rpm)
p	— perimeter (pipes)
p	— pressure
p_0	— atmospheric pressure
p_e	— external pressure
p_i	— supply pressure
$q = \dfrac{\ln \dfrac{\mu_1}{\mu_2}}{\ln \dfrac{1+\varepsilon}{1-\varepsilon}}$	— parameter yielding the law of viscosity variation with temperature
r	— radius (bearings, pipes, etc.)
r	— radius of curvature
r_1	— shaft radius
r_2	— journal radius
r_m	— centre distance between the shaft and the ball or roller (rolling bearings)
s	— sectional area (pipes)
t	— temperature

$t_{1,2}$	— cooling fluid temperatures
$t_{1,2}$	— maximum and minimum temperature in lubricant film
v	— velocity of fluid
v_c	— mean critical velocity
v_m	— mean velocity
v_1, v_2, v_3	— velocity components along directions x_1, x_2, x_3
x	— distance coordinate
x_1	— coordinate along the direction of relative motion of the solid surfaces
x_2	— coordinate along the normal to one of the solid surfaces
x_3	— coordinate normal to Ox_1x_2
z	— length (polar coordinates)
Δ	— thickness of the bearing wall
Δ_p	— pressure difference
Δ_t	— temperature difference
Θ	— angular extent of the bearing (partial journal bearings)
Θ	— angular extent of the film (rolling bearings)
Φ	— permeability (porous bearings)
Φ	— electric potential
Ω	— angular speed
α	— coefficient of thermal expansion
$\beta = \dfrac{\theta_2}{\Theta}$	— exit angle coefficient (partial journal bearings)
β_{1q}	— dimensionless parameter in oil flow formulae
γ	— specific weight
γ	— surface tension of the fluid
δ	— thickness of the metal wall
$\varepsilon = \dfrac{e}{c}$	— eccentricity ratio
ε	— ratio of the density of the heavy aqueous phase to that of the light oil phase
ε	— relative wear resistance
$\zeta = \dfrac{p\,\psi^2}{\mu_1\,\omega}$	— dimensionless load coefficient for slider bearings
σ	— electrical conductibility
σ	— unit normal stress
η	— constant in the Powell-Eyring model of grease flow
η	— volumetric efficiency of pumps
θ	— polar coordinate
θ_1	— angle corresponding to the beginning of the load-carrying film
θ_2	— angle corresponding to the end of the load-carrying film

$\varkappa$	— heat transfer coefficient
$\lambda = \dfrac{b}{2r_1}$	— slenderness ratio (journal bearing)
$\lambda = \dfrac{b}{l}$	— slenderness ratio (plane bearings)
λ	— thermal conductivity
μ	— coefficient of viscosity
μ	— micron
$\mu_{1,2}$	— coefficient of viscosity at $h = h_1$ and at $h = h_2$
μ_0	— magnetic permeability of free space
ν	— kinematic viscosity
ρ	— density
τ	— shear stress
τ_m	— shear strength of the metallic junctions
τ_r	— shear stress at wall of the pipe (greases)
$\varphi = \dfrac{\Phi \Delta}{c^3}$	— design variable (porous bearings)
φ	— fluidity (greases)
$\psi = \dfrac{c}{r_1}$	— clearance ratio
ω	— angular velocity

CHAPTER I

Friction and Wear

Friction phenomena occur wherever relative motion appears between two bodies. It is ever present in every daylife and research workers and engineers are constantly striving to reduce its effects. Only in the case of clutches, brakes and suchlike is it necessary to increase friction. In all cases of bearings, motive power drives, moving engine parts and sliding members it is important to minimize the effects of friction which cause considerable power loss and promote wear.

Modern science attempts to explain the phenomena of friction and wear, to explain its mechanism of action and to develop methods for reducing their effects in plant and machinery. In order to ensure a correct approach to satisfactory design and operation of lubricating systems, it is first necessary to understand the fundamental processes of friction and wear.

1.1. Dry Friction and Wear

Friction phenomena have long been a subject of scientific investigation and the problems are as old as man's technical activity. In spite of considerable research into fundamental detail, much of which is still valid, the fundamental mechanism of friction is still not clearly defined or fully understood.

De la Hire, more than two centuries ago recognised the existence of asperities on the surface of solid bodies, and attributed to them the appearance of friction, which accounted for their deformation and shearing, as contacting surfaces were in relative motion. In fact, the existence of the asperities, even to the cleavage plane of a single crystal, which constitutes the smoothest physical surface, has been experimentally proved. Indeed, in spite of extraordinary small dimensions (of the order of 1 to 2×10^{-8} cm) they were observed by the reflection of molecular beams off the cleavage planes of single crystals of lithium fluoride [1].

The first known experiments on friction were performed by Leonardo da Vinci, who concluded that friction force is proportional to load, and independent of contact area. Amontons rediscovered these laws (1699) stating at the same time that the value of the friction coefficient (that is to say the ratio of friction force to load) is generally about 0.3. This value is accepted even now for steel and other similar materials in standard dry conditions. Later on, Coulomb (1781) made a clear distinction between static friction and kinetic friction. Coulomb also advanced the hypothesis that friction is due to the interlocking of the surface asperities and that, generally speaking, friction represents the work necessary to lift the load over the summits of these asperities. Thus the rougher the surfaces, the higher the corresponding friction coefficient and vice-versa. Although this explanation might hold for rough surfaces (though not explaining the dissipation of energy) it is quite untenable for very smooth surfaces where very strong adherence as well as very high frictional resistance occurs in the absence of a lubricant.

Hence adhesion forces play an important part in the processes of friction. At small distances of separation the molecular forces produce a strong adhesion between clean surfaces (sometimes even welding occurs) and sliding is in consequence rendered more difficult. Although Coulomb considered the influence of molecular adhesion on friction between surfaces, he discarded this hypothesis when he discovered that friction is not dependent upon the surface area of the sliding bodies. Ewing (1892) suggested that friction depends on the interaction of the molecular forces, but the first theory of real interest using this principle was published by Tomlinson in 1929.

1.1.1. Mechanism of Dry Friction

Tomlinson developed his theory on the basis of the existence of intermolecular forces, and it is in good agreement with his own experimental data [2]. Fig. 1—1 represents schematically the basic reasoning of this theory: molecule M is in equilibrium with molecule I, when for the distance l_1 the attractive forces are in equilibrium with the repulsive forces of the two molecules under consideration. For instance equilibrium occurs for iron when $l_1 = 3.10^{-8}$ cm. If molecule II appears in the vicinity and approaches molecule M sufficiently closely to excite sizable attractive and repulsive forces, vibration and heating will occur due to the absorption of energy by molecule M. Tomlinson thus established a formula for the friction coefficient in terms of the elastic properties of the sliding bodies [2]

$$f = 1.07 \times 10^4 \, (\psi_I + \psi_{II})^{2/3} \tag{1—1}$$

where $\psi = \dfrac{3E + 4G}{G\,(3E + G)}$; E is the longitudinal modulus of elasticity and G the transverse modulus of elasticity of each material.

Beare and Bowden observed (1935) molecular perturbations associated with dry friction extending into the material to a distance of several thousands of molecular diameters, which led them to the conclusion that the structural properties of the materials must be taken into consideration. At the same time they advanced the hypothesis that the friction force between two metallic bodies without an intervening lubricant is due to the shearing of the junctions or welds, where high surface temperatures occur due to relative motion. But even when the relative velocity is not high, so that temperature rise is very small, cold welding between asperities can occur, due to local high pressures.

Bowden, Leben and Tabor reached the conclusion that dry friction is a discontinuous process, in which the intermittent welding and shearing of the asperities determine important variations in friction forces and temperature; later, it was found that the area of contact can also produce such fluctuations. With experimental devices of Bowden and Leben (1939) fluctuations of a very short duration were observed [3]. The friction recording device had a high natural frequency and the sytem of loading had an even higher natural frequency. The motion of the slider was photographically recorded and it was found that the motion was discontinuous due to the alternative stick-slip of the surfaces in contact. Measurements of the surface temperatures showed the same frequency as the stick-slip motion. The use of mineral oils did not change the discontinuous character of the motion, but when long-chain polar lubricants were used, the motion was continuous.

All these observations led to the conclusion that in the case of two different metallic surfaces sliding one upon another, junctions are formed and broken, the process occurring at a certain frequency. This hypothesis and the stick-slip phenomenon aroused contradictory opinions. Some research workers doubted the existence of welding between asperities, since they were unable to detect temperatures in excess of 45°C. This can be attributed to the low sliding speeds and it has already been pointed out that welds can appear even at low temperatures, due to the high local pressures. Moreover, the cold welding of non-ferrous metals is now a recognised industrial process [2].

Blok (1940) showed that the stick-slip phenomenon can be obviated not only by the use of suitable boundary lubricants, but also by controlling the rigidity of the driving mechanism, the damping and inertia of the moving parts and the sliding velocity [4]; the oiliness of the lubricant plays an important part too [5]. Bowden, Leben and Tabor also pointed out the importance of these factors, and it is to be noted that even when the moving parts are rigid, the surface irregularities may be capable of microscopic elastic deformations, of the order of 10^{-5} cm, as shown by Khaikin, Lissovsky and Solomonovitch (1940). They used quartz crystals to measure the minute displacements involved. In these cases the elasticity of the surface irregularities can be sufficient to produce a discontinuous motion [3].

Bowden and Leben, (1940) using a cathode-ray oscillograph, found very rapid and violent fluctuations in both surface temperature and friction in the sliding of rigidly held lubricated surfaces. The overall surface temperature measurements can give a general idea of the local values at the asperities, attenuating their maxima but responding, to an extent, to their variations, the local temperature variation being due to the damped oscillation of a given asperity.

Even if the theories based on the assumption of welding and the discontinuous character of friction are still controversial, these concepts are in better agreement with the bulk of available experimental evidence than previous theories [4].

Schnurmann and Warlow (1942) developed a friction theory based upon the influence of electrostatic forces, which can reach important values in the case of very thin lubricant films with good dielectric properties, in which case the static charges produced by the motion can accumulate, (Fig. 1—2).

It was estimated that about 30% of the total force of friction can be attributed to electrostatic effects, when violent stick-slip occurs [1]. As the electrostatic potential increases due to the relative displacement of two sliding bodies, so does the consequent electrostatic component of friction. When the potential becomes large enough, discharge occurs between the bodies, and the electrostatic frictional force is reduced to zero. Hence friction oscillates between these two levels giving rise to stick-slip motion if the system is elastic, as it must be in practice. Naturally, the leakage of electrostatic charge through the lubricant or the metallic joints tends to reduce the difference between these two limiting values of friction.

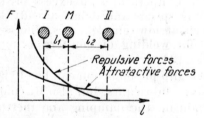

Fig. 1.1. — Equilibrium between molecules, [2].

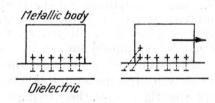

Fig. 1.2. — Increase in the electrostatic component of friction with motion, [1].

These observations, as well as more recent experimental research, have led to the general conclusion that friction is too complicated a phenomenon to be explained by means of a single mechanism.

Ernst and Merchant proposed (1940) consideration of the friction force as the resultant of the force necessary to shear the metallic junctions (as put forward by Beare and Bowden) and of the force necessary to lift the asperities of one surface over the asperities of the other, so that

$$F = F_f + F_a \qquad (1-2)$$

where F is the resultant friction force in the direction of motion, F_f the force necessary to shear the metallic junctions, and F_a that necessary to overcome the interlocking of the surface asperities (Fig. 1—3).

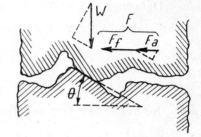

If it is supposed that the real surface of contact A_r is established by plastic deformation, then W, the normal load on the surfaces and σ_c, the yield pressure of the softer metal, give the value of A_r, thus

$$A_r = \frac{W}{\sigma_c}. \qquad (1-3)$$

Whence

$$F_f = A_r \tau \qquad (1-4)$$

Fig. 1.3. — Forces acting at a junction, [4].

where τ is the unit shear strength of the softer of the metals. Hence the coefficient of friction, defined as the ratio of the friction force parallel to the apparent area of contact to the force normal to it, can be written in the form

$$f = \frac{F_f}{W} + \frac{F_a}{W} = \frac{\tau}{\sigma_c} + \frac{F_a}{W}. \qquad (1-5)$$

For equilibrium (Fig. 1—3)

$$W \sin \theta = F_a \cos \theta \qquad (1-6)$$

so that

$$\mathrm{tg}\, \theta = \frac{F_a}{W}. \qquad (1-7)$$

where θ is the mean angle of the asperities to the direction of motion. Thus

$$f = \frac{\tau}{\sigma_c} + \mathrm{tg}\, \theta \qquad (1-8)$$

the second term on the right-hand side of the equation being important only in the case of very rough surfaces [4].

Bowden and Tabor [3] considered that, besides the force necessary to shear the asperities, the force F_p required to drag or to plow the aspe-

rities of the softer metal by the harder one must be included, and can
be written thus

$$F_p = A' \, p \qquad\qquad (1-9)$$

where A' is the area of the groove in the softer metal (Fig. 1—4), and
p is the mean pressure required to obtain this groove.

Denoting the width of the groove by b and the radius of curvature
of the slider by r, we have (Fig. 1—4a): $A' \cong \dfrac{1}{12} \cdot \dfrac{b^3}{r}$ so that [3]

$$F'_p = \frac{b^3}{12r} \, p \qquad\qquad (1-10)$$

and the resultant friction force will be

$$F = F_f + F_p = A_r \tau + A' p. \qquad\qquad (1-11)$$

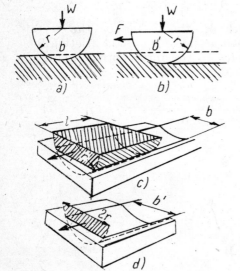

Fig. 1.4. — Deformation of a soft metallic
surface by a hard curved surface, [3]: a)
Stationary hemisphere. b) Moving hemisphere. c) Horizontal cylinder, normal to
direction of motion. d) Flat spade normal
to direction of motion.

For the above considered case
(Fig. 1—4c), the expression of F
will be

$$F = \tau \, l \, b + \frac{b^3}{12r} \, p \qquad (1-12)$$

since the projected area $l \cdot b$ may be
considered as that subjected to shear.
From the total friction force, one
can neglect shearing, by considering a cylinder of zero length (Fig.
1—4d), so that

$$F = F_p = \frac{b'^3}{12r} \, p. \qquad (1-13)$$

In the experimental work carried out to test the validity of these
formulae, the steel slider had successively the form of a hemisphere, a
cylinder and a spade. The lower plane
surface was of indium and the
sliding speed was low, so that the
temperature rise due to friction
should be negligible [3].

One of the first points of interest was that, in good agreement with
relation (1—13), the friction force due to the ploughing of the softer
material when using a spade slider (Fig. 1—4d) is proportional to the
cube of the track width (b^3). In spite of the uncertainties regarding the

physical meaning of the pressure p, the experimental results showed that the friction force F_p can be calculated with the help of geometrical data of the moving surfaces and of a factor p, which is of the same order of magnitude as the yield pressure of the softer material.

Kragelskii [6] gives considerable attention to deformation in the bulk of the material, and believes that it plays an important part in the energy balance of friction, based especially on the fact that in cutting processes one finds agglomerations of material in front of the cutting edge. However, he does not deny the importance of the adhesion phenomena, specifying that the joints between the solid surfaces and the film must be taken into consideration, but not between the solid surfaces themselves.

Fig. 1—5 represents the friction force F as a function of the width of the slider track in the softer material, for three geometric forms of slider [3]: cylinder, sphere and spade, all of steel and with the same radius of curvature. As expected, for the same width of the track, the lowest friction is produced by the spade, since the shearing of the metallic junctions is zero in this case. The sphere is placed between the spade and the cylinder, the latter yielding the maximum friction force, due to the maximum shearing. The difference between curves 1 and 3 gives precisely the shearing term F_f of the friction force, and relation 1—12 suggests that it must be proportional to b. From Fig. 1—6, where $F_f = F - F_p$ is represented, it is seen that this aspect is confirmed by the experimental data, and from the slope of the curve one obtains $\tau = 225 \ g/mm^2$.

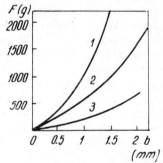

Fig. 1.5. — Friction force F as a function of the width of the slider track in the softer material, [3]: 1) Cylinder. 2) Sphere. 3) Spade.

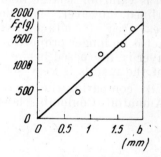

Fig. 1.6. — Shearing term F_f of the friction force, as a function of the track width, [3]

By taking into consideration both equations (1—8) and (1—11) the friction coefficient becomes [4]

$$f = \frac{\tau}{\sigma_c} + p' + \text{tg } \theta \qquad (1—14)$$

where $p' = \dfrac{F_p}{W}$ is the friction force due to the ploughing of the softer material, related to the normal load. This expression supposes either that the asperities of the slider will leave tracks in the softer material, or that they will be lifted above the asperities of the softer material, if this is only slightly less hard.

If one reconsiders now the Amontons-Coulomb laws regarding friction, their limits of validity can be established. Indeed, the relation yielding the real contact surface A_r, (1—3) shows that it does not depend upon the apparent contact area of sliding bodies. When ploughing plays a part of lesser importance, the whole friction force can be attributed to the shearing of the metallic junctions, resulting thus

$$F = A_r \tau \qquad (1{-}15)$$

that is to say that the friction force is independent of the apparent area of contact, in agreement with Amontons' first law.

If A_r is replaced by its expression in relation (1—15), one obtains

$$F = W \frac{\tau}{\sigma_c} \qquad (1{-}16)$$

which shows proportionality between the friction force and the normal load on the surfaces, that is to say the virtual independence of the friction coefficient with respect to the load. Thus we obtain the second law, which is valid for a large field of experimental conditions [3]. It must be underlined, however, that the validity of this law is conditional upon the real area of contact growing with the load. When the real area of contact is no longer proportional to the load (for instance when a metallic layer is interposed between the surfaces with relative motion, or when one of the metals is very soft) this law does not hold.

By comparing the expression of the coefficient of friction given by the Amontons-Coulomb's laws

$$f = \frac{F}{W} \qquad (1{-}17)$$

with relation (1—16) one finds

$$f = \frac{\tau}{\sigma_c} \qquad (1{-}18)$$

that is to say the coefficient of friction is equivalent to the ratio of the shearing strength of the metallic junctions and the yield pressure of the softer metal. Since the shearing takes place in the bulk of the softer metal, the value of τ corresponds to the softer metal.

Consequently, f depends only upon the physical properties of the softer metal, and since these cannot vary independently, it can be seen why f is constant, under widely varying experimental conditions, generally having values between 0.6 and 1.2, [3].

Stating that the "adhesion theory has led to notable advances in understanding of friction and wear" [7], Barwell has enumerated several specific points of criticism : 1) That the value of the coefficient of friction predicted for clean metals is too low, no explanation being provided for the variation of friction with velocity, and it is not always apparent how strong junctions can be formed in the presence of oxides or other contaminating films. 2) That the plastic deformation of the rubbing surfaces or of the material interposed between them, plays a very important part in the process of friction.

Fig. 1—7 shows a point of contact between two rubbing surfaces, or rather between two asperities on those surfaces. If this joint is considered continuous, as would be the case if the asperities were welded together, then to produce rupture along plane AB, the required forces must be in the directions given in the figure, i.e. at 45° to AB, this force configuration producing maximum shear stress on the plane AB. Hence by assuming that junctions between two surfaces are sheared along planes parallel to the direction of motion the angle of friction must be 45° and the coefficient of friction unity [7].

Barwell claims to achieve this value in many experiments between nominally clean metals of widely varying characteristics, and explains the lower values by the existence of contaminatory films. It is also mentioned that values higher than unity rarely occur and the explanation

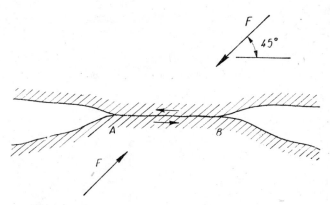

Fig. 1.7. — Shearing of a single asperity junction, [7].

advanced to cover these cases is that, due to anisotropy, glide planes are not available parallel to the direction of sliding, or that the geometry of the test specimen permits some excessive ploughing, or even a built-up leading edge.

By the same reasoning, Barwell explains the mode of action of sand when used to raise the coefficient of friction between wheels and rails : the individual grains penetrate the surfaces and may be expected to fracture along planes at 45° to the plane of principal stress, which is the resultant of the normal and tangential stresses applied to the system (Fig. 1—8).

Laboratory tests are claimed to produce a coefficient of friction of unity under the favourable conditions shown in Fig. 1—8.

Experiments with clean steel sliding on clean steel in high vacuum give the results shown in Fig. 1—9, [7].

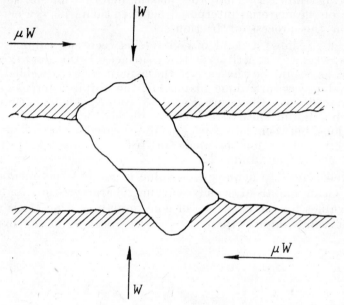

Fig. 1.8. — Hypothetical forces acting on a grain of sand, [7].

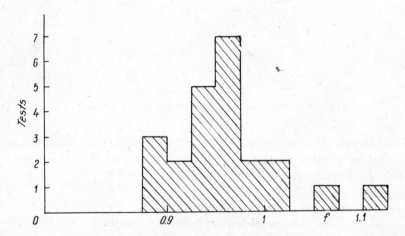

Fig. 1.9. — Friction of clean steel in vacuum, [7].

The admission of oxygen to the apparatus used in the experiments, led to a reduction of the coefficient of friction to 0.7, and this effect was found to be reversible. Low friction ($f = 0.07$) was obtained only when lubricants were used, oleic acid, oxygen and water being admitted simultaneously.

It is thus evident, from the above theories of dry friction, that the asperities of the surfaces play an important part in the process of sliding. On the one hand asperities raise the coefficient of friction due to the interference between them, and wear is thus increased, but on the other hand they have a favourable effect by lowering the molecular forces between the surfaces. Every pair of surfaces has then an optimum asperity size, for which the coefficient of friction is a minimum (Fig. 1—10); this optimum rugosity depends on the nature of the materials.

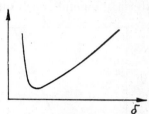

Fig. 1.10. — Variation of friction coefficient f with asperity height.

The foregoing examination of the mechanism of dry friction, assists towards an explanation of the wear process. Here again surface roughness is of prime importance, the asperities being broken off from the parent metal due to the causes outlined above, the effect being aggravated by the presence of the wear particles themselves, and the elevated temperatures consequent on the irreversibility of the process. Material can also be transferred from one surface to another, in all making wear a complex object of study.

1.1.2. Wear Measurements

Several detailed classifications of wear processes have been proposed recently. The main factors considered to have a strong influence are the following: adhesion, abrasive particles, corrosion, frictional heating, erosion, and surface fatigue.

The first quantitative relationship between wear, the properties of the materials, and the external conditions of sliding, was obtained by Tonn (1937) for abrasive wear, assuming a linear relationship between the wear resistance and the hardness H of the materials

$$\varepsilon = a H + b \qquad (1-19)$$

where $\varepsilon = \dfrac{R_2}{R_1}$ = the ratio of wear resistance of the material under investigation R_2, to that of the reference sample R_1. Khrushchov and Babichev confirmed this relationship and developed it further; for commercially pure and annealed metals, they found

$$\varepsilon = K \frac{H}{p} \qquad (1-20)$$

where p is the nominal pressure. In this case the straight line in Fig. 1—11 passes through the origin [6].

It must be pointed out that the relative wear resistance of the materials depends both on their hardness and on the nature of the inter-layer bonds, and is also influenced by the presence of inhomogeneities in the lattice structure as well as by distortions in the lattice.

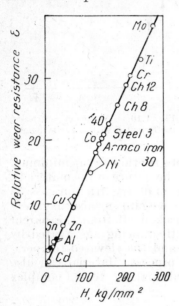

Fig. 1.11. — Relative wear resistance ε as a function of hardness H for some commercially pure metals, [6].

Bowden and Tabor consider the process of wear as the removal of welded asperities from one of the rubbing surfaces, with subsequent damage beneath the surface ; Kragelskii points out some of the drawbacks of this concept :

1) Because the harder surface can pick up a layer of the softer material, wear should be considered as between two similar metals and is therefore independent of the properties of the harder metal.

2) It is difficult to measure the amount of wear, that is to say the loss of material, or to explain how the wear particles are produced. It was shown that when adhesion exists between the surfaces, the wear process is a complex one, the softer metal being transferred to the harder metal, where it smears over the surface, and loose wear debris is produced by the destruction of this transferred layer of metal [6].

Bowden and Freitag made some wear experiments using diamond rubbing on various metals, and found that at high speeds the diamond picked up a protective film from the contacting metal, while at speeds below 200 m/s this did not occur, and the diamond suffered serious damage by heat and consequent carbonisation [3].

Holm is responsible for the relationship

$$Q = \frac{zW}{H} \qquad (1-21)$$

where Q is the quantity of wear debris produced per unit distance of sliding and z the number of atoms which are removed on encountering all the other atoms within a unit area per unit distance of sliding and it is to be noted that, (due to Archard)

$$Q = K \frac{W}{3\,\sigma_c} \qquad (1-22)$$

where σ_c is the yield pressure, and W the load, while the constant of proportionality K was found to vary between 10^{-2} and 10^{-7}.

In Great Britain and America, wear is often measured as the volume of material lost per unit distance of sliding. The equation is, according to Burwell, Strang, and Archard

$$\frac{V}{l} = K \frac{W}{p_m} \qquad\qquad (1-23)$$

where V is the volume of the material removed, l the sliding distance, K the coefficient of wear, W the load and p_m the yield stress of the material [8].

Table 1—1 gives the value obtained by Archard under dry conditions, where a cylinder of 6 mm diameter rubbed against a ring of 24 mm diameter, at a speed of 1.8 m/sec, under a load of 400 g.

Table 1—1

Coefficient of Wear [6]

Sliding against hardened tool steel, unless otherwise stated	Wear coefficient K	Hardness of the softer material $(\times 10^6 \text{ g/cm}^2)$
Mild steel on mild steel	7×10^{-3}	18.6
60/40 brass	6×10^{-4}	9.5
Teflon	2.5×10^{-5}	0.5
Perspex	7×10^{-6}	2.0
70/30 brass	1.7×10^{-4}	6.8
Bakelite (moulded)	7.5×10^{-6}	2.5
Silver steel	6×10^{-5}	32
Beryllium copper	3.7×10^{-5}	21
Hardened tool steel	1.3×10^{-4}	85
Stellite	5.5×10^{-5}	69
Ferritic stainless steel	1.7×10^{-5}	25
Laminated bakelite	1.5×10^{-6}	3.3
Tungsten carbide on mild steel	4×10^{-6}	18.6
Polyethylene	1.3×10^{-7}	0.17
Tungsten carbide on tungsten carbide	1×10^{-6}	130

Rabinowicz found that the magnitude of the wear coefficient K depends on the sharpness of the abrasive, i.e. whether the material is displaced plastically or by cutting. The values of K are, for a blunt file 0.1, for new emery paper 0.01, and for rounded abrasive particles 0.001, [9]. Table 1—2 gives the value of K for different conditions of sliding [6].

Table 1—2

Coefficient of Wear for Different Conditions of Sliding [6]

Conditions	Metal on metal		Non-metal on non-metal
	similar	different	
Dry surfaces	5×10^{-3}	1×10^{-4}	5×10^{-6}
Boundary lubrication	2×10^{-4}	1×10^{-4}	5×10^{-6}
Medium lubrication	1×10^{-5}	1×10^{-5}	5×10^{-6}
Excess lubrication	1×10^{-6}	1×10^{-5}	1×10^{-6}

Kragelskii [6] applies a different approach based on the real area of contact between sliding bodies, and consequently concentrates on the microgeometry of the surfaces. To this end he defines specific wear parameters dependent on the size of the actual contacts between the bodies and their total contact area

$$i_q = \frac{q_x}{A_r d} \ (\text{g/cm}^3)$$

and

$$i_n = \frac{V_x}{A_r d} \ (\text{dimensionless})$$

$$(1-24)$$

where i_q is the specific related wear to the mass of material q_x, worn from a single contact spot assumed to have an effective diameter d, and related to the overall geometry by the total area of actual contact A_r; i_n is similar, but based on the worn volume V_x, at an elementary point of contact.

These relations are qualitatively similar to the macroscopic wear parameter in equation (1—23) and become almost identical if the actual area of contact is assumed to consist only of plastically deformed asperities.

This method of examining the microscopic wear relies therefore on the knowledge of the roughness of the surfaces in the steady state.

The initial roughness of the harder material acts on the softer material in three ways: the hard asperities remove material by cutting and by repeated plastic deformation of the asperities of the softer surfaces, while there will always exist junctions where the elastic limit of the softer material is not exceeded, and no damage occurs.

However, the problem of putting useful values to the parameters in (1—24) is extremely complex although seemingly a valuable direction for research.

The value of A_r, the actual contact area, can be related empirically to the nominal contact area A, and the relative approach of the surfaces ε, but this relation is usually restricted to initial states of surface finish, [6]

$$\eta = \frac{A_r}{A} = b \, \varepsilon^\nu \qquad (1-25)$$

where b and ν are determined experimentally.

Furthermore the mean effective diameter of the contact spots offers an equally difficult challenge, in part resolved by Yoshimoto and Tsukizoe by statistical methods and giving as a result n, the number of predicted junctions [6].

By assuming that wear is only due to the repeated plastic deformation of the asperities of the softer surface, Kragelskii obtains the theoretical specific wear as

$$i_h = \frac{\varepsilon \, h_m}{(\nu + 1) \, n \, d} \qquad (1-26)$$

the new parameter h_m being the maximum asperity height.

By further assumptions as to the geometry of the asperities, $(1-26)$ can be reduced to

$$i_h = \frac{\tan \theta}{2 \, (\nu + 1) \, n} \qquad (1-27)$$

where θ is the base angle of a triangular asperity (Fig. 1—12).

This is taken to mean that the specific wear is independent of the material properties and this is, according to Kragelskii, supported by experimental evidence.

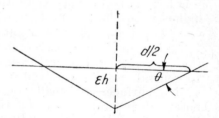

Fig. 1.12. — Model of a single asperity, [6].

1.1.3. Surface Temperature

When two solid bodies are in relative sliding motion, the energy loss will be almost totally absorbed by the rise in temperature of the lubricant, if any, and the surfaces themselves, the heat transfer from the surfaces being dispersed by radiation or conduction.

Even under conditions of light loads and low rubbing speeds, the surface temperatures can reach very high values.

The loss of energy due to friction, Q, can be written thus

$$Q = \frac{f g \, V \, W}{J} \, \text{Kcal/sec} \qquad (1-28)$$

f being the coefficient of friction, W the load in kg, and V the velocity in m/s.

Bowden and Tabor [3] carried out experiments with a constantan cylinder of radius $r = 0.5$ mm whose base slid on a mild steel plate at a velocity V of 200 cm/sec, measuring the coefficient of friction as 0.3. They assumed a value of 0.001 cal/cm² °C for $\varkappa$, the heat transfer coefficient at the constantan surface, and 0.05 cal/cm sec °C for its thermal conductivity λ.

It is possible to estimate the surface temperature T by means of the following equation

$$T - T_0 = \frac{\alpha f g \, V \, W}{\pi \, r \, J} \sqrt{\frac{1}{2 \, \varkappa \, \lambda}} \qquad (1-29)$$

where T_0 is the ambient temperature and α is a constant representing the proportion of heat transfer through the cylindrical slider, taking for the purpose of calculation in this case a value of 0.5. Under the above conditions, equation (1−29) yields a surface temperature $T - T_0$ of about 200°C.

Taking into account that the true contact surface is not equal to the apparent area as was supposed in the above calculation, but much smaller, it is evident that the rise in temperature is considerably higher than the estimated one.

These temperatures cannot be easily determined experimentally. Measuring devices embedded in the surfaces cannot be expected to record the true surface temperatures, since the temperature gradients are large. In general, results achieved by these means will be too small. When the sliding surfaces are made of two different metals, the thermo-electric potential generated between them offers a possibility of measuring the temperature. When the sliding solids are non-conducting materials, this method is no longer applicable and other solutions must be sought.

Bowden and Ridler [3] constructed an experimental device for measuring temperature using the thermo-electric method, and obtained confirmation of their theoretical estimates. They observed that for each metal, the temperature increased with speed and rose to a maximum value corresponding to the melting-point of the metal. Even under moderate conditions of load and speed, temperatures of 500−1000°C are easily reached at the metallic surfaces. An interesting point to be noted is that there are no obvious signs of this heating : the mass of the metal appears to be cool, thus it is evident that the intense heating is confined to a thin layer in the region of actual rubbing.

Experiments were also carried out with various lubricant films between polished surfaces and even under these conditions of boundary lubrication, the surface temperatures reached very high values. Fig. 1−13 represents these results for steel-constantan interfacial temperatures [3].

For non-conducting solids, temperature measurements were made by visual means [3]: one of the sliding surfaces was of glass, so that a number of tiny stars, corresponding to the hot spots at the interface

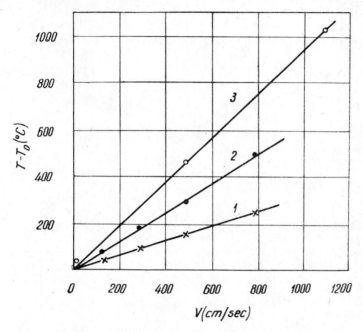

Fig. 1.13. — Temperature at the points of contact between a constantan pin and a steel disc, [3]: 1) Oleic acid. 2) Commercial lubricant. 3) No lubricant.

of the rubbing surfaces could be observed. Fig. 1—14 shows the frictional force at which visible hot spots occur, for certain speeds, as a function of the thermal conductivity of the metals in contact with the glass plate [3]. It is seen that the lower the thermal conductivity of the slider, the sooner hot spots appear.

It can be observed that equation (1—29) is based on an assumption which must be reconsidered if the estimate of the surface temperature is to be improved, since it is improbable, except in the case of a cylinder of very small diameter, that the real area of contact is an appreciable part of the cross-section of the slider. In most cases, the points at which rubbing occurs are distributed over the rubbing surface at relatively large intervals, and the temperature of the rubbing surface will not be uniform. The frictional heat is then dissipated into the bulk of the solids, and the thermal flow will depend mainly upon their bulk conductivities. In the case of two massive bodies touching over a small circular region of radius a, Bowden and Tabor established that [3]

$$T - T_0 = \frac{f\,g\,V\,W}{4\,a\,J} \cdot \frac{1}{\lambda_1 + \lambda_2} \qquad (1-30)$$

where λ_1 and λ_2 are the thermal conductivities of the bodies.

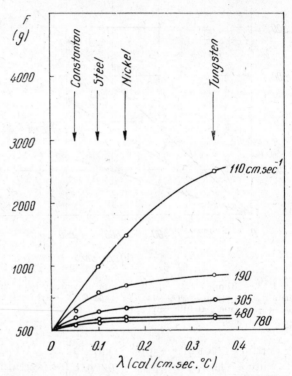

Fig. 1.14. — Frictional force F at which hot spots appear for various sliding speeds, using metallic pins sliding on a glass surface, [3].

For a square junction of side $2l$, and low sliding speeds, Jaeger found that [3]

$$T - T_0 = \frac{f\,g\,V\,W}{4 \cdot 24\,l\,J} \cdot \frac{1}{\lambda_1 + \lambda_2} \qquad (1-31)$$

a relation identical to (1—30), except for the numerical constant. This equation was obtained for low sliding speeds, and for high speeds it is necessary to allow for the cooling effect of fresh material being brought into contact with the asperity

$$\left.\begin{aligned} T - T_0 &= \frac{x_1^{1/2} f \, W \, g \, V}{3 \cdot 76 \, l \, J \, (125 \, \lambda_2 \, x_1^{1/2} + \lambda_1 \, \sqrt{l \, V})} \\ x_1 &= \frac{\lambda_1}{\rho_1 \, c_1} \end{aligned}\right\} \qquad (1-32)$$

where ρ_1 is the density and c_1 the specific heat of body I. Body I is the smooth surface (the disk) and body II the surface which carries the junction (the slider). It is seen, in this case, that the temperature increases less rapidly than the first power of V.

As pointed out, the experiments confirm that when solid bodies slide one upon another, extremely high surface temperatures may be developed, even for low speeds and loads. These high temperatures are confined to a very thin layer close to the rubbing interface of the bodies, and bulk heating can be very small. Furthermore, the hot spots are subject to very rapid fluctuations of temperature over a wide range of materials, loads and speeds; the life of the hot spot at the glass surface was found to be from 10^{-4} to 10^{-3} sec and its area to be of the order 10^{-3} cm, [3].

The surface temperature exceeds several hundred degrees Centigrade even in the presence of lubricating films, although there may be little bulk heating of the bodies and the surfaces may appear well lubricated; high temperatures occur through the lubricant film at the points of metal to metal contact. This fact is of a great importance, since local high temperatures can cause deterioration of the lubricant by volatilisation and chemical reaction.

Thus the intense local heating plays an important part in abrasion and seizure of metals.

1.1.4. Surface Damage and Thermal Effects

The high temperatures generated by friction may lead to severe surface damage. Depending on the shape of the rubbing bodies and the materials involved, various types of surface damage can occur: scoring of the surface of a cylinder by a piston, melting of antifriction materials, seizure and subsequent fracture of shafts, etc. In the case of gear teeth, scuffing may occur either directly as a result of heavy loads and low speed, or due to the high temperatures generated during sliding.

Ductile and brittle materials react differently to thermal stresses: ductile materials can support important loads for long periods without failure, while brittle materials can withstand loadings of short duration only. The speed of application of the thermal shock is then of great importance.

Repeated stressing of the surface during sliding leads to alternate contraction and expansion at the material surface, and the possibility of crack formation.

A parameter of considerable importance in the problem of crack formation in brittle materials is the ratio s of the resistance to crack formation σ_0 to the maximum thermal stress σ, [6]

$$s = \frac{\sigma_0}{\sigma}. \tag{1--33}$$

If $s > 1$ failure will not occur. Thermal fatigue must be distinguished from thermal stress arising from a single cycle. The number of cycles, n, and the resistance to thermal shock, s, are connected by the following relation [6]

$$n = e^{m(s-1)} \tag{1--34}$$

where $s > 1$ and m is an empirically determined constant.

It was found that an increase in the resistance of a material to thermal shock requires an increase in the quantity

$$\frac{\lambda \sigma_0}{\alpha E} \tag{1--35}$$

where α is the coefficient of thermal expansion and E the modulus of elasticity [6].

Several criteria have been proposed to evaluate the wear resistance of materials, by taking into account both their thermal and mechanical properties. The thermal stresses are usually higher than the mechanical ones, and this aspect must be taken into account when selecting materials.

In addition to cold welding due to high pressures between the materials, as specified in § 1.1.1., a phenomenon of important practical consequence is welding caused by frictional heating. Indeed, it is known from experimental work that in severe conditions of sliding, at high speeds and pressures, that is to say when large quantities of frictional heat are produced, one material may remain welded to the other after removing the load.

It is therefore important to check whether or not friction materials have any tendency to weld. In the case of brakes this is of major importance, since seizure can occur. During metal working operations welding between chip and cutting tool is quite a common experience.

It was found that frictional welding is due to the plastic deformation of the asperities, without melting of the metal; the impurities between the rubbing surfaces are destroyed during the welding process by the combined action of deformation and temperature. Welds produced in this way are without blisters, oxides, foreign inclusions or pores, and the joints possess high strength and ductility. Thus, a large field of practical applications is open, not only for welding similar metals but also for a large number of dissimilar combinations [6] : steel and brass, steel and copper, copper and brass, etc.

1.2. Boundary Lubrication

It is clear from the preceding sections, that under dry conditions wear between sliding bodies is heavy. In order to avoid this, it is normal practice at the present time to attempt to separate rubbing surfaces with a lubricant film, be it liquid, solid, or gaseous.

When this film has sufficient thickness, such that direct contact between the rubbing surfaces is avoided, its behaviour is considered to be governed solely by the laws of hydrodynamics. However there are many situations when purely hydrodynamic lubrication cannot be established, since the provision of a lubricant film of the necessary thickness is not always possible. In these cases the lubrication process is of a mixed character, the load being supported by both metal to metal contact and the hydrodynamic pressure generated between the surfaces. This type of lubrication has complex and distinct characteristics and may be classified as semifluid, boundary, semidry, or mixed lubrication. Nearly all research workers have differing opinions on these, for example mixed lubrication is defined sometimes as a combination of hydrodynamic and boundary lubrication [10].

Boundary lubrication is recognised now as occurring in many practical cases. Even journal bearings, when starting and stopping, operate in the regime of boundary lubrication. The rubbing surfaces of pistons and rings, crosshead-shoes, the guides of machine-tools, etc. usually work under conditions of boundary lubrication. This is also the case for gears, especially hypoid gears, wire dies and cutting tools. Finally, starved bearings (gravity fed, or fed by rings, wicks or felt-pads, etc.) due to the small amount of lubricant present between the surfaces, can occasionally work under these conditions. Boundary lubrication is also characteristic of running-in.

Thus we are obliged to study the mechanism of boundary lubrication and a large amount of work has been done in this field.

When trying to explain the mechanism of boundary lubrication it must be pointed out at the beginning that it is very difficult to obtain dry friction, *stricto senso*; severely controlled laboratory conditions are necessary, and the task is far from easy. What in practical cases is named "dry friction", is in reality a limiting form of boundary friction, since oxides, impurities, watery vapours, air, etc., are present between the rubbing surfaces and influence the friction process, even when no special lubricant is used.

In order to give an idea of the importance of these contaminating films, it is sufficient to note that the coefficient of friction for unlubricated metallic surfaces is close to 1.0, while that for surfaces lubricated with boundary films falls to 0.15 or even 0.05, depending upon the efficiency of the film involved.

1.2.1. Mechanism of Boundary Lubrication

The modern concept of boundary lubrication began with the works of Hardy (quoted in [3]) who showed that boundary lubrication depends not only upon the chemical nature of the lubricant, but also upon the nature of the rubbing surfaces. Indeed, the experimental work carried out with several fatty acids, paraffins and alcohols on various surfaces, showed the part played in boundary lubrication by the chemical nature of the surfaces. These observations caused Hardy to advance the hypothesis that friction phenomena in these conditions depend upon the surface fields of force, since the lubricant molecules are adsorbed and oriented at each of the solid surfaces to form unimolecular films which can support the load (see Fig. 1—15a). Since these polar groups adhere to the metal surfaces, sliding will take place between the layers of non-polar groups, and the efficiency of a boundary lubricant is measured by the extent to which these layers can counteract the molecular forces at the underlying surface. The dependence of the phenomenon upon the polarity of the lubricant molecule, and upon its chain length is thus obvious. Hardy concluded that for each class of lubricant there is a linear decrease in friction with increasing molecular weight.

This theory received confirmation from the X-ray experiments of Trillat, Bragg and Müller, who observed the existence of oriented films on the metal surface; similar results were obtained by investigating the structure of surface films by electron diffraction [3].

However, Hardy's theory is an over simplification: even with the best lubricants and with very light loads, traces of wear can be detected on the sliding surfaces, once motion begins. Electrographic analysis of the surfaces and radioactive tracer techniques enabled metallic contacts through the lubricant film to be observed; in the case of some metals, these effects were observed by electron microscope even for extremely small loads [3]. Moreover, it is hard to obtain effective lubrication with adsorbed monolayers of long-chain compounds: the liquid alcohols are highly polar and thus well adsorbed on the metal surface, but they provide poor boundary lubrication.

Finally, even with chain molecules, the friction does not fall below a certain finite value. Thus friction under conditions of boundary lubrication is not confined to a sliding motion between the monolayers of lubricant. The actual level of knowledge in this field does not afford the elaboration of a satisfactory quantitative theory of boundary lubrication, ready to be applied to practical cases. It is obvious that such a theory must take into consideration the metallic contacts and the adhesion through the lubricant film. It must be pointed out that in addition to the load bearing capacity of the metallic contacts and the adsorbed lubricant layers, the hydrodynamic pressures generated between the surface rugosities can also be of importance (Fig. 1—15b), [3].

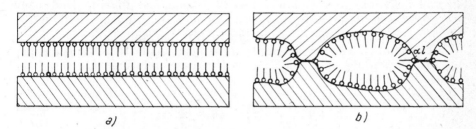

Fig. 1.15. — Sliding under conditions of boundary lubrication, [3]: a) Hardy's hypothesis of adsorbed monolayers of lubricant. b) Mechanism involving breakdown of the lubricant film on an area αA.

The area of metallic contact will increase with rise in surface temperatures, since plastic flow of the asperities will be more easily accomplished, so decreasing the area supporting the load by hydrodynamic effects or through adsorbed layers of lubricant. The resulting friction force F will consist of the force necessary to break the metallic junctions and to shear the lubricant layer separating the surfaces [3]

$$F = A \left[\alpha \, \tau_m + (1 - \alpha) \, \tau_l\right] \qquad (1—36)$$

where A is the area supporting the load, α a coefficient expressing the fraction of the area over which breakdown of the film has occurred, τ_m the shear strength of the metallic junctions and τ_l the frictional resistance between the sheared layers of lubricant.

When a good lubricant is used, the area occupied by the metallic junctions can be very small, but the shear strength of these junctions may be very high compared with that of the lubricant, so that some part of the resistance to motion appears to be due to them. The metallic contacts shown in Fig. 1—15b are also responsible for the wear and damage of the rubbing surfaces. Hence the main function of the lubricant is to reduce the amount of metallic contact between the surfaces with a layer which is not easily broken and is characterized by a very low shear strength, so that friction is kept to a minimum. If the lubricant has the necessary chemical properties, it can react with the rubbing surfaces and the resulting compounds often diminish friction, since they adhere to the surfaces and provide good separation. Moreover, boundary lubricants must have a strong lateral adhesion and a high melting point.

Because of their high lateral cohesion, their ability to resist sufficiently high temperatures and their resistance to appreciable deformation without rupture, metallic soap films are useful as extreme pressure

lubricants. Fatty acids are therefore valuable additives, since their metallic soaps, formed at the rubbing surfaces, fulfil the role of boundary
lubricants. It is also to be noted that the formation of viscous soap films
may lead to an efficient separation of the surfaces, even at speeds well
below those at which hydrodynamic effects can be established. These
conditions are no longer those of true boundary lubrication, but the friction and wear falls to very low values; this so-called quasi-hydrodynamic
effect has been described by Beeck, Givens and Smith (cited in [3]).

By considering the relation due to Bowden and Tabor (1—36) for
the friction force, various attempts have been made to establish experimentally the values of α and τ_l; in this case, relation (1 — 36) is put
in the form

$$f = \frac{1}{p} \left[\alpha \tau_m + (1 - \alpha) \tau_l \right] \qquad (1\text{—}37)$$

where p is the yield pressure of the material.

The method recently used by Tamai and Rightmire consisted in
measuring the friction with a pin-and-rotating-disk type machine, for
various degrees of purity of the surfaces [11].

From relation (1 — 37) put in the form

$$f = \alpha f_m + (1 - \alpha) f_l \qquad (1\text{—}38)$$

where $f_m = \dfrac{\tau_m}{p}$ and $f_l = \dfrac{\tau_l}{p}$, the values of α and f_l can be deduced from
the systems of equations built up with known values f and f_m.

Thus, for a 0.001 percent palmitic acid solution in cetane, the
values were

$$\left. \begin{array}{l} 0.53 = 2.5 \, \alpha + (1 - \alpha)\, f_l \text{ for fresh surfaces (without oxides)} \\[2mm] 0.25 = 1.0 \, \alpha + (1 - \alpha)\, f_l \text{ for aged surfaces} \\[2mm] 0.12 = 0.3 \, \alpha + (1 - \alpha)\, f_l \text{ for oxidized surfaces} \end{array} \right\} \qquad (1\text{—}39)$$

and from any pair of equations, $\alpha = 0.18$ and $f_l = 0.079$. Tamai and Rightmire therefore consider the accuracy of Eq. (1—37) proved in this case,
in spite of a great variation of friction values. In Fig. 1— 16 the results
obtained with various amounts of palmitic acid in cetane are given, and a
comparison is made with previous work (Rabinowicz and Tabor,
1951), [11].

By comparing the results obtained using a thin film of lubricant with
those obtained with large quantities of lubricant, the authors found that
in the latter case friction is always larger. This results in τ_l having higher
values in bulk-liquid lubrication. In order to explain this phenomenon, the
hypothesis of an edge effect was proposed. This edge effect results in higher

friction, since in bulk-lubrication the spaces around load-carrying areas are more likely to be filled with lubricant than in the case of thin-film lubrication. The large discrepancy in measurements of friction have not yet received a complete explanation, but some research workers think that the extension of the oxide layer is the cause of increased shearing force [11].

Considering Eq. (1 — 38) and stating that $f_m = 1$, Barwell finds : $f = \alpha + (1 - \alpha)f_i$, so that [6]

$$f = \alpha(1 - f_i) + f_i \quad , \quad (1-40)$$

and further on, based on experimental data furnished by Rabinowicz

$$\frac{\text{Wear lubricated}}{\text{Wear dry}} = \left[\alpha + (1 - \alpha)\frac{W_e}{W_m} \right]$$

$$(1-41)$$

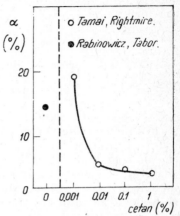

Fig. 1.16. — Values of coefficient α for cetane solutions, [11].

where W_e is the energy of adhesion of fully lubricated areas and W_m the energy of adhesion of metallic junctions. However, the values of f and α are still a matter of speculation, but it sheds some light on the influence of lubrication upon wear.

Vinogradov and his co-workers think that in conditions of boundary lubrication not only the adsorption properties of the lubricants at the metal-lubricant interface are to be considered, but also the chemical processes at the surfaces [12].

The consensus of scientific opinion nowadays is that the efficiency of boundary lubricants depends on their ability to produce solid or semi-solid coatings on the rubbing surfaces.

In conclusion, it must be pointed out that modern design techniques exploiting the new insight into the mechanism of elastohydrodynamic lubrication (Dowson, Cameron etc. [13]) can in many cases provide a more fortuitous solution to certain design problems.

A field in which lubrication presents a particular interest is that of gearing; quite important hydrodynamic effects, even under these conditions, have been demonstrated by Cameron [13], and great importance was assigned to chemical reactions.

In the case of gearing the method of failure is generally by scuffing. In certain cases an amount of scuffing may be tolerated (low speeds and light loads) but this is the exception. The criteria for the onset of scuffing have been posed in the form [5]

$$C = C(f, \alpha, V_1, V_2, l) = f^a \cdot \sigma^b \cdot V_{sc}^c \cdot V_t^d \cdot l^e = \text{const.} \qquad (1-42)$$

where a, b, c, d, e, are dimensionless constants, f is the coefficient of friction, σ the stress, V_1, V_2, the speeds of rolling, $V_{sc} = V_1 - V_2$, $V_t = V_1 + V_2$, $(V_1 > V_2)$ and l is the linear dimension. The characteristic parameter of scuffing, C, (according to Almen-Straubb) when considering the dimensions of the independent variables involved, will be in the form

$$C = [MT^{-3}L] \qquad\qquad (1-43)$$

so that, considering again $(1-42)$

$$[MT^{-3}L] = [O]^a \, [ML^{-1}T^{-2}]^b \, [LT^{-1}]^c \, [LT^{-1}]^d \, [L]^e . \qquad (1-44)$$

When the unknowns are eliminated and the independent variables with similar indices grouped, dimensionless complexes can be isolated, but to introduce this type of dimension analysis is meaningless unless the independent variables reflecting the properties of the lubricant, the conditions of heat transfer, the properties of the materials and so on are included. Table $1-3$ contains some of the more verified scuffing criteria, as well as the values of the dimensionless constants a, b, c, d, and e, [6].

It can be seen from Table $1-3$ that the empirical scuffing criteria have no general validity and are relevant only to particular designs and types.

1.2.2. Applications

Knowledge of the mechanism and peculiarities of boundary lubrication can be applied in many practical situations to keep friction to a minimum, when bulk-lubrication is not possible. Thus, extreme-pressure (temperature) lubrication relies on the use of chlorine, sulphur and phosphorous based additives. The compounds of these active chemicals with metal surfaces, i.e. chlorides, sulphides and phosphides have a relatively low shear strength, so that rubbing between the contacting surfaces occurs in the film, and the surfaces are protected; the compounds have also a high resistance to pressure and temperature. However, these compounds are solids, and hence their performance as lubricants is subjected to a different mechanism and is discussed later.

The chemical action of some agents upon the metallic asperities at the high temperature produced by friction, leads to so-called "running-in", so that the necessary corrections of the micro-and-macro-geometry of the surfaces are obtained in a much shorter time and with a better surface finish. Thus, some phosphorous based additives (lecitine or tricresyl phosphate) when mixed with oils, level the asperities in the areas of metallic contact by chemical action and produce a very good surface finish in a remarkably short time [14]. It has also been found that phosphorous based additives permit heavier loads than sulphur ones, and even seized surfaces can be made operational again.

Table 1—3

Formulae for Scuffing Criteria [6]

Author	Basic premises for deducing scuffing criteria	a	b	c	d	e	Initial relationship	Formula for calculating scuffing criteria	Limiting values of calculated criteria	Types of gears to which criteria are applicable
Almen		0	1	1	0	0	σV_{sc}	$\sigma V_{sc} > C_0$	$C_0 = 32,000$ kgm/cm² sec	Special conical gears in rear axles of cars
Almen-Straub	Empirical formula	0	1	1	0	1	$\sigma V_{sc}\, l$	$\sigma V_{sc} \leqslant C_{0m}$	$C_{0m} = 81,000$ kgm/cm² . sec. mm	Cylindrical aircraft spur gears
Kist'yan		0	1	0	0	0	σ_p	$\sigma_p \leqslant \sigma_{sc\,uf}$	—	Cylindrical spur gears
Blok	Scuffing occurs when oil film temperature reaches a critical value	1	$\frac{3}{2}$	1	$\varphi(V_1, V_2)$	$\frac{1}{2}$	$\dfrac{f\sigma^{3/2}V_{sc}^{1/2}}{V_t\, d}$ (for steel surfaces)	$T_0 + \dfrac{1.85\, f P^{3/4}\,(\sqrt{V_1} - \sqrt{V_2})}{\rho^{1/4}}$	Depends on oil and material of contacting surface	All types involving line contact and lubricated with mineral oil

In some cases of metal-working, for instance in the case of wire-drawing, spectacular reductions in friction, with a corresponding increase in efficiency of the process, can be obtained by creating small deposits of lubricant on the metal surfaces, by phosphating or shell-blasting.

The lubricant must possess good boundary adhesion, since only in these conditions it is possible to force it between tool and wire.; usually mineral oils with 5% of oleic acid or sodium stearate are used.

An important field of research is the determination of the dependence of the sliding friction behaviour of the surfaces upon their structure, in order to make possible a correct selection of antifriction materials. To this end some aluminum based alloys (96% Al — 3.5% Sb and 91% Al — 5.6% Sn) have been studied, and it was found that the first alloy, characterized by hard inclusions of AlSb in a semi-hard matrix of aluminum solid solution presented a very good resistance to wear, with the exception of cases of lubrication with contaminated oils. The second alloy, with a semi-hard matrix of aluminum and soft inclusions of tin, exhibited low wear when the lubricant was contaminated, since the hard particles in the lubricant showed the tendency to embed themselves in the softer material [15].

1.3. Transition from Boundary to Hydrodynamic Lubrication

As pointed out in §1.2, between boundary to full hydrodynamic lubrication a series of transient regimes can appear. Thus, Dobry believes that a so-called "mixed regime" occurs between the boundary and the full hydrodynamic regimes, displaying some of the characteristics of both [10]. Considering Lenning's experiments and assuming that the surface asperities generate pressure by hydrodynamic action, (see Fig. 1—17) Dobry obtains the following relation for the transition from boundary to mixed lubrication

$$v_{bm} = K_1 \frac{p_e \delta}{\mu} (1 - \alpha p^{1/4}) \qquad (1-45)$$

where v_{bm} is the velocity at which the transition occurs, K and α are constants of proportionality, p_e the external pressure, p the unit load, σ the surface roughness, and μ the viscosity of the lubricant [10].

In the same way, for the transition from mixed to fluid or hydrodynamic lubrication, the relation advanced is

$$v_{mh} = K_2 \frac{p \delta}{\mu} \qquad (1-46)$$

where K_2 is a constant of proportionality.

It is to be noted that in the later case the external pressure no longer has any effect, while the unit load is of more importance.

If the total load W is divided into W_h, the load supported by hydrodynamic forces, and W_b, the load supported by metallic contacts, one finds [10]

$$\left.\begin{array}{l} \text{for } v < v_{bm}; \ W = W_b \ \text{boundary lubrication,} \\[2mm] \text{for } v_{bm} < v < v_{mh}; \ W = W_b + W_h \ \text{mixed lubrication,} \\[2mm] \text{for } v \gg v_{mh}; \ W = W_h \ \text{hydrodynamic lubrication.} \end{array}\right\} \quad (1-47)$$

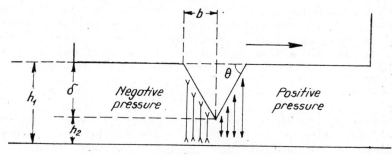

Fig. 1.17. — A single asperity as a slider bearing, [10].

However, the criterion for these definitions consists of friction measurements, and the discrepancies are large ; the situation may be clarified by improvement in experimental techniques.

1.4. Fluid Lubrication

In the case of fluid lubrication no contact between the surfaces occurs ; the surfaces are completely separated by a fluid film, supporting the load. It has been shown that a lubricant layer with a thickness of as little as 10,000 molecules (that is to say about 10^{-4} cm) is quite sufficient to prevent contact [1].

The part played by the lubricant between the sliding surfaces is much more complex than merely to keep the asperities apart as in boundary lubrication : the lubricant modifies the phenomenon qualitatively by producing a smooth distribution of the pressure in the lubricant film, by dissipating the heat generated by friction, by avoiding corrosion phenomena and by preventing the intrusion of foreign matter.

In the case of sufficiently thick films, the motion of the lubricant is governed by the laws of hydrodynamics, all the friction forces being generated by the relative sliding of the inner layers of the lubricant film.

Measurements have shown that hydrodynamic frictional losses are $20-100$ times less than in the case of boundary lubrication and incomparably smaller than for dry friction.

The internal friction of the lubricant film, i.e. the viscosity, conveys the motion from one layer of the film to another, and the resistance to motion is generally given by Newton's law [16]

$$\tau = \mu \frac{\partial v}{\partial n} \tag{1-48}$$

where μ is the absolute viscosity, v the velocity and n the normal to the surface.

When considering a cylindrical shaft rotating in a journal with dry contact surfaces, a resultant force $-W$, equal and opposite to the load W, will act upon the shaft at the point of contact (see Fig. 1—18a, [16]). The resultant can be broken into the normal force N and the frictional force F. The friction torque opposing rotation is

$$M = Fr = fNr. \tag{1-49}$$

Considering now the same surfaces separated by an oil film (see Fig. 1—18b) which adheres to the shaft and to the journal surfaces, the velocities within the lubricant layer will vary from zero on the bearing surface, to $r\omega$ on the shaft surface, if this variation is assumed, to a first approximation

$$\frac{\partial v}{\partial n} = \frac{r\omega}{c} \tag{1-50}$$

where c is the radial clearance of the bearing, that is to say the average thickness of the lubricant layer.

The friction force per unit length of shaft can be written as [16]

$$F = 2\pi r^2 \mu \frac{\omega}{c} \tag{1-51}$$

and the friction torque as

$$M = 2\pi r^3 \mu \frac{\omega}{c}. \tag{1-52}$$

It is readily seen that the nature of hydrodynamic friction torque is fundamentally different from that of dry friction: it no longer depends on the load, nor on a coefficient of friction, but varies with the cube of the radius, proportionally with viscosity, and angular velocity, and inversely with radial clearance. Moreover, considerations of equilibrium

show that the shaft no longer tends to climb the journal in the opposite
direction to its rotation, as in the case of dry friction (compare Figs.
1—18a and 1—18b).

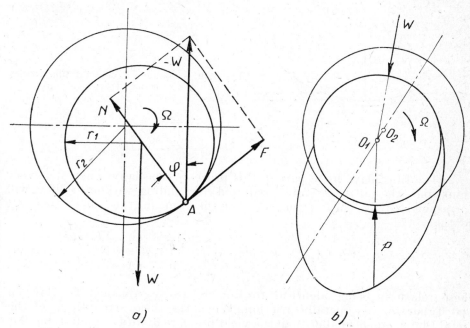

Fig. 1.18. — Equilibrium of forces in : a) Dry friction. b) Hydrodynamic friction.

The results of the hydrodynamic theory of lubrication cover a wide
field of application : journal and thrust bearings with constant or variable
forces and velocities lubricated with liquids or gases, rolling bearings,
and recently gears, rings and cylinders of internal combustion engines, etc.

1.5. Solid Film Lubrication

Under certain stringent conditions of operation, where a continuous
supply of lubricant is rendered impractical, the only method of lubricating rubbing surfaces may be to provide a layer of material that will
behave as a lubricant in reducing the friction and wear between the
moving parts.

The principle is shown schematically in Fig. 1—19 [17], where a
large ball under load rests on a flat surface ; the surface is covered by a thin
adherent solid film with a shear strength τ. The ball penetrates the flat

surface until the contact area A_1 reaches a value $A_1 = \dfrac{W}{\sigma_{c_1}}$, so that the load W is supported by the yield pressure σ_{c_1}.

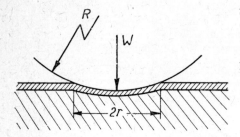

Fig. 1.19. — Mechanism of solid film lubrication, [17].

The film plays little part in this process, especially when it is very thin; but the ultimate force required for sliding without rolling will correspond to the shear strength τ_2 of the film in the same area A_1, so that [17]

$$W = A_1 \sigma_{c_1} \; ; \; F = A_1 \tau_2 \; ; \; f = \frac{F}{W} = \frac{\tau_2}{\sigma_{c_1}}, \qquad (1-53)$$

these relations being identical to Eq. (1—18), established by Bowden and Tabor for dry metallic friction. When the shear strength τ_2 of the metal film is much smaller than the yield pressure σ_{c_1} of the underlying flat surface, the coefficient of friction can reach very low values. It will be seen later on that this principle can be used to obtain efficient lubrication with solid metallic films. It can also be seen that the friction does not depend upon the modulus of elasticity E_1 and E_2 of the materials involved [17]

$$A_2 = k W^{2/3} \; ; \; k = 1.2\pi \left[\frac{r}{2} \left(\frac{1}{E_1} + \frac{1}{E_2} \right) \right]^{2/3}. \qquad (1-54)$$

Since f defined as above — relation (1—53) — will depend upon W, the term "coefficient of friction" is no longer suitable

$$F = A_2 \tau_2 = k \tau_2 W^{2/3} \; ; \; f' = \frac{F}{W} = k \tau_2 W^{-\frac{1}{3}}. \qquad (1-55)$$

An explanation of the decreasing value in friction with increasing load is thus obtained [17].

When severe deformation occurs, for instance in metal-working, the thickness of the solid film plays an important part : when the film is thick, its yield pressure will determine the contact area, but when the contact area is determined by the resistant substrate, a wide variety of soft materials can be used to reduce friction, due to their low shear strength (polymers, long-chain organic solids, very soft materials in general). In metal working the lubricant film exceeds the height of the asperities, so that the coefficient of friction is low. As already stated, one of the main functions of the lubricant film is to separate the rubbing surfaces, in order to avoid metallic junctions; in this case friction is kept to a minimum, since the shear strength of the lubricant is very low as compared with that of the materials involved, [17].

In the case of extreme pressure additives, the superficial chemical processes can produce adherent solid films. The temperature at which these compounds decompose determines their range of action. The chloride films for instance, formed with steel specimens, are effective up to 350°C in the absence of air, while the sulphide films remain useful up to 700°C.

1.5.1. Lubrication with Lamellar Solids

The recent advent of graphite and molybdenum disulphide lubricants has thrown into question the mode of action of lamellar solids as antifriction and antiwear (and seizure) materials. Since both of these materials have a layer-lattice crystal structure, it is reasonable to expect most materials of similar structure to behave as low friction coatings.

The anisotropy of these materials was first believed to be the explanation for their low friction, an explanation later considered unsatisfactory in the light of new experiments. Savage discovered the influence of water vapour on the behaviour of graphite surfaces in relative motion and found the interlayer bounds to be much stronger than theory suggests. In order to explain this effect he considered that the lattice arrangement of carbon atoms caused the cohesion forces to be much larger in one of three distinct regions of the lattice, where a C atom is bonded to three others. Subsequent measurements have not confirmed this supposition. Because of the beneficial effect of water vapour, even in a hydrogeneous atmosphere, Savage considered facial adsorption to be the main factor in the process [17].

On the other hand, extensive research with molybdenum disulphide demonstrated its low friction in high vacuum, while the adsorbed vapours proved not only unnecessary, but detrimental, due to their reactions with MoS_2, resulting in compounds without lamellar structure, or volatile [17]. It was also established that outgassed graphite, molybdenum disulphide and other lamellar solids do not behave in the same way when the temperature is raised : the friction of graphite and boron nitride falls considerably, while MoS_2, $CrCl_3$ and TiI_2 have the same low friction, until their structure is modified. The variation of interlayer bonding was considered the cause of this phenomenon, but here again not all lamellar solids conform to this explanation.

The presence of impurities reduces the efficiency of molybdenum disulphide, so that an explanation based on the modification of the inter-layer bonds gains further support [18].

Thin films of these substances deposited on metallic surfaces in powder form, or merely in suspension in the surrounding atmosphere, behaved differently. Thus it was found that the forces of major importance in the frictional behaviour of deposited layers of solid lubricants were those occurring between crystallites [17].

The friction between graphite films increases when the temperature exceeds 400 to 600°C, while the weight loss indicates rapid oxidation above 600°C. Boron nitride and molybdenum disulphide also presented increased friction associated with rapid oxidation. The removal of adsorbed gases from graphite, boron nitride and talc, increased the friction, which fact was attributed to increased adhesion between crystallite edges, while MoS_2 showed the opposite effect, thought to originate from additional hydrogen bonding between crystallites. Electron diffraction methods confirmed the intercrystallite bonding hypothesis. Braithwaite supported this hypothesis using a different approach, and suggested the existence of a third type of lubrication, the so-called "contact lubrication", in order to cover the lubrication phenomena of lamellar solids [17]. This is concerned with systems where the distances between moving surfaces are small, and there are contacts at the high spots protruding through the adsorbed layers of liquid boundary lubricants. Contact lubrication is not to be considered as merely an extension of boundary lubrication, since liquid boundary lubricants are only attached to the metal surface, while lamellar solid lubricants are actually a part of the metallic surface, since they are mechanically worked into the surface during running-in.

This mechanical process occurs during the running-in of surfaces, the asperities being subject to large scale deformation. The lamellar solids are located between the asperities not removed by welding or breaking; these layers of solid lubricant cannot be removed by ordinary chemical methods which are quite efficient for removing liquid boundary lubricants. Even after surfaces have been rubbed and washed in warm solvents and detergents they continue to run under low wear conditions if initial running-in with lamellar solid lubricants has been performed.

This concept of contact lubrication explains why lamellar solids may be less efficient during the running-in of very hard metals : the hardness of the metal can exceed the edge hardness of the lamellar solid, which can no longer embed itself in the metal.

During certain metal-working operations, the chemical treatment of the surfaces with phosphoric acid, or the electro-deposition of a metallic film, simulates the action of the plastic surface layer produced by a solid lubricant on a metal. The layer of metal plastically deformed in conjunction with the solid lubricant during metal-working is much more elastic than the underlying metal and is thus capable of absorbing any extra-deformation produced during the operation or subsequently ; it also allows a greater proportion of the energy to be usefully employed in the reduction of the metal, and produces a better finish. The solid lubricant between the rubbing surfaces consists of a series of distinct interfaces (see Fig. 1—20, [19]):

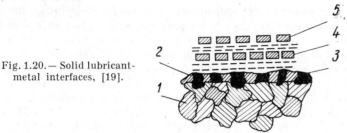

Fig. 1.20.— Solid lubricant-
metal interfaces, [19].

1. The grain boundary interfaces within the metal.
2. The metal on metal oxide (or adsorbed film) interface.
3. The metal oxide (or adsorbed film) on solid lubricant envelope interface.
4. The solid lubricant envelope on solid lubricant interface.
5. The intramolecular or intercrystallite interfaces within the solid lubricant.

Solid lubricants are useful, according to Braithwaite, at two stages during the working life of metals : a) During its fabrication (extrusion, forging, drawing, etc.) when their action will determine the nature of the interfaces (1) and (2). Interface (1) will determine such properties as hardness and tensile strength while in later use interface (2) will determine the surface finish in both a chemical and physical sense. b) During its running life, when the efficiency of the surfaces will be determined by the characteristics of interface (3). Here the film-forming additives in a dispersion of solid lubricant are referred to as a lubricant "envelope".

The study of interfaces (1) and (2) is largely a metallurgical problem — to determine the texture of the metal surface — while the properties of interfaces (3), (4) and (5) are determined by the surface-chemistry of the finely divided solid lubricant [19].

Measurements have been made of the friction coefficient and wear life of graphite- and molybdenum disulphide-coated surfaces, working in dry oxygen, dry nitrogen and wet air. In general, graphite exhibits good lubricating qualities in moist air, poor ones in dry oxygen and practically no lubrication in dry nitrogen; molybdenum disulphide provides good lubrication in dry nitrogen, worse in dry oxygen and poor in wet air. A general theory of lubrication must explain these apparent anomalies.

An illustration of the above mechanism of lubrication with graphite consists in the measurement in vacuum of its interlamellar binding energy, as performed by Bryant, Gutshall and Taylor [20]. It was found that in vacuum this energy has a degree of magnitude greater than in air, so that graphite must be removed from the general category of weakly bound lamellar materials which exhibit the phenomenon of intrinsic lubrication. Based on the correlation between interlayer binding energy and frictional phenomena (depending upon actual conditions : uncontaminating environment (ultrahigh vacuum) or interacting environment (air)) the authors conclude that "There exists between the binding energy of lamellar solids and the ambient atmosphere, a relationship which is correlatable with frictional behaviour". According to this hypothesis, muscovite also would be considered as a nonlubricant, because its intrinsic interlayer binding energy is too high to permit easy shear or cleavage. In the same way MoS_2 would be declared an intrinsic lubricant since it has weak interlayer binding. The observed behaviour of MoS_2 in ultra-high vacuum supports this statement [21]. Thus, while for MoS_2 no contaminant is necessary to weaken the interlayer binding, graphite is a satisfactory lubricant only in interacting atmospheres, i.e. air, oxygen or water vapour. Table 1—4 summarizes the relationship between the binding energy and the ambient atmosphere of several lamellar solids ; according to the above theory it is to be expected that good lubrication will be obtained in the presence of interacting gases, if the binding energy is high in vacuo, and this is the case [20].

Table 1—4

Relationship between the Binding Energy and Ambient Atmosphere for Some Lamellar Solids, [20]

Lamellar solid	Easy cleavage in ultrahigh vacuum	Beneficially interacting gases
Graphite	No	Air, O_2, H_2O
Molybdenum disulphide	Yes	—
Talc	Yes	—
Phlogopite	No	Air, H_2O
Pyrophyllite	Yes	—
Muscovite	No	Air, H_2O
Margarite	No	Air, H_2O

In order to apply the same approach for MoS_2, as for graphite, it is necessary to assume that the shear strength of the lattice is less than the adhesion of clean basal planes to the metallic substrate, and that in oxygen or wet air this adhesion is reduced or prevented, due to the contamination of the basal planes. The validity of the first assumption has already been pointed out, and it has been shown that although clean molybdenum disulphide basal planes also are hydrophobic, a non-lubricating monolayer of hydrophilic trioxide is formed in oxygen at low temperatures, which reduces the binding forces between planes. A complete destruction of the MoS_2 lattice is possible as a result of oxide formation increased by high relative humidity and localised frictional heating. On the other hand, in the presence of nitrogen vapours no adhesion can occur between the basal planes ; they will be free to adhere to the metal substrate and thus adequate surface lubrication and protection will follow [17].

The influence of humidity upon the performance of molybdenum disulphide was explained according to Salomon, de Gee and Zaat, [22], by the formation of H₂S. The variation of the coefficient of friction of MoS₂ on steel as a function of humidity is shown in Fig. 1—21; the humidity of the surface is lower than that of the surrounding atmosphere, because the former is warm [22].

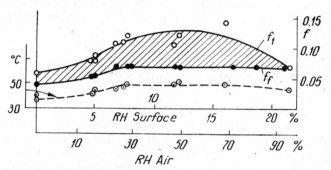

Fig. 1.21. — Influence of relative humidity (*RH*) on the coefficient of friction of a MoS₂ film on steel, [22].

The coefficient of friction is seen to increase with humidity, and its values are higher at the beginning of the run (f_i) than near its end (f_f).

In a nitrogen atmosphere no adhesion is possible to the basal planes, so that adherence to the metal substrate will not be reduced and good protection will result. In oxygen or wet air the adsorption phenomena will have no influence on lubrication, since even in this case, as has been pointed out, the shear strength of the lattice is lower than the adhesion to the metal substrate.

The sliding behaviour of MoS₂ in air, controlled atmospheres, and high vacuum (pressures down to 10^{-9} torr) was investigated by Haltner [21] who reached the conclusion that, unlike graphite, the good lubricating properties of MoS₂ do not depend upon the interference of water vapour. It was concluded thus that MoS₂ can be an excellent lubricant in high vacuum conditions.

In conclusion, the diversity of opinion regarding the mechanism of lubrication with lamellar solids does not obscure the fact that layer lattice compounds with weak interlayer forces are useful low friction materials. It also seems that the weaker the forces, the lower the friction, but details of bonding to the metal surface and orientation are important. It has also been shown that large numbers of dislocations take place in the basal planes of these lamellar solids, and speculation has been made about their eventual influence upon the lubrication phenomena. Hence the necessity of a brief record of the actual experimental data available.

By examining, for instance, crystals of graphite and MoS₂ with an electron microscope, it can be seen that the basal planes are well supplied with dislocations; it appears that they are generated at the cleavage steps and interact to form extensive hexagonal networks. Delavignette and Amelinckx have also shown that dislocations can move very easily on the glide planes, but are hindered by the smallest obstacle [17], [23].

The presence of laminar rolls of graphite in wear debris was observed with electron microscope techniques by Bollman and Spreadborough. It is suggested that these rolls form small roller bearings and so might account for low friction. Spreadborough thinks that a surface orientation of the crystallites precedes the formation of the rolls [24].

1.5.2. Lubrication with Thin Metallic Films

By considering the friction force rendered by relation $F = A\tau$ (established when the effect of the ploughing term is small compared with the shearing term) it is seen that in order to achieve minimum friction between unlubricated surfaces with relative sliding, both the contact surface A and the shear strength τ must be small. With most metals this is not possible, since the metals with low shearing strength are usually soft, so that the contact area A becomes larger under load, and when both metals are hard τ is also important, so that F reaches high values. This idea is presented schematically in Fig. 1—22 a and b.

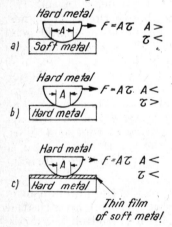

Fig. 1.22. — Mode of lubrication with thin metallic films, [3].

A useful exception is found in anisotropic solids, capable of withstanding high normal pressures, but readily sheared by a tangential force. As was previously seen, solid lamellar lubricants exploit this principle, but it is difficult to achieve similar results with metals, since they are far less anisotropic. For this reason the coefficient of friction of most metals is of the same order of magnitude, and the values range between 0.6 and 1.2, [3].

However, effective anisotropy can be achieved by depositing a very thin film of a soft metal on the surface of a hard one (Fig. 1—22c). In this way low shear strength of the soft metal is matched by a small contact surface, since the hard substrate will bear the load. As a result, the product $A\tau$ will be small and the friction low. Thin metallic films thus present particular interest, and studies have been made of the behaviour of, for instance, indium, lead and copper films laid upon various substrates. It was discovered that the thinner the metallic layer, the smaller the friction, the thinnest effective film being 10^{-5} cm, [3]. On the other hand, thicker films withstand higher loads, and wear is kept at a minimum, so that the optimum thickness will be a compromise, i.e. sufficient to avoid a rapid wiping out, but thin enough to keep friction to a reasonable level.

In the same way, investigations of the influence of temperature have shown that friction decreases when the temperature is raised, and reaches a minimum at the melting point of the metal, at which point the friction increases sharply. Thus with lead films the coefficient of friction is reduced to half its value over a temperature range of 20°C to 270°C [3]. The explanation lies in the decrease of shear strength with increasing temperature, while the contact area remains almost constant, since the load is supported by the hard substrate. When the melting point is reached the film is broken, and friction rises rapidly.

The experiments performed in order to establish the extent to which the coefficient of friction conforms to Amontons' law, are summarized in Fig. 1—23, [3]. It is seen that the coefficient of friction for unlubricated steel or for steel lubricated with mineral oil obeys Amontons' law, remaining independent of load, but for steel lubricated with a thin film of indium, f decreases sensibly with load.

The explanation is consistent with the foregoing theory : for unlubricated steel (or lubricated with mineral oil) the area of metallic contact is proportional to the applied load, but when the lubricant consists of a thin film of soft metal, the deformation of the substrate resulting from the increased load causes only a small increase of the area of real contact; consequently there is only a slight growth of the friction force as the load increases, backed by a decrease of the coefficient of friction f, an effect quite evident in Fig. 1—23.

The behaviour of metallic films in some ways resembles that of ordinary lubricant films : they produce a substantial reduction in friction, the metallic substrate is protected and the resulting sliding is smooth. Metallic films also wear away by successive sliding, but at a higher rate than conventional lubricants. Finally, friction increases when the metallic films melt, an effect analogous to that occurring when solid hydrocarbon films reach their melting point.

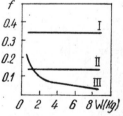

There are also sensible differences between conventional lubricating films and metallic films : boundary lubricants are efficient in layers of one or two molecules thick, while a metallic film must be considerably thicker to be efficient, i.e. it must be of the order of 10^{-5} cm, that is to say about 30 atomic layers. Another difference is that conventional lubricant films obey Amontons' law regarding the variation of the coefficient of friction, and metallic films do not.

Fig. 1.23. — Effect of load on the coefficient of friction : 1) Unlubricated tool steel. 2) Steel lubricated with mineral oil. 3) Steel lubricated with indium film of thickness 4.10^{-4} cm, [3].

Lubrication with thin metallic layers has a wide field of practical application, especially where very heavy loads must be supported and conventional lubricants cannot be used. Very thin lead films for instance are efficient in deep drawing operations : a 0.001 in film deposited on steel permits the use of unlubricated dies and results in an excellent surface finish [3].

Thin metal films can produce coefficients of friction as low as 0.04, for heavily loaded indium films for example, and this is comparable with the performance of the best boundary lubricants.

References

1. R. SCHNURMANN, *Friction and Wear*. Wear, **5**, *1*, 1962.
2. D. D. FULLER, *Theory and Practice of Lubrication for Engineers*. John Wiley, New York, 1956.
3. F. P. BOWDEN, D. TABOR, *The Friction and Lubrication of Solids*. Oxford, at the Clarendon Press, 1964.
4. M. C. SHAW, F. E. MACKS, *Analysis and Lubrication of Bearings*. McGraw Hill, New York, 1949.
5. D. PAVELESCU, *Dependence of Friction and Stick-Slip on the Main Wear Factors*. Rev. Roum. Sci. Techn., Méc. Appl., **13**, *1*, 1968.
6. I. V. KRAGELSKII, *Friction and Wear*. Butterworths, London, 1965.
7. F. T. BARWELL, *Some Further Thoughts on the Nature of Boundary Lubrication*. Rev. Roum. Sci. Techn., Méc. Appl., **11**, *3*, 1966.
8. J. F. ARCHARD, *Contact and Rubbing of Flat Surfaces*. Journ. Phys., **24**, 1953.
9. E. RABINOWICZ, *Predicting the Wear of the Metal Parts*. Production Engineering, **29**, 1958.
10. A. DOBRY, *The Transition Between Boundary, Mixed and Hydrodynamic Lubrication*. Wear, **7**, *3*, 1964.
11. Y. TAMAI, B. G. RIGHTMIRE, *Mechanism of Boundary Lubrication and Edge Effect*. Trans. ASME, Journ. Basic Eng. **87**, Series D, *3*, 1965.
12. G. VINOGRADOV, I. V. KOREPOVA, Y. Y. PODOLSKY, N. T. PAVLOVSKAYA, *Effect of Oxidation on the Boundary Friction of Steel in Hydrocarbon Media and Critical Friction Duties Under which Cold and Hot Seizure (or Welding) Develop*. Trans. ASME, Journ. Basic Eng., **87**, Series D, *3*, 1965,
13. A. CAMERON, *Principles of Lubrication*. Longmans, London, 1966.
14. O. BIȚĂ, I. DINCĂ, *Comportement aux charges lourdes de quelques additifs à base de phosphore*. Rev. Méc. Appl., **8**, 3, Bucarest, 1963.
15. GH. VASILCA, AL. NICA, O. BIȚĂ, I. DINCĂ, *Some Aspects of the Effects of the Structural Type of Two Aluminum Alloys on Their Sliding and Wear Resisting Performance*. Rev. Roum. Sci. Techn., Méc. Appl., **9**, *5*, 1964.
16. N. TIPEI, *Theory of Lubrication*. Stanford University Press, Stanford, 1962.
17. E. R. BRAITWAITE, G. W. ROWE, *Principles and Applications of Lubrication with Solids*. Scient. Lubr., **15**, *3*, 1963.
18. O. BIȚĂ, I. DINCĂ, *Friction and Wear Aspects in Molybdenum Disulphide Lubrication*. Rev. Roum. Sci. Tech., Méc. Appl., **10**, *2*, 1965.
19. E. R. BRAITHWAITE, *Solid Lubricants and Surfaces*. Pergamon Press, Oxford, 1964.
20. P. J. BRYANT, P. L. GUTSHALL, L. H. TAYLOR, *A Study of Mechanisms of Graphite Friction and Wear*. Wear, **7**, *1*, 1964.
21. A. J. HALTNER, *An Evaluation of the Role of Vapour Lubrication Mechanisms in* MoS_2. Wear, **7**, *1*, 1964.
22. G. SALOMON, A. W. J. DE GEE, J. H. ZAAT, *Mechano-Chemical Factors in* MoS_2 *Film Lubrication*. Wear, **7**, *1*, 1964.
23. P. DELAVIGNETTE, S. AMELINCKX, *Dislocation Patterns in Graphite*. Jour. Nucl. Metals, **5**, *1*, 1962.
24. J. SPREADBOROUGH, *The Frictional Behaviour of Graphite*. Wear, **5**, *1*, 1962.

CHAPTER II

Design of Lubrication Systems

Having studied at some length the detailed behaviour of lubricants and bearing surfaces, and having demonstrated the necessity of lubricating any moving contact to reduce frictional wear, we must now examine the ways in which such lubricant can be provided.

The lubricants of most pragmatic interest are oils and greases, and these are generally distributed to the bearings of a machine by means of a central system [1] being automatic to varying degrees, and consequently of some complexity.

2.1. Design of Lubrication Systems with Fluid Lubricants

Centralized lubrication systems have a large number of lubrication points, fed from a main unit, so that the pipe network is complex. The head losses must be calculated as a function of the pressure and amount of lubricant required at the various points of lubrication, in order to determine the operating parameters of the supply devices. The present section deals with the problem of conveying Newtonian fluids through pipes and networks. The large majority of mineral oils are Newtonian, characterized by shear rates depending only on the imposed shear stress, that is to say $\tau = \mu \dfrac{\partial v}{\partial n}$,

where τ is the shearing stress, μ the absolute viscosity and $\dfrac{\partial v}{\partial n}$ the velocity gradient along the normal to the surface, [2].

The unit of measurement of viscosity in the cgs system is the poise, p (dyne.sec/cm²); generally, the centipoise is used (1 cp = 1/100 poise), a unit which corresponds approximately to the viscosity of water at 20°C. The equivalent unit in the gravitational system is kg.sec/m² = 98.1 dyne. sec/cm² = 10^4 cp.

The absolute or dynamic viscosity μ is sometimes replaced by the ratio of μ and density ρ, named kinematic viscosity : $\nu = \dfrac{\mu}{\rho}$. The unit of kinematic viscosity in the cgs system (cm²/sec) is the stoke (St); the usual unit is the centistoke (1 cSt = 1/100 St), [2].

2.1.1. Formulae for Calculating the System Parameters

Motion of fluid in a pipe has two distinct modes : laminar and turbulent flow. Laminar flow responds to a theoretical description and the relation obtained for such flow is [3]

$$Q = \frac{\pi (p_1 - p_2) r^4}{8 \mu L} \tag{2-1}$$

where Q is the flow and $p_1 - p_2$ the pressure drop along a length of pipe L, of radius r.

This predicts a parabolic velocity distribution, and expresses the Hagen-Poiseuille law, entirely supported by observation.

If the pressure drop $p_1 - p_2$ is expressed in terms of gravitational heads of the lubricant

$$\frac{p_1 - p_2}{L} = \rho g \, \frac{h_1 - h_2}{L} \tag{2-2}$$

the following relation is obtained for the oil flow [4]

$$Q = \frac{\pi r^4}{8 \mu} \cdot \frac{\rho g (h_1 - h_2)}{L} \tag{2-3}$$

where ρ is the density of the lubricant and g the constant acceleration due to gravity.

Denoting the hydraulic slope by

$$i = \frac{h_1 - h_2}{L} \tag{2-4}$$

relation (2−3) takes the form

$$Q = \frac{\pi r^4}{8 \mu} \rho g i \tag{2-5}$$

or

$$i = \frac{8 \mu Q}{\pi \rho g \, r^4}, \tag{2-6}$$

These equations are only applicable within a range of flow extending from zero up to a certain maximum or "critical" flow, characterized by a critical value of the Reynolds number

$$\mathbf{Re}_c = \frac{Q}{\pi \nu r}. \tag{2-7}$$

At Reynolds numbers higher than critical the flow ceases to be laminar and becomes turbulent. The value of the critical Reynolds number for the pipes used in lubrication systems is considered to be about 1000. The laws of turbulent motion are still based on experiment rather than theory. It has been established that in turbulent flow the frictional resistance of the fluid for a given length of a pipe is proportional to its surface area, to the density of the fluid, and to something lower than the second power of the mean velocity of the flow. If v_m is the mean velocity, it is possible to write

$$\pi r^2 (p_1 - p_2) = 2 \pi L k \rho v_m^n \qquad (2-8)$$

and further

$$i = \frac{h_1 - h_2}{L} = \frac{p_1 - p_2}{\rho g L} = \frac{2k v_m^n}{g r}. \qquad (2-9)$$

Since

$$v_m = \frac{Q}{\pi r^2}$$

$$i = \frac{2kQ^n}{\pi^n g r^{2n+1}} \qquad (2-10)$$

or

$$i = K \frac{Q^n}{r^{2n+1}} \qquad (2-11)$$

where $K = \dfrac{2k}{\pi^n g}$; the exponent n must be determined experimentally, for pipes of various sizes, materials and surface roughness.

The value of n depends on the magnitude of the surface irregularities relative to the diameter of the pipe and is approximately 2 for rough surfaces, while for smooth ones it diminishes to about 1.7. The factor K is nearly constant over a wide range of flow, for a given pipe, but varies widely with the size and roughness of the pipe.

If $n = 2$, equation (2-11) becomes

$$i = K \frac{Q^2}{r^5} \qquad (2-12)$$

that is to say a form similar to Darcy's formula $\left(i = k \dfrac{v^2}{2g} \right)$, the relation for Q becoming

$$Q = r^{2.5} \sqrt{\frac{i}{K}}. \qquad (2-13)$$

It can be seen that while the flow is proportional to the fourth power of the radius in the case of laminar flow, it is proportional to the 2.5 power of the radius in the case of turbulent flow.

Fig. 2—1 represents schematically the relation between the flow and the hydraulic gradient for both laminar and turbulent motion — relations (2—6) and (2—11) — for a hypothetical pipe and fluid, when $n = 1.75$, [4]. The point of intersection of the two lines, I, represents the critical

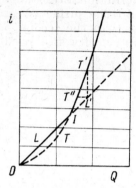

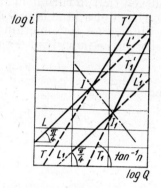

Fig. 2.1. — Variation of hydraulic gradient i with the
flow Q for, [4]:
— — — Laminar motion.
———— Turbulent motion.

Fig. 2.2. — Logarithmic re-
presentation of the variation
of hydraulic gradient i with
flow Q for, [4]:
— — — Laminar motion.
———— Turbulent motion.

point at which the motion is indeterminate as between laminar and turbulent flow. In the cases of pipes with very smooth surfaces it is possible to preserve the laminar regime beyond this critical point, if care is taken to avoid any disturbance in the fluid on entry or in the pipe.

The dotted lines are not generally useful since either subcritical turbulence, or carefully suppressed turbulence are equally abnormal. The values of Q and i are therefore predicted as those which represent, of the two alternatives, the lesser flow (or higher resistance). Calculations based on this approach will err, if at all, on the side of safety since the predicted flow will be higher than the actual one, and the calculated value of the hydraulic slope cannot be exceeded.

The flow equations for both laminar and turbulent motion are most usefully represented graphically by taking logarithms of relations (2—6) and (2—11):

$$\log i = \log Q + \log \mu + \log \frac{8}{\pi \rho g} - 4 \log r \qquad (2-14)$$

and

$$\log i = n \log Q + \log K - (2n + 1) \log r. \qquad (2-15)$$

These relations are shown in Fig. 2—2 and the linear relation between $\log Q$ and $\log i$ is evident.

The full and dotted lines have the same significance as in Fig. 2—1, and it can be seen from relations (2—14) and (2—15) that the line representing laminar flow has a slope of 45 degrees, while the line representing turbulent flow has a slope given by the parameter n ($\tan^{-1} n$); for this case, $n = 1.75$, [4]. The lines LL', TT' and $L_1 L_1'$, $T_1 T_1'$, apply for the same fluid but for different pipes, the latter representing the performance of a larger pipe.

When the operating conditions of both pipes are the same, the slopes of both corresponding lines will be the same, and for a series of various

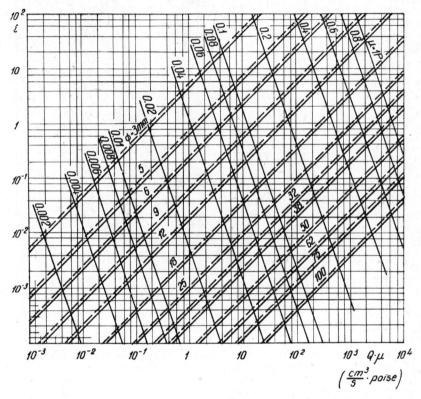

Fig. 2.3. — Hydraulic slope i as a function of the product $Q.\mu$ for various pipe diameters, in the case of laminar motion, [4]: $---\;\rho = 0.9$; ———— $\rho = 1$.

pipe diameters the points of intersection will define a locus, which in this case approximates with sufficient accuracy to a straight line.

The frictional resistance of viscous fluids in pipes can be represented very conveniently by logarithmic charts as shown in Fig. 2—2. For practical purposes it is preferable to draw the diagrams of laminar motion apart from those of turbulent motion. Fig. 2—3 thus represents the hydraulic slope i as a function of the product $Q.\mu$ for a wide range of pipe diameters (in mm) likely to be used in lubrication systems. From Eq. (2—5) it is seen that i is proportional to $Q.\mu$ so that if it is represented as a function of

$Q.\mu$ instead of Q, it is no longer necessary to repeat the same diagram for every value of μ; the flow Q is in cm³/sec and the viscosity μ in poises [4]. The full lines correspond to $\rho = 1$, and the broken ones to $\rho = 0.9$.

The critical points of transition are represented by lines corresponding to values of μ ranging from 0.001 to 1 poise. Consistent with the treat-

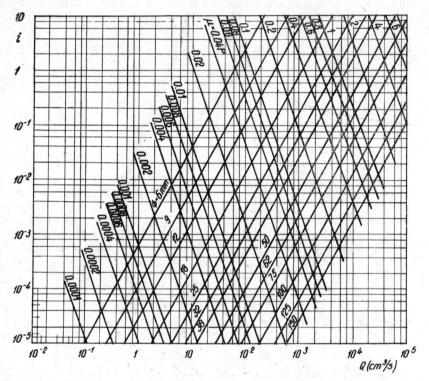

Fig. 2.4. — Hydraulic slope i as a function of the flow Q for various pipe diameters, in the case of turbulent motion, [4].

ment of Fig. 2—2, laminar motion will occur for values of i and $Q.\mu$ beneath and to the left of these critical lines. For turbulent flow another chart is therefore necessary (Fig. 2—4), being derived both theoretically and experimentally, [4]. It is noteworthy that turbulent flow characterised by relation (2—11) is not influenced by density variations.

Surface roughness has an important effect on the flow of viscous liquids in pipes, especially when it is turbulent, but charts 2—3, 2—4 are meant only to apply to smooth and clean pipes, a not unreasonable requirement in practice.

The results of laminar analysis can be applied to smoothly curved pipes as long as the curvature is not great and the section of the pipe is constant.

The losses in elbows, tees, valves, etc. can be estimated with the help of relation (2—16):

$$\Delta h = h_1 - h_2 = K\frac{v^2}{2g} \qquad (2-16)$$

where h_1 is the head before the obstacle, h_2 the head after it and K an experimentally determined coefficient; table 2—1 for instance, yields some values of K for elbows and bends [3], [5], while table 2—2 presents values of K for valves [5]. In this way Δh can be determined and added directly to the pipe head losses; the average velocity v is readily determined when the flow rate is known: $v = \dfrac{Q}{\pi r^2}$.

By equating Darcy's relation and the fitting-loss formula

$$k\frac{L}{r} \cdot \frac{v^2}{2g} = K\frac{v^2}{2g} \qquad (2-17)$$

one obtains an equivalent length L_e [3]

$$L_e = \frac{K}{k}\,r. \qquad (2-18)$$

The coefficient k can be easily deduced from Fig. 2—5 (drawn after [3] regardless of roughness influence) as a function of the Reynolds number $\mathbf{R_e}$ for $\mathbf{R_e} > 1000$ and from relation $k = \dfrac{32}{\mathbf{R_e}}$ for $\mathbf{R_e} < 1000$, since the full turbulent regime is considered to appear when $\mathbf{R_e}$ exceeds 1000, [3].

It is thus possible to determine the equivalent length L_e, with the help of coefficients K and k, so that the head loss results finally as

$$\Delta h = h_1 - h_2 = i\sum_{i=1}^{N} L_{e_i}. \qquad (2-19)$$

For sudden enlargements the results are similar

$$\Delta h = \frac{(v_1-v_2)^2}{2g} = \frac{v_1^2}{2g}\left(1 - \frac{r_1}{r_2}\right)^2 = K\frac{v_1^2}{2g} \qquad (2-20)$$

where v_1 is the average velocity before the enlargement and v_2 after it. When $v_2 = 0$ (discharge into reservoirs or large areas, $r_2 = \infty$) one finds

$$\Delta h = \frac{v_1^2}{2g} \qquad (2-21)$$

that is to say the entire velocity head is lost in turbulence. The variation of the coefficient K as a function of radii r_1 and r_2 is shown in Fig. 2—6, [5].

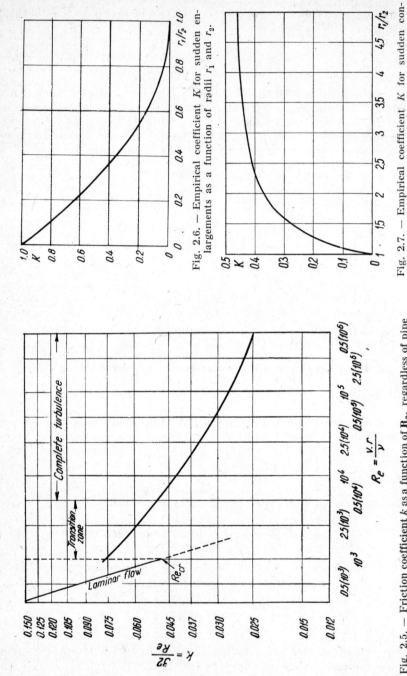

Fig. 2.6. — Empirical coefficient K for sudden enlargements as a function of radii r_1 and r_2.

Fig. 2.7. — Empirical coefficient K for sudden contractions, as a function of radii r_1 and r_2.

Fig. 2.5. — Friction coefficient k as a function of R_e, regardless of pipe roughness influence.

Table 2—1

Values of K for elbows and bends

Element	Dimension	Coefficient K
Screwed elbows	up to 2 in	0.72
Smooth right-angled bends	$\dfrac{\text{radius of curvature}}{\text{radius of pipe}} = 1$	0.25
,,	,, $= 2$	0.15
,,	,, $= 10$	0.10
Tees	—	1.50

Table 2—2

Values of K for valves [5]

Element	Conditions	Coefficient K
Globe valve	Fully open	10.0
Angle valve	,, ,,	5.0
Swing checkvalve	,, ,,	2.5
Gate valve	,, ,,	0.20
,, ,,	3/4 open	1.15
,, ,,	1/2 open	5.6
,, ,,	1/4 open	24.0
Stop valve	Fully open (600 psi)	4.0
,, ,,	3/4 open	4.6
,, ,,	1/2 open	6.4
,, ,,	1/4 open	780.0
Diaphragm valve	Fully open	2.3
,, ,,	3/4 open	2.6
,, ,,	1/2 open	4.3
,, ,,	1/4 open	21.0
Plug valve with screwed bends (1/4 turn from closed to full open)	Fully open	0.77
,,	99 % open	0.86
,,	98 % open	0.95
,,	95 % open	1.45
,,	90 % open	2.86
,,	80 % open	9.6
,,	70 % open	28.0

For sudden contractions no simple mathematical analysis is available, but experimental investigations have led to the relation [3]

$$\Delta h = K \frac{v_2^2}{2g} \qquad (2—22)$$

where v_2 is the velocity in the smaller pipe. The coefficient K depends upon the ratio of the diameters and Fig. 2—7 gives its values for the usual case, [3].

In order to design the supply network as a whole, the flows and head losses in the various distinct elements of the system must be combined to provide the pressures and flow rates required at the various working points of the installation.

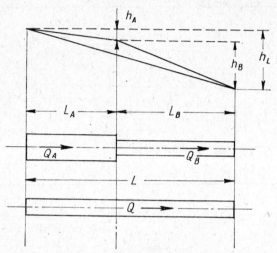

Fig. 2.8. — Pipes in series and the equivalent pipe.

2.1.1.1. *Pipes in Series.* For this case (Fig. 2 — 8) the total head loss can be obtained by summing the losses for each pipe [6]

$$\Delta h_L = (k_r\,Q^n)_A + (k_r\,Q^n)_B + \ldots + (k_r\,Q^n)_N = \sum_{i=1}^{N} (k_r\,Q^n)_i. \quad (2\text{--}23)$$

For other elements (elbows, bends, valves and so on, or sudden contractions and enlargements), relations (2—16), (2—20) and (2—22) with the respective tables and figures rapidly yield the equivalent head losses Δh_j, so that finally

$$\Delta h_L = \sum_{i=1}^{N} (k_r\,Q^n)_i + \sum_{j=1}^{M} (\Delta h)_j \qquad (2\text{--}24)$$

and the fall of pressure Δp will result from Eq. (2—2) as

$$\Delta p = \gamma\,\Delta h \qquad (2\text{--}25)$$

since γ is the specific weight of the fluid ($\gamma = \rho\,g$).
The flow through each pipe must be the same, or

$$Q = Q_A = Q_B = \ldots = Q_N \qquad (2\text{--}26)$$

and hence :

$$k_r = (k_r)_A + (k_r)_B + \ldots + (k_r)_N = \sum_{i=1}^{N} (k_r)_i . \qquad (2-27)$$

But, by definition

$$k_r = \frac{\Delta h_L}{Q^n} = \frac{iL}{Q^n} ; \qquad \left\{ \begin{array}{l} (n = 1 \text{ for laminar motion}) \\ (n = 2 \text{ for turbulent motion}) \end{array} \right. \qquad (2-28)$$

so that for laminar motion one can write, when relation $(2-6)$ is used

$$\Delta h_L = iL = \frac{8 \, \mu \, LQ}{\pi \, \rho \, gr^4} = k_r \, Q^n \qquad (2-29)$$

and further, that

$$k_r = \frac{8 \, \mu \, L}{\pi \, \rho \, gr^4} ; \qquad (n = 1) . \quad (2-30)$$

For turbulent motion, relation $(2-11)$ can be used

$$\Delta h_L = iL = K \frac{LQ^n}{r^{2n+1}} = k_r Q^n \qquad (2-31)$$

which gives

$$k_r = K \frac{L}{r^{2n+1}} ; \qquad (n = 1.70 \div 2). \quad (2-32)$$

If n is taken to be 2, relation $(2-32)$ becomes

$$k_r = K \frac{L}{r^5} . \qquad (2-33)$$

The equivalent pipe. It is sometimes useful to reduce all the pipes in series, to an equivalent single pipe, which for the same overall length and total head loss will allow the same flow through it.

For the head loss in this case, relation $(2-27)$ can be used, as well as relations $(2-30)$ and $(2-32)$; the head losses for each pipe can also be determined by means of the charts in Figs. $2-3$ and $2-4$.

The flow through the equivalent pipe is equal to the flow passing through each pipe — relation $(2-26)$ — and its length will equal the total length of the pipes under consideration

$$L = L_A + L_B + \ldots + L_N = \sum_{i=1}^{N} L_i. \qquad (2-34)$$

It is convenient to use relation (2—18) for bends, elbows, valves, etc., and the chart in Fig. 2—5, to express the head losses in the form of equivalent lengths, so that

$$L_e = \sum_{i=1}^{N} L_i + \sum_{j=1}^{M} (L_e)_j \qquad (2-35)$$

while relations (2—27) or (2—24) will give the overall head loss to a good approximation.

The radius of the equivalent pipe can be determined after the calculation of the total head loss, by means of relations (2—30) or (2—33), which for laminar motion give

$$r = \sqrt[4]{\frac{8\,\mu\,L}{\pi\,\varrho g\,k_r}} \qquad (2-36)$$

and for turbulent motion

$$r = \sqrt[5]{\frac{KL}{k_r}}. \qquad (2-37)$$

These computations can be verified by deriving the hydraulic slope i from relation

$$i = \frac{\Delta h_L}{L} = \frac{\sum\limits_{i=1}^{N} (\Delta h)_i}{\sum\limits_{i=1}^{N} L_i + \sum\limits_{j=1}^{M} (L_e)_j} \qquad (2-38)$$

and by establishing later on the dimensions of the pipes from Fig. 2—3 for laminar motion, as a function of the product $Q.\,\mu$, or from Fig. 2—4 for turbulent motion as a function of Q.

The equivalent pipe which can replace pipes and other elements in series is a particularly convenient concept when the whole system under analysis contains parallel circuits, or other complications.

2.1.1.2. *Pipes in Parallel.* Pipes of various diameters disposed in parallel (emerging from a common supply point) may be considered (Fig. 2—9).

In this case the head loss is the same for all pipes [5]

$$\Delta h_L = k_r\,Q^n = (k_r\,Q^n)_A = (k_r\,Q^n)_B = \ldots (k_r\,Q^n)_N \qquad (2-39)$$

and the total flow will equal the sum of partial flows

$$Q = Q_A + Q_B + \ldots + Q_N = \sum_{i=1}^{N} Q_i \qquad (2-40)$$

so that

$$\left(\frac{1}{k_r}\right)^{\frac{1}{n}} = \left(\frac{1}{k_r}\right)_A^{\frac{1}{n}} + \left(\frac{1}{k_r}\right)_B^{\frac{1}{n}} + \ldots + \left(\frac{1}{k_r}\right)_N^{\frac{1}{n}} = \sum_{i=1}^{N} \left(\frac{1}{k_r}\right)_i^{\frac{1}{n}}. \qquad (2-41)$$

If each pipe is taken to be of the same length (Fig. 2—9)
$$L = L_A = L_B = \ldots = L_N. \qquad (2-42)$$
It is sometimes necessary to know how much oil flows through each pipe. One can assume a flow for one of the pipes and introduce it in the

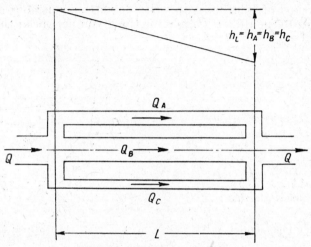

Fig. 2.9. — Pipes in parallel.

calculations, to establish the common head loss of the pipes, which is readily accomplished by means of the charts in Figs. 2—3 and 2—4.

All other assumed flow rates Q'_A, Q'_B, ..., etc. can be calculated later on with the help of the calculated head loss. Apportioning the real total flow Q to the assumed flows, the real flow rates Q_A, Q_B, ..., etc. can be deduced, [6]

$$
\left.
\begin{aligned}
Q_A &= \frac{Q'_A \times Q}{\sum\limits_{i=1}^{N} Q'_i} \\[2ex]
Q_B &= \frac{Q'_B \times Q}{\sum\limits_{i=1}^{N} Q'_i} \\[2ex]
&\quad \cdot \quad \cdot \quad \cdot \quad \cdot \\[1ex]
Q_N &= \frac{Q'_N \times Q}{\sum\limits_{i=1}^{N} Q'_i}
\end{aligned}
\right\} \qquad (2-43)
$$

The head loss for every pipe is then determined as a function of the flow rates Q_A, Q_B, ..., etc. If the resulting differences are negligible, the problem is solved; if they are important, the procedure is repeated, by considering as assumed flow rates the calculated flows Q_A, Q_B, ..., etc., until the differences are as small as desired.

2.1.1.3. *Pipe Networks.* As has been already mentioned, quite complicated pipe networks are frequently found in lubrication practice, due to the numerous points of an installation at which lubrication is required (Fig. 2—10), so that a general method of computation must be outlined.

One method of solution is to write down the equations derived from continuity and Bernoulli's principle for the given network; the continuity

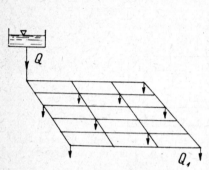

Fig. 2.10. — Pipe network.

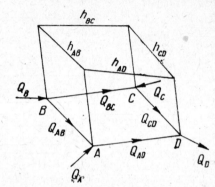

Fig. 2.11. — Loop from a pipe network.

principle states that the total flow rates towards and away from any junction must be equal, while Bernoulli's principle states that the net head loss around any single loop (Fig. 2—11) of the network must be zero. The direction of flow must always be in the direction of the falling energy line. It is possible thus to write, for a loop of the network (Fig. 2—11), the following relations [6]

$$\left. \begin{array}{l} Q_B = Q_{BC} + Q_{AB} \\ Q_{BC} + Q_C = Q_{CD} \\ Q_{CD} + Q_{AD} = Q_D \\ Q_A + Q_{AB} = Q_{AD} \end{array} \right\} \tag{2—44}$$

and

$$(k_r\, Q^n)_{BC} + (k_r\, Q^n)_{CD} = (k_r\, Q^n)_{AB} + (k_r\, Q^n)_{AD}. \tag{2—45}$$

If the flow rates Q_A, Q_B, Q_C and Q_D are known, as well as the characteristics of the pipes, the flows Q_{AD}, Q_{CD}, Q_{BC} and Q_{AB} can be deduced by trial-and-error. From knowledge of the flow rates, one can calculate the dimensions of the pipes as functions of the head losses.

In spite of its simplicity, this method is inconvenient for complicated snetworks, where all the effects are interrelated. For these situations it is advisable to use a systematic trial-and-error method, based on Cross, method [6] for viscous fluids. Each loop of the network is studied separately, and values of the flow in each branch chosen to be consistent with the continuity equations.

For example with equation (2—44), take $Q'_{AB} = Q_0$, then

$$
\left.
\begin{aligned}
Q'_{BC} &= Q_B - Q_0 \\
Q'_{CD} &= Q_C + Q_B - Q_0 \\
Q'_{AD} &= Q_D - Q_C - Q_B + Q_0
\end{aligned}
\right\}
\qquad (2\text{—}46)
$$

Assuming that Q the flow through branch AB is also consistent with the head loss equation (in this case (2—45)) and that

$$
Q - Q_0 = \Delta Q
\qquad (2\text{—}47)
$$

t is clear from (2—46) that a better estimate of the flow would be

$$
\left.
\begin{aligned}
Q''_{AB} &= Q'_{AB} + \Delta Q \\
Q''_{BC} &= Q'_{BC} - \Delta Q \\
Q''_{CD} &= Q'_{CD} - \Delta Q \\
Q''_{AD} &= Q'_{AD} + \Delta Q
\end{aligned}
\right\}
\qquad (2\text{—}48)
$$

Substituting these new values of the branch flows in the head loss equation (in this example (2—45))

$$
\begin{aligned}
k_{r_{BC}} \, (Q'_{BC} - \Delta Q)^n + k_{r_{CD}} \, (Q'_{CD} - \Delta Q)^n - \\
- k_{r_{AB}} \, (Q'_{AB} + \Delta Q)^n + k_{r_{AD}} \, (Q'_{AD} + \Delta Q)^n = 0.
\end{aligned}
\qquad (2\text{—}49)
$$

Then expanding the brackets and ignoring the second powers of the small quantity ΔQ

$$
\begin{aligned}
k_{r_{BC}} \, (Q'^n_{BC} - n \, \Delta Q \, Q'^{\,n-1}_{BC}) + k_{r_{CD}} \, (Q'^n_{CD} - n \, \Delta Q \, Q'^{\,n-1}_{CD}) - \\
- k_{r_{AB}} \, (Q'^n_{AB} + n \, \Delta Q \, Q'^{\,n-1}_{AB}) - k_{r_{AD}} \, (Q'^n_{AD} + n \, \Delta Q \, Q'^{\,n-1}_{AD}) = 0.
\end{aligned}
\qquad (2\text{—}50)
$$

This equation thus yields an estimate of ΔQ, i. e.

$$
\Delta Q = \frac{k_{r_{BC}} \, Q'^n_{BC} + k_{r_{CD}} \, Q'^n_{CD} - k_{r_{AB}} \, Q'^n_{AB} - k_{r_{AD}} \, Q'^n_{AD}}{n \, (k_{r_{BC}} \, Q'^{\,n-1}_{BC} + k_{r_{CD}} \, Q'^{\,n-1}_{CD} + k_{r_{AB}} \, Q'^{\,n-1}_{AB} + k_{r_{AD}} \, Q'^{\,n-1}_{AD})}
\qquad (2\text{—}51)
$$

ΔQ being positive in the direction of Q'_{AB}.

This method can be generalized if it is remembered to keep a consistent sign (say clockwise flow positive) and negative ΔQ when the head loss term is negative; since in relation (2—51) it is the term ΔQ which contains the sign change, the denominator is a sum of absolute terms.

Then (2—51) can be written generally

$$
\Delta Q = \frac{\displaystyle\sum_{i=1}^{N} (k_r \, Q^n)_i}{\displaystyle\sum_{i=1}^{N} (n k_r \, Q_0^{n-1})} .
\qquad (2\text{—}52)
$$

By returning to the example, Q''_{AB} can now be taken as $Q'_{AB} + \Delta Q$ and similarly for the rest of (2—48). The process is continued using these better values of the flow, until ΔQ is acceptably small.

The values k_r can be determined either in the usual way, by use of the diagrams $i = f(Q.\mu)$ or $i = f(Q)$ (Figs. 2—3 and 2—4) for the initially assumed flows, or by the use of any theoretical or experimental relation. The head losses deduced initially can be used until the end of the process, in spite of their approximate value, since they occur in both the numerator and the denominator of expression (2—51), and small corrections to their values will have a negligible effect.

If it is considered necessary a more precise estimate of the head losses may be obtained from the final flow values.

The whole process may be summarized as follows :

a). The equations of continuity and head loss must be used with a sign convention (clockwise positive).

b). It must be remembered that the same sign convention applies to ΔQ, and thus if the flow in a branch is anti-clockwise ΔQ must be taken away.

c). Each loop of a circuit is treated separately, and common branches must be considered subject to the increments from both loops.

For the rapid calculation of the complicated networks, it is useful to apply an electrical analogy, the voltage drop and the current corresponding respectively to the head loss and flow rate. Information on the head loss, flow distribution, etc. may thus be obtained without trial-and-error calculations, and the effects of changes in the pipe dimensions can be rapidly predicted.

The advent of digital computers has meant that complicated lubrication networks can be solved swiftly by their use, if the cost is justified [6].

2.1.2. Numerical Examples

2.1.2.1. *The Supply System.* Consider a lubricating circuit (Fig. 2—12) fed by a pump having a capacity of 200 cm³/sec of oil ($\gamma = 0.0009$ g/cm³ and $\mu = 0.9$ poise at 30°C). The length and inside diameter of the pipes are specified in the figure. The values of the coefficient K are the following : for the entrance loss (a), $K = 0.5$ (from Fig. 2—7); for the elbow (b), $K = 0.72$ (from Table 2—1); for the gate valve (c) 1/4 open, $K = 24$ (from Table 2—2); for the stop valve (d) 1/2 open, $K = 6.4$ (from Table 2—2).

In order to establish the total pressure drop Δp, it is convenient to find the equivalent length L_e for elbow, valves, etc. and then to use relation (2—35) for the total length L

$$L = \sum_{i=1}^{N} L_i + \sum_{j=1}^{M} (L_e)_j$$

It is readily seen that $\Sigma L_i = L_A + L_B + L_C = 0.5 + 1 + 1 = 2.5$ m and relation (2—18) $L_e = \dfrac{K}{k} r$ and the graph in Fig. 2—5 are used for the equivalent lengths.

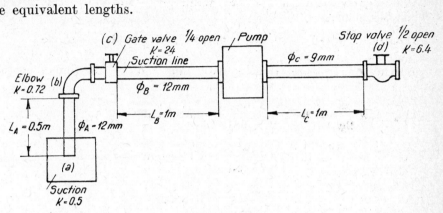

Fig. 2.12. — Lubricating circuit.

Upstream of the pump, the velocity $v = \dfrac{Q}{\pi r^2} = \dfrac{200}{\pi \times 0.6^2} = 176$ cm/sec, so that $\mathbf{R_e} = \dfrac{\rho v r}{\mu} = \dfrac{0.9 \times 176 \times 0.6}{0.9} = 106$; since $\mathbf{R_e} < 1000$ the regime is laminar and $k = \dfrac{32}{\mathbf{R_e}} = 0.302$. Downstream of the pump, $v = \dfrac{200}{\pi \times 0.45} = 317$ cm/sec, $\mathbf{R_e} = 191$ and $k = 0.168$.

Thus $\Sigma (L_e) = L_{e_a} + L_{e_b} + L_{e_c} + L_{e_d} = \dfrac{0.6}{0.302}\, 0.6 + \dfrac{0.72}{0.302}\, 0.6 +$

$+ \dfrac{6.4}{0.302}\, 0.6 + \dfrac{6.4}{0.168}\, 0.45 = 66$ cm, and $L = 2.5 + 0.66 = 3.16$ m.

The head loss is obtained from relation (2—24)

$$\Delta h_L = \sum_{i=1}^{N} (k_r\, Q^n)_i + \sum_{j=1}^{M} (\Delta h)_j$$

and relation (2—28) gives : $k_r = \dfrac{iL}{Q^n}$ ($n = 1$, since the motion is laminar) and one finds for the pipes ($Q_A = Q_B = Q_C = 200$ cm^3/sec) $k_{r_A} = \dfrac{i_A L_A}{Q_A} =$

$= \dfrac{1.15 \times 50}{200} = 0.287$ sec/cm^2, $k_{r_B} = \dfrac{i_B\, L_B}{Q_B} = \dfrac{1.15 \times 100}{200} = 0.575$ sec/cm^2

and $k_{r_C} = \dfrac{i_c L_c}{Q_c} = \dfrac{1.50 \times 100}{200} = 0.75$ sec/cm^2; i_A, i_B, i_C are deduced from Fig. 2—3 as a function of the diameter of the pipes, the product $Q.\mu$ and the density ρ.

Finally, $\overset{N}{\underset{i=1}{\Sigma}}(k_r Q^n)_i = (0.287 + 0.575 + 0.750)\,200 \cong 322$ cm.

Further on, from relation (2—16) : $\Delta h = K \dfrac{v^2}{2g}$ one finds

$$\Delta h_a = K\,\frac{v_2^2}{2g} = 0.5\,\frac{176^2}{2 \times 981} = 7.85 \text{ cm}$$

$$\Delta h_b = K\,\frac{v^2}{2g} = 0.72\,\frac{176^2}{2 \times 981} = 11.4 \text{ cm}$$

$$\Delta h_c = K\,\frac{v^2}{2g} = 24\,\frac{176^2}{2 \times 981} = 378 \text{ cm}$$

$$\Delta h_d = K\,\frac{v^2}{2g} = 6.4\,\frac{317^2}{2 \times 981} = 316 \text{ cm}$$

so that $\overset{M}{\underset{j=1}{\Sigma}}(\Delta h)_j = 7.85 + 11.40 + 378 + 316 = 713$ cm, the total head loss $\Delta h_L = 322 + 713 = 1035$ cm, and the fall of pressure in the system $\Delta p = \gamma\,\Delta h_L$ — relation (2—25) — will be : $\Delta p = 0.0009 \times 1035 = 0.93186$ kg/cm^2 = 0.932 atm, i. e. in circulating through the system, the oil pressure drops nearly 1 atm.

If formula (2—38) is used $i = \dfrac{\Delta h_L}{L} = \dfrac{1035}{316} = 3.27$, one can find the equivalent diameter from Fig. 2—3, as a function of i, the product $Q.\mu$ and the density. Its value is found to be $\Phi_e \cong 10$ mm, quite acceptable for the given system (pipes A, B, have $\Phi_{A,B} = 12$ cm, pipe C has $\Phi_C = 9$ mm, and there are also losses in elbow and valves) so that it constitutes a satisfactory check of the previous calculation.

For other elements of the lubrication system, downstream of the stop valve (d), one of the following methods can be used.

2.1.2.2. *Parallel Pipes*. Three parallel pipes emerging from the same joint are considered (see Fig. 2—9) ; the dimensions are the following : $\Phi_A = 12$ mm ; $\Phi_B = 8$ mm ; $\Phi_C = 18$ mm ; $L = L_A = L_B = L_C = 10$ m. The total flow $Q = 100$ cm^3/sec. The viscosity μ of the oil is 0.9 P at 30°C. The motion is laminar, as can be observed from Fig. 2—3, so that $n = 1$.

The flow rates in pipes A, B, C, must be established, as well as the head loss. Using the method obtained in § 2.1.1.2., an arbitrary flow must be chosen, say $Q'_A = 30$ cm^3/sec, then Fig. 2—3 gives $i_A = 0.5$. Since from relation (2—39) $\Delta h_{L_A} = \Delta h_{L_B} = \Delta h_{L_C}$ and $L_A = L_B = L_C$, one finds $i_A = i_B = i_C = 0.5$. For $i = 0.5$, Fig. 2—3 gives $Q'_B = 8$ cm^3/sec for $\Phi_B = 8$ mm and $Q'_C = 100$ cm³/sec for $\Phi_C = 18$ mm, so that $Q' = Q'_A + Q'_B + Q'_C = 138$ cm³/sec.

When relations (2—43) are applied, it is found that

$$Q_A = \frac{Q'_A \times Q}{Q'} = \frac{30 \times 100}{138} \cong 22 \text{ cm}^3/\text{sec}$$

$$Q_B = \frac{Q'_B \times Q}{Q'} = \frac{8 \times 100}{138} \cong 6 \text{ cm}^3/\text{sec}$$

$$Q_C = \frac{Q'_C \times Q}{Q'} = \frac{100 \times 100}{138} \cong 72 \text{ cm}^3/\text{sec}$$

From Fig. 2 — 3 one finds for the above deduced flow rates: $i_A = 0.40$, $i_B = 0.39$, $i_C = 0.38$. These values are sufficiently close to the original values of 0.5 and the calculation is not continued further. The mean value for the head loss is (Eq. (2—9)) : $\Delta h_L = iL = 0.39 \times 10 = 3.9$ m, and the corresponding pressure drop $\Delta p = 0.35/\text{cm}^2$ ($\Delta p = \gamma \Delta h$ and $\gamma = 0.0009$ kg/cm²).

If greater precision is required, the new value of $i_A = 0.4$ can be used to calculate a closer estimate of the system performance.

2.1.2.3. *Pipe Network.* The pipe network in Fig. 2 — 13 is considered, its characteristics being: $\Phi_{AB} = 12$ mm; $\Phi_{AC} = 18$ mm; $\Phi_{BC} = 10$ mm; $\Phi_{BD} = 18$ mm; $\Phi_{CD} = 12$ mm; $L_{AB} = L_{AC} = L_{BD} = L_{CD} = 5$ m; $L_{BC} = 8$ m. The oil circulates in the system at 60°C and $\mu = 0.046$ P.

The flow rates through the pipes must be determined, only the total flow $Q = 1200$ cm³/sec being known.

By assuming a flow distribution as shown in Fig. 2—13a : $Q_{0_{AB}} = Q_{0_{BC}} = Q_{0_{CD}} = 400$ cm³/sec; $Q_{0_{AC}} = Q_{0_{BD}} = 800$ cm³/sec, Fig. 2—4 gives (the motion is turbulent, $n = 2$) : $i_{AB} = 1$; $i_{AC} = 0.6$; $i_{BC} = 3$; $i_{CD} = 1$; $i_{BD} = 0.6$.

The values of k_r are deduced from relation (2—28) :

$$k_{r_{AB}} = \frac{i_{AB} L_{AB}}{Q^2_{0_{AB}}} = \frac{1 \times 500}{400^2} = 0.31 \times 10^{-2} \text{ sec/cm}^2$$

In a similar way one finds : $k_{r_{AC}} = k_{r_{BD}} = 0.47 \times 10^{-3}$ sec/cm²; $k_{r_{BC}} = 1.5 \times 10^{-2}$ sec/cm²; $k_{r_{CD}} = 0.31 \times 10^{-2}$ sec/cm².

If the method of controlled trial-and-error (§ 2.1.1.3.) is applied, the value ΔQ is established from relation (2—52) for the loop ABC of the system, as follows

$$\Delta Q = \frac{k_{r_{AB}} \times Q_{0_{AB}}^2 - k_{r_{AC}} \times Q_{0_{AC}}^2 - k_{r_{BC}} \times Q_{0_{BC}}^2}{n\,(k_{r_{AB}} \times Q_{0_{AB}} + k_{r_{AC}} \times Q_{0_{AC}} + k_{r_{BC}} \times Q_{0_{BC}})} =$$

$$= \frac{0.31 \times 10^{-2} \times 400^2 - 0.47 \times 10^{-3} \times 800^2 - 1.5 \times 10^{-2} \times 400}{2\,(0.31 \times 10^{-2} \times 400 + 0.47 \times 10^{-3} \times 800 + 1.5 \times 10^{-2} \times 400)} =$$

$$= + 144 \ \text{cm}^3/\text{sec}$$

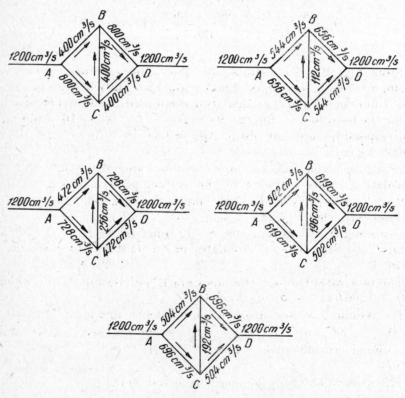

Fig. 2.13. — Successive steps in the iterative calculation of oil flows in a loop.

For the loop BCD one obtains in the same way $\Delta Q = -144$ cm³/sec. When these corrections are applied to the system, in conformity to relation (2—47) and to the specified indications, the flow rates from Fig. 2—13b are found : $Q_{AB} = Q_{CD} = 544$ cm³/sec ; $Q_{AC} = Q_{BD} = 656$ cm³/sec ; $Q_{BC} = 112$ cm³/sec.

By considering now these flow rates as assumed flow rates for a new procedure, and preserving the values of k_r, one finds for the loop ABC, $\Delta Q = -72$ cm³/sec, for the loop BCD, $\Delta Q = 72$ cm³/sec, and the resulting flow rates are shown in Fig. 2—13 c. Repeating the procedure, $\Delta Q = 30$ cm³/sec for the loop ABC and $\Delta Q = -30$ cm³/sec for the loop BCD, the effect of this alteration is shown in Fig. 2—13 d.

Finally, ΔQ is found to be 2 cm³/sec for the loop ABC and $\Delta Q = -2$ cm³/sec for loop BCD, and the corresponding flow distribution is shown in Fig. 2—13 e: $Q_{AB} = Q_{CD} = 504$ cm³/sec; $Q_{AC} = Q_{BD} = 696$ cm³/sec; $Q_{BC} = 192$ cm³/sec.

Since these last values of ΔQ are small, the calculation can be considered complete and the final values of Q retained.

2.2. Design of Lubrication Systems for Non-Newtonian Fluids

Although the large majority of oils obey Newton's law of shearing, there are a number of lubricants which must be considered non-Newtonian. Thus, some synthetic oils, and all of the greases have characteristics which may change in use, the same lubricant presenting different shearing stresses under the same boundary conditions after a period of time.

Viscosity, as has been pointed out, is a notion generally applied to Newtonian fluids [7]; their behaviour is exhibited by line one of Fig. 2—14. Other liquids follow the non-linear relation $\tau = f\left(\dfrac{\partial v_1}{\partial x_2}\right)$; for them the curve passes through the origin, which means that the shearing stresses become zero at the same time as does the velocity; non-Newtonian liquids of this type include those synthetic oils not obeying Newton's law of shearing. Since deviations from Newton's law $\left(\tau = \mu\dfrac{\partial v_1}{\partial x_2}\right)$ are not large, it

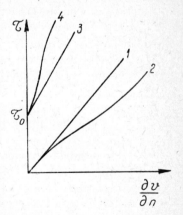

Fig. 2.14.— Behaviour of various classes of lubricants.

will be assumed that this law is valid for any oil.

The characteristic curves for greases, lines 3 and 4 of Fig. 2—2, do not pass through the origin, indicating that a unit effort τ_0 is needed at zero relative velocity to start the motion, and the expression $\tau = f\left(\dfrac{\delta v_1}{\partial x_2}\right)$ can be either linear or nonlinear.

For non--Newtonian lubricants, the term "consistency" is used; the consistency of a grease is analogous to the viscosity of an oil, the corresponding coefficient being defined in the same way as viscosity, but sometimes the reciprocal relation between the normal velocity gradient and the shear stress is used, this reciprocal relation being called "mobility".

The consistency is determined by the grease structure, elasticity and ductility and is affected by different factors: the nature and quality of metallic soap, the percentage of free grease and alkaline substances used in the saponification process, the water content, thermal conditions, manufacturing methods and so on [2].

The consistency of greases during operation is modified by the time of utilisation and by the degree of mixing and stirring. The consistency of greases and plastic materials depends on the shearing action to which they have been previously submitted i.e. the materials are time-dependent, and usually reffered to as thixotropic. It must be pointed out, however, that thixotropic fluids show a decrease in consistency or shear stress with time, under isothermal conditions and steady shear, while those showing an increase are termed as rheopectic, or antithixotropic; however, the latter mode of behaviour is relatively uncommon.

The friction developed in pipes and bearings, the flow of grease, and the operating characteristics of bearings depend on the consistency, which should be considered the fundamental property of these lubricants.

Consistency is measured by the rate of flow of grease through various capillary tubes [2], at various pressures. Another method of determining the consistency is the measurement of the depth to which a standard body subjected to a given force penetrates into a mass of grease.

In order to design grease-lubricated systems correctly, the flow properties of greases must be determined over the whole range of shear strain rates likely to be met with in the system. There are two main types of mechanical lubrication systems. The first one works with one pumping unit feeding a main pipe, from which there are separate lines to individual points, and it must be remarked that this system works at high strain rates. The second type has individual pumps for each lubrication point; in this case very low strain rates are encountered.

The "equivalent flow rate" can be defined as

$$\frac{Q_v}{\pi r^3} = \frac{1}{\tau_r^3} \int_0^{\tau_r} \varphi \ \tau_{ri}^3 \ \mathrm{d}\tau_{ri} \qquad\qquad (2-53)$$

which is independent of the pipe size; Q_v is the volume rate of flow, $\tau_r = \dfrac{pr}{2L}$ the shear stress at wall of the pipe, L the length of the pipe,

τ_{rt} the shear stress at radius r in pipe, p the pressure and φ the fluidity at shear stress τ_r. For the first type of system incorporating a main pump with several branches, values of this parameter lie between 0.1 and 100 sec^{-1}, while for the second case, an individual pump for every feed point, the value of the equivalent flow rate never exceeds 1 sec^{-1}, [8].

2.2.1. Experimental Evidence

Very useful experimental data has been obtained by Summers-Smith [8], in order to examine the validity of relation (2—53) and to check the reproducibility of the results. The pipe test rig consisted of a cylindrical reservoir and a length of pipe, both immersed in a water bath at a constant temperature; the grease was forced through the pipe by gas pressure and a floating piston. Four sizes of pipe covered a range from 3/16 in up to 1 in nominal bore, and the pipes were sandblasted. The pressure drop for 11 ft length of pipe was obtained from calibrated oil-filled Bourdon gauges and the rate of flow was measured by collecting the efflux.

Two types of laboratory viscometers have been used: the S.O.D. capillary viscometer (ASTM 1954) and the Amner and Blott plunger viscometer. The characteristics of the greases used in the tests (lime-based cup greases of no. 1 N.L.G.I. consistency) are given in Table 2—3, [8]

Table 2—3

Characteristics of Greases [8]

Grease	Worked penetration at 25°C	Viscosity of base oil at 38°C (cSt)	Approximate soap content (%)
A	314	113	14.0
B	337	54	12.5

The results obtained with the above mentioned test rig are plotted in Fig. 2—15, for grease A at 0°C and 24°C, and for grease B at 18°C [8]. Considerable experimental scatter can be observed, but in spite of the systematic errors, no systematic variation with the pipe diameter is to be detected.

The results obtained with the S.O.D. viscometer, where the grease is forced from the cylinder through the capillaries by means of hydraulic pressure, do not agree with the experimental results obtained with the Summers-Smith test rig.

The results taken from the plunger viscometer can be converted to compare with those measured by Summers-Smith, but there is little agreement in this case also.

2.2.2. Calculation Data

The mechanism of the flow of greases through pipes is not yet sufficiently understood, so that empirical methods must be employed. One of these equations assumes that the grease behaves like a Bingham plastic, i.e. it presents a definite yield point; Buckingham's relation gives values of the flow parameter thus:

$$\frac{Qv}{\pi r^3} = \frac{rm}{8L}\left(p - \frac{4p_0}{3} + \frac{p_0^4}{3p^3}\right) \tag{2—54}$$

where p_0 is the pressure necessary to initiate the flow and m is the mobility. McMillen solved graphically this equation in terms of two parameters: m and $f = \tau_r \cdot c$ (c is the ratio of the radius of the unsheared central plug of grease to the radius of the pipe). Fig. 2—15 shows reasonable agreement between Buckingham's equation (2—54) and the experimental results for values of $\frac{Q_v}{\pi r^3} > 1$, [8].

When the grease is considered as a pseudo-plastic material, the Powell-Eyring model can be used, yielding [8]

$$\tau_r = \eta\,\frac{Q_v}{\pi r^3} + a\,\log\,\frac{Q_v}{\pi r^3} + b. \tag{2—55}$$

In this equation the flow is considered as a rate process, involving both a Newtonian and a non-Newtonian flow and η, a and b are constants depending upon the nature of the grease and the temperature. As it can be seen in Fig. 2—15, the agreement with the experimental results is better than with Buckingham's equation, but not for values $\frac{Q_v}{\pi r^3} < 0.01$.

It should be pointed out that at low equivalent shear rates anomalous results are obtained with the plunger viscometer, which gives a discontinuity in the shear stress/flow rate curve, so that results below this discontinuity must not be considered.

Moreover, the range covered by laboratory viscometers represents only a part of the range likely to be met with in grease-lubrication systems, and no mathematical expression allows an extrapolation of the viscometer results to low rates of flow.

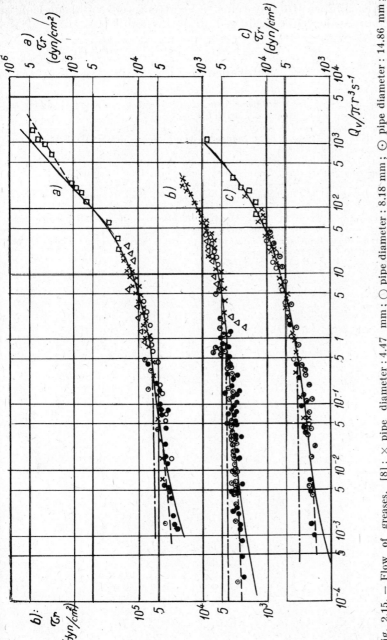

Fig. 2.15. — Flow of greases, [8]: $\times$ pipe diameter: 4.47 mm; $\bigcirc$ pipe diameter: 8.18 mm; $\odot$ pipe diameter: 14.86 mm; $\bullet$ pipe diameter: 25.43 mm; $\triangle$ piston viscometer; $\square$ S.O.D. viscometer.

— — — Experimental flow patterns. — · — · — Buckingham's equation: a) f = 5,580 dyn/cm²; m = 0.0083 W^{-1} b) f = 4,100 dyn/cm²; m = 0.067 W^{-1} c) f = 3,130 dyn/cm²; m = 0.037 W^{-1}

——— Powell-Eyring's equation: a) $\tau_r = 440 \dfrac{Q_v}{\pi r^3} + 1,400 \log\left(\dfrac{Q_v}{\pi r^3}\right) + 6,340$ b) $\tau_r = 56 \dfrac{Q_v}{\pi r^3} + 650 \log\left(\dfrac{Q_v}{\pi r^3}\right) + 4,100$

c) $\tau_r = 92 \dfrac{Q_v}{\pi r^3} + 690 \log\left(\dfrac{Q_v}{\pi r^3}\right) + 3,400$ a) Grease A at 0°C. b) Grease B at 24°C. c) Grease B at 18°C.

However, experimental results in the form of Fig. 2—15 enable the design of grease lubrication systems to be attempted with some confidence. Much more research is required into this subject.

References

1. AL. NICA, *Sisteme noi de ungere a utilajelor industriale* (New Lubrication Systems for Industrial Equipment). Bucharest, I.D.T., 1960.
2. N. TIPEI, *Theory of Lubrication*. Stanford University Press, Stanford, 1962.
3. W. ERNST, *Oil Hydraulic Power and its Industrial Applications*. McGraw-Hill Book Company, New York, 1949.
4. A. G. M. MICHELL, *Lubrication*. Blackie and Son, London, 1950.
5. H. ROUSE, *Engineering Hydraulics*. John Wiley, New York, 1950 (Chapter VI, by V. L. Streeter).
6. V. L. STREETER, *Handbook of Fluid Dynamics*. McGraw-Hill Book Company, New York, 1961.
7. N. TIPEI, V. N. CONSTANTINESCU, AL. NICA, O. BIŢĂ, *Lagăre cu alunecare* (Sliding Bearings), Editura Academiei R.P.R., Bucharest, 1961.
8. D. SUMMERS-SMITH, *Flow Properties of Lubricating Grease*. Proceedings of the Conference on Lubrication and Wear, Paper 25, London 1957.

CHAPTER III

Principal Elements and Construction of Lubrication Systems

A general classification of the methods of distributing oil or grease to the moving parts of a machine or installation, can be best summarized in tabular form (Table 3—1), [1]. It should be pointed out that some of the supply methods can be used for both oils and greases.

Table 3—1

			Total loss systems	Recuperative systems
Semiauto-matic	Low pressure	Oils	Drip feed Wick feed Oil Mist Manual, mechanical or pneumatic oil feed by shots	Ring or chain and oil bath Splash feed from sump Porous rubbing surfaces
		Greases	Pre-packing Funnel feed Routine pressure packing by piston or external pump	
Auto-matic	Low pressure	Oils and greases	Open circuit	Closed circuit
			Gravity feed from reservoir Hydrostatic, pneumatic, electric or mechanically controlled pumps	Recovery with wet or dry sump
	High pressure		Centralised open systems Oil sprays	Recovery with wet or dry sump

3.1. Semiautomatic Systems

Bearings lubricated by rings, wicks or gravity feed, do not need regular attention, and the oil bath and means of supply are usually integral with the load bearing elements.

The design of such bearings is outlined in [2] and in other works on hydrodynamic lubrication [3], [4]. These systems are prone to oil contamination since they are usually difficult to seal effectively against the intrusion of foreign matter.

Greasing methods are widely described in published literature. It is worth pointing out at this stage, that although the use of greases generally permits the simple and inexpensive design of supply devices, they have certain intrinsic disadvantages since a complete lubricant layer is difficult to provide before the bearing reaches its running temperature, and therefore greases do not lend themselves to application in cases of intermittent motion and intermittent use, high starting loads, etc.

Hence, for more stringent environments, loads, and usage, where reliability is a costly commodity, a pressurized centralised oil supply is generally used to overcome these difficulties.

One intermediate solution which does not involve a central supply system but provides lubricant under pressure, at a given moving contact, leads to the applications shown in Figs. 3—1, 3—2, 3—3 and 3—4, [5].

Fig. 3—1 shows a manually operated oil or grease supply unit, which is used where no continuous power source is available and in situations when human surveillance is practical, e.g. farm implements or light production machinery. This system cannot provide a continuous lubricant supply and relies upon the operator for its successful application.

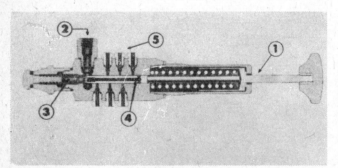

Fig. 3.1. — Manually operated semiautomatic lubricating system [5]: 1 — pump handle and piston; 2 — lubricant inlet; 3 — measuring chamber; 4 — supply duct; 5 — supply ports.

Where the lubricant requirements can be linked to some action of the machinery and a source of energy is available, the feed system can be made semiautomatic, usually with some overriding manual control.

Fig. 3—2 shows a vacuum operated device used, for instance, where manifold pressure, or the application of vacuum brakes indicates to some measure the extent to which the bearings are used, or simply, where negative air pressure is readily available and manual contact is inconvenient.

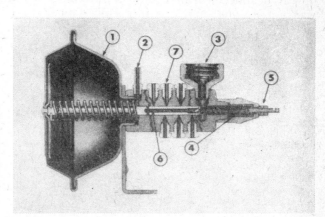

Fig. 3.2. — Vacuum operated semiautomatic lubricating system [5]: 1 — vacuum diaphragm; 2 — vacuum inlet; 3 — lubricant inlet; 4 — measuring chamber; 5 — electric contact assembly; 6 — supply duct; 7 — supply ports.

This device requires a minimum vacuum of 42 mm Hg for operation, and is provided with an electrical display system for manual control.

A compressed air supply is generally available, and Fig. 3—3 shows a similar device used on heavy transport vehicles and various factory equipment. This particular device lends itself to control by mechanical means, linked to some degree with the requirements of the bearings it supplies, or even to control by fixed time cycle devices.

The minimum air supply pressure is of the order of 50 psi (4 kg/cm²).

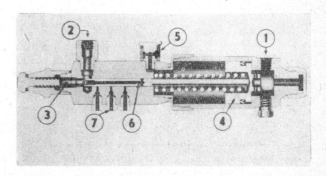

Fig. 3.3. — Air operated semiautomatic lubricating system [5]: 1 — air inlet; 2 — lubricant inlet; 3 — measuring chamber; 4 — air piston; 5 — filter; 6 — supply duct; 7 — supply ports.

Fig. 3—4 shows a mechanically operated device, employing reciprocating or rotary motion as its motive force. This device can supply as many as 12 lubrication points at once, and the feed to each can be metered to meet its individual requirements [5].

3.2. Automatic Systems

The devices outlined in the previous section were either manually operated and controlled, or semiautomatic (inasmuch as the motive force was not manual and the metering dependent on the functioning of the

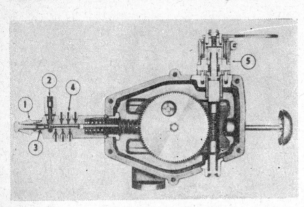

Fig. 3.4. — Mechanically operated semiautomatic lubricating system, [5] : 1 — nose plug ; 2 — lubricating inlet ; 3 — measuring chamber ; 4 — supply ports ; 5 — clutch assembly.

installation) with provision for overriding manual control. To remove reliance on the operator, and to provide continuous lubricant control, it is clearly necessary to use pumps and to centralize the distribution to a greater extent so as to reduce costs.

Automatic systems provide economic and reliable means of supplying lubricant to multiple bearing installations, their design being of some technical complication involving work on pipe flow developed in the previous chapter. It is worth noting that the systems outlined in this section are generally for cycle operation, that is with discontinuous metering to the lubrication points.

3.2.1. Low Pressure Centralized Systems

This category of automatic feed devices includes gravity fed systems as well as low pressure pumped systems ($1 - 5$ kg/cm^2).

3.2.1.1. *Gravity Feed*. The lubricant is ʃstored at a high level in a large reservoir and the system is simply closed by the addition of a scavenging pump.

Clearly these systems can only be used in low flow applications under light loads. Fig. 3—5 represents one example of such a device used in this case to lubricate a steam engine.

3.2.1.2. *Low Pressure Pump Systems*. As in the previous example these supply systems can be closed or open circuits depending on the economic justification of the inclusion of a scavenge pump to recuperate the used oil. However this method allows the use of a single pump for both supply and scavenging, instead of two separate pumps and a reservoir.

The design of these devices is simple, since the lubricant is metered through fixed valves or jets, but due to their low pressure, the pipes cannot be too long, and no hydro-static effects to relieve starting torque and wear can be expected.

Fig. 3—6 shows two practical variants, one using a gear pump (Fig. 3—6 a) and the other a piston pump (Fig. 3—6 b).

The pumps can be powered from any convenient source and it is also possible to control their action to match the supply to the requirements of the installation. It is possible to feed numerous lubrication points from one central pump system, and lubricant contamination presents no problem.

Certain problems concerning the metering of oil to each lubrication point are encountered with this method and the means of overcoming these disadvantages are discussed in Chapter V.

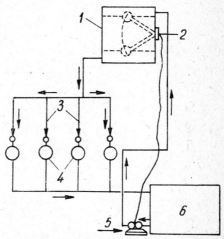

Fig. 3.5. — Gravity feed centralized system : 1 — oil sump ; 2 — electric switch for the pump ; 3 — supply ducts ; 4 — bearings ; 5 — recirculating pump ; 6 — main sump.

3.2.2. High Pressure Centralized Systems

These systems generally employ metering devices actuated by the lubricant supply pressure, to overcome the uncertainties intrinsic in low pressure circuits. They can be used efficiently to provide lubricant to a few points or several thousand, and when correctly designed and operated can bring important direct and indirect savings in the operating costs of an installation. This being mainly due to increased reliability and more precise metering possible with these systems, in addition to the removal of costly operator supervision by full instrumentation and the provision of display panels to indicate directly and immediately the functioning of the entire installation.

In order to outline the design of these networks it is helpful to divide them into classes. For instance, the metering elements can be installed in series or parallel. The network can be based on a single or double pressure line, and the flow can be unidirectional or reversible. The metering devices themselves can be of different forms e.g. piston valves or springs.

Fig. 3—7 compares the series and parallel flow systems: Fig. 3—7a shows the parallel type, with the main line supplying each metering valve independently, while Fig. 3—7b shows the series system where the metering to each point is performed successively, each metering valve being fed from the main line only after the previous one has received its charge. This latter system has the advantage that any blockage in the feed lines is immediately accompanied by a positive indication at the pump, with the obvious disadvantage that subsequent lubrication to any of the points is interrupted, which does not apply to the former system.

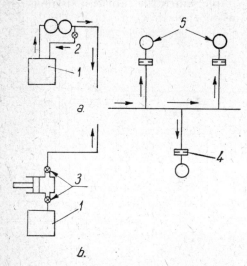

Fig. 3.6. — Low pressure centralized system:

a) With gear pump.
b) With piston pump.

1 — Oil sump; 2 — by-pass; 3 — admission and exhaust valves; 4 — fixed orifice valves; 5 — bearings.

Both of these supply methods can be fed from single-line or double-line ducts, the double line systems putting each line alternatively under pressure. The flow can be also reversed and any combination of these circuits can be employed.

3.2.2.1. *Single Line Automatic Systems.* Fig. 3—8 represents a single line system with spring loaded metering valves, being one of the simplest examples of this type. The design of this class of circuit is adequately described in [1].

The spring loaded metering devices are subject to certain disadvantages, particularly that of the spring being blocked by foreign matter, weakening or breaking.

The principle of operation can be followed from the figure: In Fig. 3 — 8a the supply line is under pressure and the piston is forced downwards to open the valve to the metering cavity. Fig. 3 — 8b shows the lower piston opening to allow

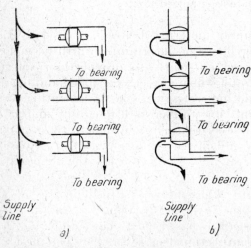

a)   b)

Fig. 3.7. — Comparison of parallel (a) and series (b) flow systems.

pressurized lubricant to flow through the one-way valve to the bearing. The shot of lubricant is interrupted in Fig. 3—8c as the lower piston stops the supply pressure reaching the one-way valve, and the supply line is disconnected from the pump by the rotary valve (4) and the

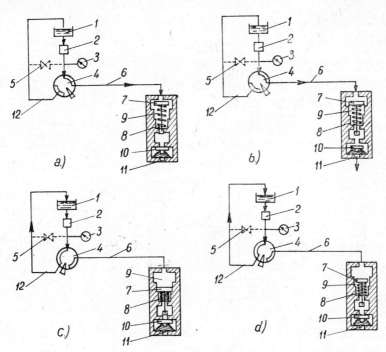

Fig. 3.8. — Single-line centralized system :
1 — lubricant reservoir; 2 — pump; 3 — manometer; 4 — three-way rotating valve; 5 — by-pass; 6 — supply line; 7 — piston; 8 — spring; 9 — measuring chamber; 10 — non-return valve; 11 — supply port; 12 — shut-down line.

piston is returned to its inital position by the spring to complete the cycle (Fig. 3—8d).

This system feeds a shot of lubricant, approximately equal to the internal volume of the metering valve, to the bearing, whenever the rotary valve puts its supply line under pressure.

3.2.2.2. *Double Line Automatic Systems.* For multiple port applications, provision is shown in Fig. 3—9 for the parallel ducting of several double line valves into one manifold, and a complete assembly using one of these units is shown in Fig. 3—13.

The example given in Fig. 3—9 incorporates piston valves, and the cycle is as follows [1]. The upper supply line is first opened to the pumped lubricant which moves the landed control piston (Fig. 3—9a) to allow lubricant into the metering chamber. The process is continued in Fig. 3—9b, the pressurized lubricant forcing the second piston down to supply the metered volume of oil (remaining from the previous cycle) to one of the bearings. The end of this movement of the piston in the metering chamber is shown in Fig. 3—9c, the lower supply

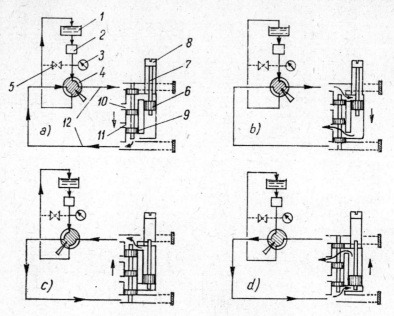

Fig. 3.9. — Double line centralized system :

1 — lubricant reservoir; 2 — pump; 3 — manometer; 4 — four-way rotating valve; 5 — by-pass; 6 — measuring piston; 7 — indicator rod; 8 — control assembly; 9 — landed piston; 10 — supply port no. 1; 11 — supply port no. 2; 12 — double supply line of the system.

line being opened to return the piston to its original position, and to supply the second bearing with lubricant. Fig. 3—9d shows this being accomplished in the same way as in the down stroke (Fig. 3—9 b).

This device can clearly be used to supply a single bearing with double the metering cylinder volume.

3.2.2.3. *Centralized Systems with Reverse Flow.* Fig. 3—10 represents the piston metering valves utilized in such systems. These are connected in series to the pump via a four-way valve, which changes the direction of flow in the same manner as does the supply line circuit in Fig. 3—9. The only essential difference between this system and the previous double line system is the automatic by-pass of lubricant through the metering valve after the metered quantity has been delivered to the bearing, and before the flow is reversed, [6].

3.2.2.4. *Centralized Systems with Non-Reversing Multiple Port Valves.* All the previous high pressure systems rely upon a rotary valve for controlling the distribution cycle. Non-reversing piston valve feed circuits remove this complication while clearly adding complication to the structure of the metering valves themselves (see Fig. 3—11, [6]).

However, the principle of operation of these unidirectional metering valves simplifies the unit construction of multiple port distributors,

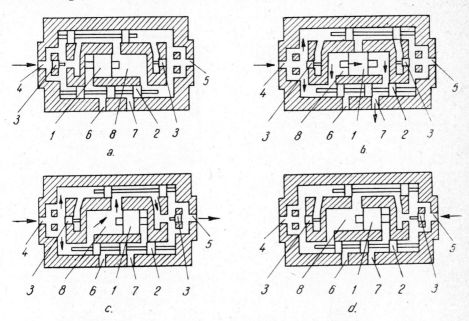

Fig. 3.10. — Piston metering valve for centralized systems with reverse flow [6]:
1 — main piston; 2 — landed piston; 3 — check piston; 4 — first sense supply line;
5 — second sense supply line; 6 — supply port no. 1; 7 — supply port no. 2.

one manifold being capable of containing an almost unlimited number of valves in series, although currently the limit is practically set at about ten.

For applications of greater complexity where groups of lubrication points are situated far apart, a central metering valve of the same basic construction can be used as a central control to reduce the pipe losses and such a system is shown in Fig. 3—12. This system is used in heavy machine tool applications, and in this example some 50 lubrication points are effectively served by only 7 manifolds [7].

The greater flexibility of these systems can be compared to that of a system using double line, or reversible flow valves connected in parallel in one manifold (Fig. 3—13) [8]. It must also be remembered that the warning device is much more reliable in series systems, and for these reasons are more commonly used.

Conclusions. This introduction to the construction of centralized automatic lubrication systems will enable the engineer to choose a multitude of design solutions for a wide range of applications for use with both oils and greases.

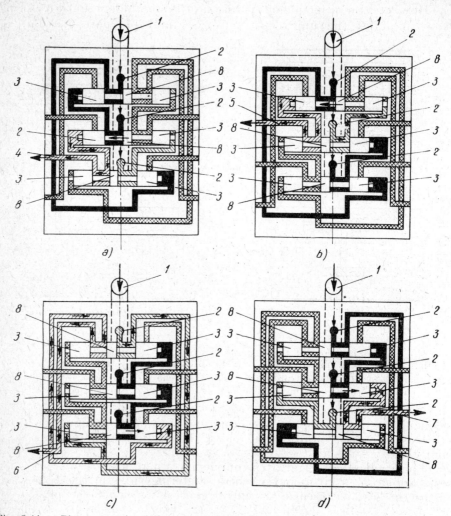

Fig. 3.11. — Piston metering valves for centralized systems with non-reversing flow, [6]: 1—main supply line; 2—supply lines to measuring devices; 3—metering pistons; 4,5,6,7—supply ports to bearings; 8—landed pistons.

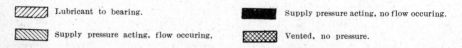

Lubricant to bearing.   Supply pressure acting, no flow occuring.

Supply pressure acting, flow occuring.   Vented, no pressure.

The component parts of these systems (pumps, filters, etc.) will be dealt with in the subsequent chapter to complete the design information.

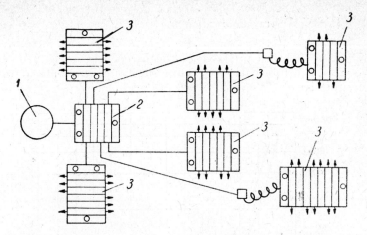

Fig. 3.12. — Single line centralized system with non-reversing flow and manifolds, [7].:

1 — automatic pump; 2 — master manifold; 3 — metering manifolds.

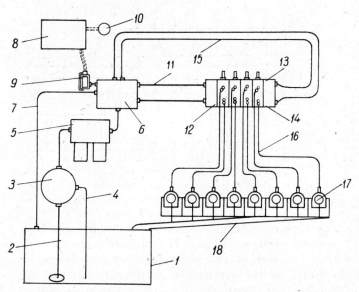

Fig. 3.13. — Double line centralized system with reverse flow [8]:

1 — lubricant reservoir; 2 — supply line with finemesh screen; 3 — pump; 4 — by-pass; 5 — high-pressure filter; 6 — automatic valve; 7 — drain-pipe; 8 — time relay; 9 — automatic valve switch; 10 — warning system; 11 — double supply line; 12 — intake to manifold; 13 — metering manifold; 14 — exit from manifold; 15 — returning lubricant lines; 16 — supply lines to bearings; 17 — bearings; 18 — recuperation lines.

3.2.3. Spray Lubrication

This means of lubricant feed has been recently developed for application in centralized lubrication systems, similar in principle to the widely used single units.

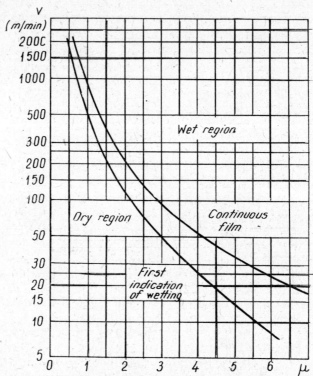

Fig. 3.14. — Effect of velocity and particle size on the wetting capacity of lubricant spray, [9].

The general principle has several designations : oil-fog, oil-mist, aerosol lubricators, sprayed lubricant, etc., but there is little justification for sub-dividing a class of lubricant feed which consists essentially of lubricant dispersed in fine particles suspended in a jet of high speed air.

However, two distinct applications of this principle do lead to a certain confusion in terms. For lubricating the moving parts of compressed air systems the air flow can be very large and the metered lubricant supply much lower than in rolling bearings, chains and gear applications, where the air flow is kept to a minimum.

Although both categories are similar in essence, they cannot employ the same mixing elements and supply equipment.

3.2.3.1. *Design Principles and Data.* The size of the particles of lubricant in suspension influences the distance over which the emulsion can be transported without danger of drop formation in the supply lines.

Particles less than 2 μ in diameter can be moved through several hundreds yards of piping without agglomeration, and this means that a high degree of centralization can be obtained without the inefficiencies intrinsic in long distance oil or grease supply systems.

The formation of a lubricant film at the point of application of the spray depends on the emulsion velocity as well as the particle size. Fig. 3—14 shows the limiting combination of these parameters for particle agglomeration, [9].

Clearly there are two regimes of interest : the particles must be transported without drop formation (low speed, small particle size) and must be condensed to form a film at the lubrication point (by accelerating the emulsion flow, or increasing the particle size).

For different bearing applications three distinct methods of condensing the spray can be used.

In ball bearings, for instance, with surface speeds of at least 1 m/sec and diameters up to 150 mm, a nozz'e can be employed, of about 1 mm diameter. The nozzle works in yet another manner to condense the emulsion, by destroying the surface tension of the lubricant particles in the turbulence produced by the running bearing.

For low speed rolling bearings the lubricant is condensed in the spray unit by adding a tube of some 40 to 45 mm in length and 1.5 mm in diameter to the nozzle. It has been found that one such tube is necessary for every 60 mm of the bearing diameter and each row of the bearing is considered separately, [10], (e.g. a four row roller bearing of 300 mm diameter will be equipped with 20 such nozzles and tubes).

The third method of condensing the air-oil emulsion was originally used in journal bearing applications, but can be successfully employed with plane bearings and guides. It consists of a threaded plug inserted in the feed line, containing several small diameter orifices directing the fluid onto a condensing wall which completes the particle agglomeration, and directs a stream of droplets into the areas of contact.

Spray lubrication is not only an efficient method of supplying and metering lubricant to widely distributed lubrication points, but also provides considerable cooling of the bearings, because of the pressurized air stream ; it also eases the exclusion of foreign matter from the bearing casing by maintaining it above ambient pressure, [9].

By heating the air stream it is possible to form droplets from even high viscosity oils (220 cP at 38°C) and because of the expansion of the air at the delivery point there is no danger of supplying heated oil to the bearings. Thus, for example, the air stream can be heated to 150°C in some cases, and yet the inlet oil temperature at the bearing will still not exceed 30°C.

A simple method of calculating the oil consumption is to take the figure of 0.5 g/hr for each "row — cm" of bearing. This figure is generally accepted to provide a continuous lubricant film without wastage. This parameter, "row — cm", is chosen for rolling bearings, being the product of the bearing diameter and the number of rows; for journal bearings the projected surface area in square cm is divided by 4, [11].

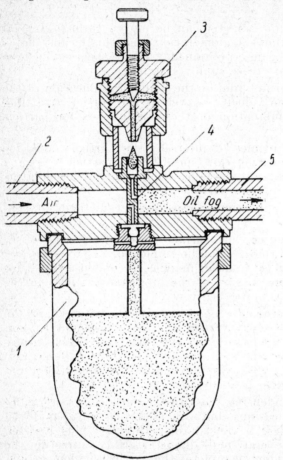

Fig. 3.15. — Oil-fog lubricator, [11]: 1 — oil sump; 2 — compressed air supply; 3 — metering device; 4 — venturi tube; 5 — oil-fog duct.

Thus, for a two row roller bearing of 20 mm diameter the oil requirement is 2 g/hr, while for a journal bearing of similar overall dimensions, 20 mm diameter and 20 mm width, the oil consumption should be 0.5 g/hr.

For plane guides the "row — cm" number is obtained by dividing the area of contact in square cm by 20, while for gears the product of tooth width and pinion diameter is divided by 4, [11].

Spray lubrication systems supplying up to 1000 row — cm have been constructed and used successfully.

3.2.3.2. *Detail Design Considerations.* As was mentioned above, there are two main types of spray lubrication equipment: 1) Those designed to lubricate pneumatically operated equipment, the air being primarily the means of power transmission and only secondarily the oil mist vehicle. 2) Those systems with an independent compressed air supply, which can be optimized to produce efficient oil-spray delivery, usually operating at much lower pressures and flow rates with a higher concentration of lubricant in suspension.

Fig. 3—15 illustrates an example of an aerosol unit suitable for air operated equipment, and usually employed to supply a limited number of elements. The mode of operation of such a device is simple, but the oil mist it produces is somewhat irregular in concentration and droplet size.

Oil is forced from the reservoir through the venturi tube (4), where it enters the air stream through a fine orifice. Not all the oil is broken up sufficiently and the delivery duct (5) usually contains lubricant particles of various sizes.

Spray lubrication of pneumatically operated equipment with a greater number of widely dispersed elements requires a more sophisticated lubricator producing a more uniform oil mist with finer droplets.

Centralized spray lubrication systems employ the same type of lubricator with different venturi sizes and metering jets (see Fig. 3—16); almost 90% of the oil mist formed in the venturi (4) is returned to the reservoir and the particles which finally reach the outlet duct (5) vary in size from 0.5 to 2µ, sufficiently small to be transfered over long distances, even at high air stream speed, supplying thus a large number of lubrication points.

The reservoir can also be provided with a levelling device to improve the constancy of the oil-air mixture, [11].

The complete assembly of a centralized aerosol system is shown in Fig. 3 — 17. Compressed air (1) at something like

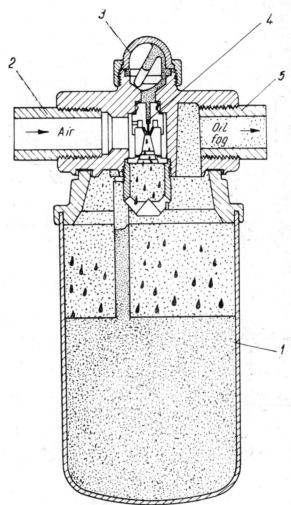

Fig. 3.16. — Uniform oil-mist lubricator, [11] : 1 — oil sump ; 2 — compressed air supply ; 3 — metering device ; 4 — venturi tube ; 5 — oil fog duct.

6 atm is first filtered (2) before being directed (3) to the several aerosol devices which may exist in a machine shop installation. The pressure is generally reduced to an optimum value consistent with the performance of the lubricator and the characteristics of the distribution

network (4). The air supply can be interrupted to conform with the operating cycle of the lubricated machinery by a pressure switch (5), and

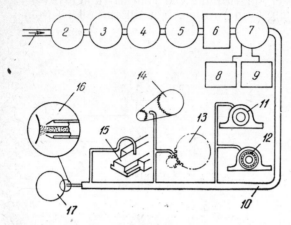

Fig. 3.17. — Components of centralized aerosol systems, [11] : 1 — compressed air supply ; 2 — filter ; 3 — solenoid valve ; 4 — pressure regulator ; 5 — pressure switch ; 6 — air heater ; 7 — oil-fog lubricator ; 8 — liquid-level indicator ; 9 — reservoir heater ; 10 — oil-fog supply duct ; 11 — sliding bearings ; 12 — anti-friction bearings ; 13 — gears ; 14 — chain ; 15 — slides and ways ; 16 — micro-fog reclassifier ; 17 — other utilization points of the oil-fog.

is then fed to the lubricator through a heater, if necessary (6). Various measuring systems can be included, both for checking the oil level in the reservoir and the air supply pressure.

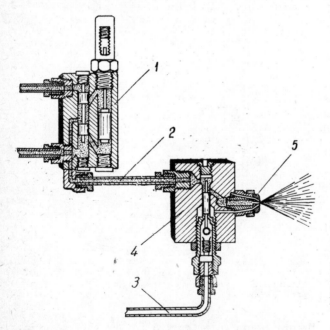

Fig. 3.18. — Individual system of spray lubrication, [12] : 1 — metering valve ; 2 — lubricant supply ; 3—air supply ; 4—ball valve ; 5 — nozzle.

The condenser head is also shown schematically in Fig. 3—17, along with the various applications for which this system is suited, [11].

Another type of centralized spray lubrication system is illustrated in Fig. 3—18, [12]. Compressed and filtered air is supplied to the spraying head (4) and controlled by the oil flow to the metering valve (1), of a form similar to the double line or reverse flow valves of Fig. 3—9.

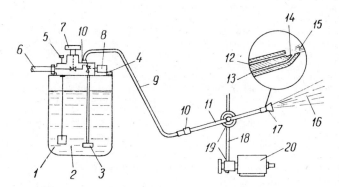

Fig. 3.19. — Mobile device for spray lubrication and cooling, [13]:
1 — reservoir; 2 — emulsion; 3 — filter; 4 — filler; 5 — level-indicator; 6 — air supply; 7 — air valve; 8 — emulsion valve; 9 — flexible duct; 10 — joint; 11 — stainless steel tube; 12 — air channel; 13 — emulsion channel; 14 — extremity of the mixing-head; 15 — point of pulverisation; 16 — oil fog spray; 17 — protection nozzle; 18 — adjustable frame; 19 — adjustable joints; 20 — fixing magnet.

Often an addition is made in the circuit before the condenser head to increase the droplet size and ease the agglomeration of the emulsion, while serving as an individual control over the amount of lubricant delivered to a particular element of the installation. These devices are called re-classifiers and are sometimes merely lengths of small diameter tubing.

The optimum positioning of the spray head depends considerably on the characteristics of the nozzle and the exit droplet size. Generally, however, a distance of 150—200 mm should be allowed between the spray head and the surface upon which the film is required to form, and in some cases, notably gear teeth, condensation is assisted if the spray makes an angle of 30° with surfaces entering into contact [1].

Portable spray lubrication devices are useful in small machine tool applications, and an example is illustrated in Fig. 3—19. This system can be supplied directly with shop air or provided with a small independent compressor.

The spray can be directed on to the tool bit and considerable cooling can be achieved either with oil-water emulsion or cutting fluids in suspension, [13].

References

1. AL. NICA, *Sisteme noi de ungere a utilajelor industriale* (New Lubrication Systems for Industrial Equipment). Bucharest, I.D.T., 1960.
2. N. TIPEI, V. N. CONSTANTINESCU, AL. NICA, O. BIȚĂ, *Lagăre cu alunecare* (Sliding Bearings), in Romanian. Editura Academiei R.P.R., Bucharest, 1961.
3. D. D. FULLER, *Theory and Practice of Lubrication for Engineers.* Wiley, New York, 1956.
4. G. VOGELPOHL, *Betriebssichere Gleitlager.* Springer-Verlag, Berlin, 1967.
5. Lincoln Engineering Co., Saint Louis, U. S. A., *Catalog-82.*
6. A. F. BREWER, *A Survey of Lubrication Methods.* Lubr. Eng., **16**, *11*, 1960, **17**, *8*, 1961.
7. Trabon Engineering Corporation, Solon, Ohio, U.S.A., *Bulletin no. 5410.*
8. Farval Division, Eaton Manufacturing Co., Cleveland, Ohio, U.S.A., *Bulletin no. 26—T.*
9. D. G. FAUST, *Fog Lubrication of Machine Tools.* Lubr. Eng., **14**, *2*, 1958.
10. R. FRAZIER, *Oil Mist Lubrication on Roll Neck Bearings.* Iron and Steel Engineer, **11**, *8*, 1963.
11. D. G. FAUST, *Oil Fog Lubrication — Past, Present and Future.* Lubr. Eng., vol. **17**, *8*, 1961.
12. E. J. GESDORF, *Modern Techniques for Spray Lubricating Industrial Gearing.* Lubr. Eng., **15**, *10* 1959.
13.   —   *Precise Vapor Lub Cooling System.* Scient. Lubr., **11**, *10*, 1959.

CHAPTER IV

Auxiliary Components of Lubrication Systems

4.1. Pumping Devices

4.1.1. Gear Pumps

This type of pump is perhaps the most widely used method of lubricant supply, mainly due to its wide range of operating parameters, and its ability to cope with almost any form of lubricant.

The mode of operation of a typical spur-gear pump is illustrated by Fig. 4—1. The fluid is carried around the periphery of each of the meshing gears in the cavities between their teeth, and is obstructed from returning to the input port by the mating of the teeth in the contact region.

Small quantities of fluid may be trapped between approaching teeth in this region, and this can give rise to considerable pressures and consequent additional loading of the gear shafts and bearings. This effect can be minimised by the provision of relief grooves in the side plates, exhausting the excess oil to the output side of the pump casing.

The oil flow Q obtained from a gear pump is given by a simple relation

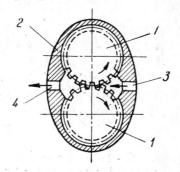

Fig. 4.1. — Operating principle of gear pumps : 1— gears ; 2 — housing ; 3 — suction ; 4 — pressure zone.

$$Q = \pi \, d \, l \, m \, n \, h \, \eta \, 10^{-6} \, \text{litres/min} \quad (4-1)$$

where m and d are the pitch and pitch diameter of each pinion (in mm), h the tooth height and l its width (in mm), and n the rotational speed in rpm ; η is the volumetric efficiency of the pump and generally lies between 0.7 and 0.8.

The efficiency is much influenced by the viscosity of the pumped medium as shown in Fig. 4—2, which also gives an idea of the range of application of this type of pump, [1].

The pump speed is generally found to be between 900 and 1800 rpm and outlet pressures can rise to 100 atm or more, with flow rates reaching values of 200 to 300 l/min.

The disadvantage of this type of pump is its intrinsic hydraulic inbalance which causes a drop in mechanical efficiency because of high bearing loads.

The radial pressure distribution can be made more uniform by ducting oil from the high pressure outlet region through channels in

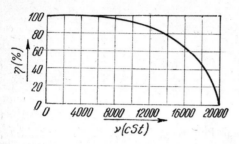

Fig. 4.2. — Volumetric efficiency of gear pumps as a function of viscosity.

the side plates to the low pressure regions without a large reduction in volumetric efficiency [2].

Two types of gear pump employing a slightly different principle of operation are shown in Figs 4—3, [3] and 4—4, [2].

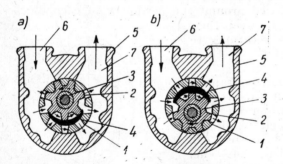

Fig. 4.3. — Internal gear pump, [3]: 1 — rotor; 2 — idler; 3 — bushing; 4 — crescent; 5 — housing; 6 — suction zone; 7 — pressure zone.

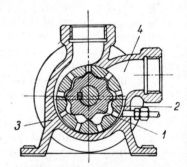

Fig. 4.4. — Internal gear pump, [2]: 1 — rotor; 2 — idler; 3 — housing; 4 — suction zone.

The first pump can be used in situations where the drive is reversed without reversing the flow of oil, the crescent shaped segment shifting to accomodate the reversed rotation of the outer gear (Figs. 4—3a and 4—3b), [3].

The second internal gear pump uses specially profiled teeth, and dispenses with the third moving part. The pinion has one less tooth than the outer ring, and the pitch and pitch diameters are chosen to provide a difference in diameters equal to the height of one tooth. The tooth shape is constructed of logarithmic spirals and the flow is reversed with the drive.

4.1.2. Vane Pumps

Slightly higher volumetric efficiencies can generally be achieved with vane pumps at the expense of lower delivery pressures (see Fig. 4—5) [2]. The rotor is placed eccentrically in the pump housing (Fig. 4—5a) and the degree (and even sense) of the eccentricity e determines the flow through the pump, thus

$$Q = 2\pi\, D\, e\, l\, n\, \eta\ 10^{-6}\ \text{l/min} \qquad (4-2)$$

where η generally lies between 0.8 and 0.9 and where the dimensions (see Fig. 4—5b) are in mm.

The sealing at the vane tips and the wear between the vanes and the housing and rotor slots are the main sources of mechanical and volumetric inefficiencies. By careful construction the flow rate can rise to values comparable with that of a gear pump providing the pressure difference across the pump is less than 70 to 80 atm. The hydraulic balance can be improved by rearranging the ports in diametrically opposed pairs.

Higher delivery pressures can be achieved by connecting such pumps in series. The flow can also be varied or reversed by altering the eccentricity of the rotor shaft and this can also be realised automatically.

4.1.3. Piston Pumps

The reciprocating motion of the piston in this type of pump can be provided by a simple crank, but is more usually effected in two ways: the first category uses a radial disposition of the pump cylinders, and the second uses axial cylinders arranged around the central drive shaft.

These pumps are generally used in high pressure applications and also for variable flow devices [2].

4.1.3.1. *Radial Piston Pumps.* This type is especially suitable for supplying variable quantities of fluid at a constant driving speed. Fig. 4—6 shows three positions of the outer ring controlling the pump stroke, the flow being positive, zero, and negative respectively in (a), (b) and (c), [2]. When the ring is eccentric to the rotor the pistons will each have the same stroke (equal to $2\,e$) and the flow will be

$$Q = 2A\, n\, e\, i\, \eta\ 10^{-6}\ \text{l/min} \qquad (4-3)$$

where A is the area of the piston face in mm^2, e the eccentricity in mm, i the number of pistons and n the speed of rotation in rpm. The volumetric efficiency η is generally between 0.8 and 0.9. These pumps can deliver pressures of up to 250 atm and are used in lubrication systems where continuously variable flow or precisely fixed flow is required.

The design of the piston thrust faces can vary considerably, and the eccentric cam can also be placed inside the cylinder block, which may be fixed, the cam then rotating to provide the pumping action.

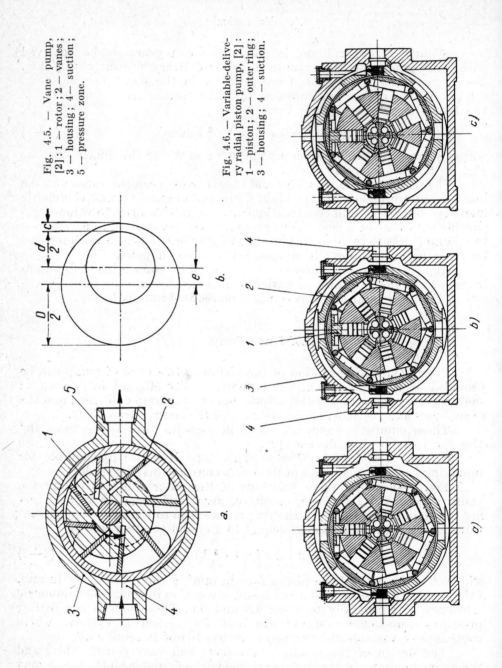

Fig. 4.5. — Vane pump, [2]: 1 — rotor; 2 — vanes; 3 — housing; 4 — suction; 5 — pressure zone.

Fig. 4.6. — Variable-delivery radial piston pump, [2]: 1 — piston; 2 — outer ring; 3 — housing; 4 — suction.

4.1.3.2. *Axial Piston Pumps*. A more compact design can be achieved by placing the pump cylinders parallel to the axis of rotation and providing the pumping action by some form of angled plate (see Fig. 4—7) [2].

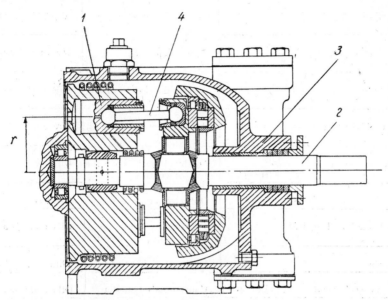

Fig. 4.7. — Variable-delivery axial piston pump, [2]: 1 — piston; 2 — shaft; 3 — housing; 4 — connecting rod.

The flow is (similar to (4—3))

$$Q = 2An\, e\, i\, \eta\, 10^{-6}\ \text{l/min} \qquad\qquad (4-4)$$

where the eccentricity $e = r \tan \beta$, r being the radius of the piston circle (neglecting connecting-rod tilt) and β the maximum swash-plate angle (usually 20°), [2].

The general performance of this pump is very similar to that of a radial piston pump, with the same shortcomings of difficult lubrication and complicated construction.

4.2. Sealing Devices

The exclusion of foreign matter and the conservation of lubricant are essential to the efficacy of a lubrication system. A good sealing device must achieve these ends with a minimum of friction and wear, consistent with the demands of simplicity.

Table 4—1 lists the various types of seals with their respective fields of application, [4].

Table 4—1, [4]

Type of seal	Application	Suitable lubricant
Stamped pieces	Low velocities; clean environment	Very thick greases
Stamped and turned pieces	Usual bearings	Medium thick greases
Radial grooves	Variable velocities; contaminated media	Oils and greases
Grooves filled with grease	Antifriction bearings	Greases
Stuffing-boxes	Oil level well above the line of centres	Oils
Rings	Only for greases	Greases
Spring loaded sealing lips	Bearings working in uncontaminated media	Oils and greases
Labyrinths	High-speed bearings	Thin oils
Face type seals (leather or synthetic)	Contaminated media	Oils and greases
Felt, leather, cork, synthetic rubber (eventually with grooves or labyrinths)	Contaminated media (cork); felt only for low velocities	Oils and greases
Rubber (eventually in combination with other systems)	Bearings	Water; turbine oils

4.2.1. Hydraulic Seals

4.2.1.1. *Calculation Data.* The flow of fluid through the small annular spaces between shaft and seal lip exhibits certain peculiarities which must be observed for effective seal design. One notable fact is that the critical Reynolds number for turbulent flow based on the annular clearance c and the fluid velocity v, is much lower than for pipe flow, varying as it does between 600 and 1000: $\mathbf{R}_c = \dfrac{cv}{\nu}$, ν being the kinematic viscosity of the fluid.

The fluid velocity v is given by the relation

$$v = \frac{c^2 \, \Delta p}{12 \mu \, l} \qquad\qquad (4\text{—}5)$$

where Δp is the pressure drop over the length of seal l and μ the dynamic viscosity, the other parameters being in consistent units, [5].

The consequent fluid loss is thus

$$Q = \pi d c v = \frac{\pi d c^3 \Delta p}{12 \mu l} \qquad (4-6)$$

d being the shaft diameter. From this relation it is clear that the efficiency of a seal in reducing lubricant losses is predominantly dependent on the radial clearance c, since this parameter is raised to the third power. This means that rigid seals must be made to very close tolerances.

The orientation of the seal is of equal importance since the flow through an eccentric annular cavity can be written, [5]

$$Q = \pi d e v_m \qquad (4-7)$$

and

$$v_m = \frac{5e^2 \Delta p}{24 \mu l} \qquad (4-8)$$

where e is the eccentricity and v_m the mean velocity.

It is clear from this expression that if the seal is fully eccentric ($e = c$) then the flow is increased by a factor 2.5 over its concentric value. If the seal surface is provided with annular grooves to induce turbulence, this factor can be reduced. For example if $\mathbf{R}_e$ is in the range 2,000 to 13,000 the flow is 1.15 times the laminar value and if the seal is provided with grooves and $\mathbf{R}_e$ lies between 1,000 and 10,000, the factor becomes 1.25.

The radial clearance between shaft and seal alters with temperature if the pieces are made of different materials, and if c_0 is the radial clearance at the initial temperature t_0, then the radial clearance will be

$$c = c_0 + \frac{d}{2} (\alpha_e - \alpha_i) (t - t_0) \qquad (4-9)$$

at the operating temperature t, if the coefficient of linear expansion of the seal and shaft are respectively α_e and α_i.

The fluid viscosity also changes with temperature and constant oil flow through the seal over a wide temperature range ($t_2 - t_1$) can be achieved by choosing the materials thus

$$\alpha_e - \alpha_i = \frac{2c_0 \left[\left(\frac{\mu_1}{\mu_2} \right)^{1/3} - 1 \right]}{d \left[(t_1 - t_0) - (t_2 - t_0) \left(\frac{\mu_1}{\mu_2} \right)^{1/3} \right]} . \qquad (4-10)$$

The radial clearance is also affected by the deflections of the surfaces with fluid pressure :

$$\Delta c = \frac{\Delta p \, d_e \, d_i^2}{E (d_e^2 - d_i^2)} \qquad (4-11)$$

where E is the elastic modulus of the materials.

Experimental work has suggested that the flow through capillary annuli is not only a function of the predictable physical phenomena already treated but also of the physico-chemical properties of the lubricant.

The flow through annular spaces has been observed to fall over a period of time and this has been explained as being due to the deposition of particles carried in the fluid. However, experiments with carefully filtered fluids produced the same results, and led to the conclusion that a thick adsorbed boundary layer is formed in time, whose effect on the velocity profile is shown in Fig. 4—8.

The thickness of this layer of polarized molecules varies from situation to situation, but polymolecular fatty acids for example can form layers of between 0.05 to 10 microns thick, [5]. The effect of this boundary layer, be it due to adsorption or the deposition of foreign matter, is shown in Fig. 4—9 as a function of time.

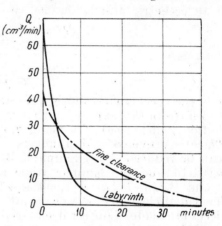

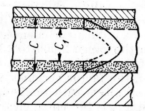

Fig. 4.8. — Influence of the boundary adsorbed layer on the velocity profile.

Fig. 4.9. — Variation of flow with time through a seal.

It is also to be noted that as oil flow is reduced by decreasing clearance, so friction increases ($f = 0.005 - 0.3$), [6].

Because of the complication of taking into account all the various factors already mentioned which govern the oil loss through hydraulic seals, it is more usual to employ certain empirical relations.

For a mobile seal

$$\Delta p = \frac{25\, l\, v\, \mu}{c^2\, c_\mu^{0.32}} \text{ kg/cm}^2 \tag{4—12}$$

and

$$Q = \frac{c_\mu^{0.32}\, c^3\, \pi\, d\, \Delta p}{25\, \mu\, l} \text{ cm}^3/\text{sec.} \tag{4—13}$$

For a fixed seal

$$\Delta p = \frac{32\, l\, v\, \mu}{c^2\, c_\mu^{0.32}} \text{ kg/cm}^2 \tag{4—14}$$

and

$$Q = \frac{c_{\mu}^{0.32}\, c^3\, \pi\, d\, \Delta p}{25\, \mu\, l} \quad \text{cm}^3/\text{sec} \tag{4—15}$$

where c_{μ} is the radial clearance in microns.

The effect of annular grooves is different depending on whether the oil flow is laminar or turbulent. They increase the leakage if the flow is sub-critical and reduce it if the flow is turbulent up until a limiting value of $\mathbf{R}_e = 20{,}000$ for concentric and $\mathbf{R}_e = 11{,}000$ for eccentric seals.

Hence calculation of the Reynolds number characterising the seal application is a necessary step in the design procedure.

4.2.1.2. *Detail Design*. Because the precise mechanism of flow in narrow annular passages is not completely understood, a purely theoretical design method is impossible, and empirical laws or indications must remain the basis of constructing a given sealing device. Hence extensive experimental work has been carried out on the various distinct types of seals.

Teichmann and others [6] have studied the performance of face seals from 1″ to 2″ in diameter, operating at normal electric motor speeds of 1800 and 3600 rpm with aqueous liquids.

Synthetic rubber seals have become increasingly important in recent years and a series of experiments to determine their performance was

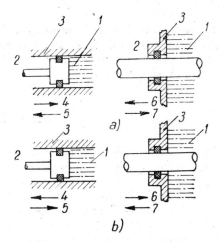

Fig. 4.10. — Effect of direction of shaft motion on rubber seals [7]: 1 — oil; 2 — atmosphere; 3 — stationary cylinder or seal; 4 — piston direction, oil pressure high; 5 — piston direction, low pressure; 6 — shaft direction, oil pressure high; 7 — shaft direction, low pressure.

made by Denny [7]. This type of seal is particularly sensitive to the fluid pressure behind it, the frictional torque rising considerably.

Friction is also proportional to the surface roughness and hardness of the shaft. Leakage past such a seal is affected by the direction of motion of the shaft and the conditions for various amounts of lubricant flow are illustrated in Fig. 4—10, [7].

Synthetic rubber seals are subject to yet another peculiarity of performance in that after a few days of inactivity the friction increases considerably — up to five times the steady running value — due to the gradual disappearance of the boundary oil film.

The use of O rings is a particularly simple and attractive solution to sealing problems for low speed concentric shafts, while for eccentric rotating shafts the best solution is often a variation of the thrust ring.

Seals made of plastic materials rely to a considerable extent on the surface finish of the mating metal for their wear life and sealing properties [8].

Graphite, however, is an attractive seal material because the surface finish requirements are not so stringent and it can sustain high rubbing

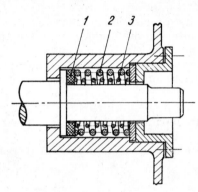

Fig. 4.11. — Face type seal with stationary graphite ring: 1 — graphite ring; 2 — spring; 3 — flexible cover.

speeds, temperatures and pressures, [9]. Considerable simplicity can be achieved in exploiting this material and seals such as that illustrated in Fig. 4—11 maintain their performance for a wide range of fluids, including water and water vapour.

4.2.2. Rolling Bearing Seals

The common categories of sealing methods used in conjunction with ball and roller bearings in particular are as follows [10]:

a). Non-contacting seals: fine annular clearances with or without grooves, labyrinths radial and axial, deflectors and pressure bleeding.

b). Contact seals: felt rings, stuffing boxes, spring loaded synthetic rubber lips (sometimes skew).

c). Sealed bearings: manufacturers of rolling bearings supply sealed units to the user, generally prepacked with grease and complete with some simple sealing system, such as felt rings, chip shields and synthetic rubber O rings.

The choice of sealing method depends considerably on the following: the type of lubricant (grease or oil), the mode of supply (bath or spray), the permissable oil loss, the operating environment (for the exclusion of impurities), the pressure and temperature of fluid within the bearing, and of course, cost.

One of the most common solutions for a wide range of applications has been the spring loaded rubber lip shown in Fig. 4—12, [10].

Fig. 4—13 represents the general limits of applicability of the usual seal types [11], the most obvious indication to be drawn from this

Fig. 4.12. — Seal incorporating spring loaded flexible lip, [10] : 1 — shaft ; 2 — rubber lip ; 3 — spring ; 4 — metallic frame ; 5 — housing.

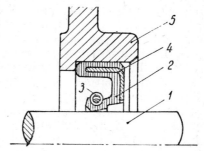

Fig. 4.13. — General limits of applicability of usual seal types, as a function of shaft diameter (d) and velocity (V) or speed (n) : 1 — felt seals ; 2 — plastic and leather spring loaded seals ; 3 — ring seals ; 4 — best friction seals ; 5 — deflection flingers for oil ; 6 — limit of utilization of self-sealing stuffing boxes ; 7 — grooves and labyrinths ; 8 — radial labyrinths ; 9 — umbrellas ; 10 — deflection thread.

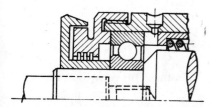

Fig. 4.14. — Combined seal : grooves and labyrinths.

being that contact seals cease to be practical at high rubbing speeds, where a form of labyrinth or groove seal is most attractive (see for instance Fig. 4—14, [12]).

4.3. Lubricant Recuperation Elements

Under ideal conditions the useful life of a mineral oil should be unlimited, and there have been examples of bearings and machines working for many years with the same oil.

In general, however, the lubricant tends to lose certain of its qualities with use, due to the following causes :

a). High working temperatures lead to oxidation and polymerisation of the lubricant, the products being soluble or carried in suspension.

b). Contamination with either foreign matter from the ambient media or wear debris.

c). Contamination with water either from the other working parts of the machine or installation, or by condensation from the atmosphere, causing emulsification of the oil.

Internal combustion engines for example, present a whole range of lubricant degeneration problems from all three categories, e.g. carbon particles from the combustion process entering the oil system, oil carbonisation with fuel and condensed water, etc.

In machine-tools the problem is usually to exclude or remove water contaminants and swarf.

The lubricant may also suffer change in its physical and chemical properties purely because of mechanical stress (the rupture of long chain molecules) or chemical action. Hence the necessity for periodic oil changes, even with the most elaborate oil recuperation systems.

It must be mentioned that recovery systems for greases are non-existent.

The elements of an oil recovery system are usually therefore filters, oil coolers to keep the steady state working temperature of the oil low, mechanism to avoid oxidation and reduce the chemical deterioration of the additives, and a device or devices for continual purification of the lubricant.

The lubricant can also be regenerated after a period in a separate installation.

4.3.1. Oil Filtration

There are two ways by which impurities may be removed from the lubrication system :

a) Regular oil changes.

b) Filtration in service.

The former is simple and efficient, the used oil being treated by settling, filtration, separation and eventually chemically regenerated before being replaced at the next oil change. The disadvantage of this method is that not all the oil can be drained from the system (in the case of some internal combustion engines up to 40% may remain). The residue immediately contaminates the fresh oil and where oil is easily trapped, so are the contaminants.

The latter process, of oil purification in service, is thus more attractive and more economical in many cases, because of reduced shut-down time and labour.

An example of the effect of the continuous oil treatment can be taken from aero-engine operation. Without filtration the oil change period is something like 300 to 400 hours, but with merely intermittent filtration of all the lubricant as part of the routine checking, the change period is extended to 1200 hours [13].

Filtration in service can be effected in several ways:

a) Full flow purification, eventually with the aid of a separate unit for periodic application.

b) Partial flow purification where a by-pass system permits its continuous efficient operation.

4.3.1.1. *The Efficiency of Purifying Systems.* The continuous full flow method employs the purifying device or devices in series with the rest of the system allowing complete filtration of the oil once per cycle. The filter is chosen to exclude the contaminating particles of a size likely to cause damage or blockage, but cannot remove the soluble impurities, and is in general coarser than a by-pass filter, to reduce pumping losses.

The efficiency of these systems can be increased by the addition of a finer filter in parallel with the main filter.

The partial flow system places the filtration unit in parallel with the main lubricant supply-line, and only a fraction of the oil flow is filtered in one cycle. The possibility of impurities remaining unfiltered for more than a number of cycles (clearly linked to the percentage of the by-pass flow) is statistically small.

By careful positioning of the by-pass circuit, more of the contaminated oil can be filtered for a given fraction of the total flow. The by-pass system should be designed to balance the production of intrinsic or foreign matter with its filtering capacity.

Denoting the total oil flow by Q and the filtered flow which returns to the sump by Q_f, this idea can be expressed thus, [14]

$$n_f = n \frac{Q_f}{Q} \qquad (4-16)$$

where n particles are present in the system at a given moment and n_f particles remain in the filter.

When equilibrium is established between the number of particles entrained in the lubricant in unit time (n_0), and that removed (n_f) the relation becomes

$$n = n_0 \frac{Q}{Q_f} \qquad (4-17)$$

Thus the number of particles passing through the lubrication point is

$$n \frac{Q - Q_f}{Q} = n_0 \frac{Q - Q_f}{Q_f}. \qquad (4-18)$$

The relation (4—18) may be summed up by the simple statement that the particles entrained in the lubricant in a given time, pass through the bearings in proportion to their entrainment, in the case of full flow filtration, where the filtered flow is fed to the bearings instead of to the sump.

The ratio of the filtered oil flow to oil fed to the lubrication points $(Q_u = Q - Q_f)$, $\frac{Q_f}{Q_u}$ is generally about one fifth and hence the contamination at the bearings will be five times the rate of entrainment. However, to keep the level of contamination to within the limits achieved with a by-pass system such as this, a batch filtration system requires very frequent changes or short filtration cycles.

Independent filtration systems can be applied intermittently or continuously in parallel with the supply system, or with full-flow in shut-down periods, as in the aero-engine example above. Such a unit consists of a separate pump which draws off lubricant from the supply system and returns the filtered oil at a convenient point in the circuit. These devices can remain in position and operation in conjunction with a given lubrication system, or be made mobile. The quantity of oil taken from the system in by-pass applications is usually about 10% of the total flow.

The same general approach can be used in designing such apparatus as was outlined above for integral by-pass systems with the advantage that this device can be placed so as to filter the oil passing through the elements contributing most to the contamination of the whole system.

Fig. 4—15 shows an example of full-flow and partial-flow arrangements for engines, [15] and Fig. 4—16 shows an independent by-pass

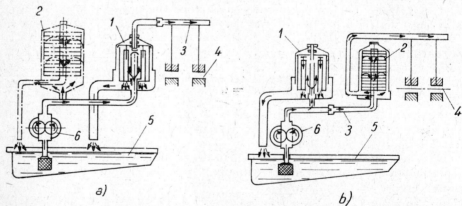

a)   b)

Fig. 4.15. — Filter arrangements for engines, [15]: a) Full-flow. b) Partial flow. 1 — centrifugal filter; 2 — coarse filter; 3 — valve; 4 — crank-shaft bearings; 5 — oil sump; 6 — gear pump.

filter unit serving a large marine engine installation, [13]. In this general field of application where the combustion processes lead to a high level of lubricant contamination and where space limitations are not severe, the filtration equipment may reach a high degree of sophistication in order to reduce maintenance costs considerably.

In diesel electric locomotives the space allowed for ancillary equipment is not as generous and for similar engines the oil changes need to be much more frequent than in the marine applications.

Fig. 4—17 shows schematically the effect and efficiency of various methods of lubricant maintenance in the case of an internal combustion engine [15].

The contribution of an air filter in such applications is to be noted.

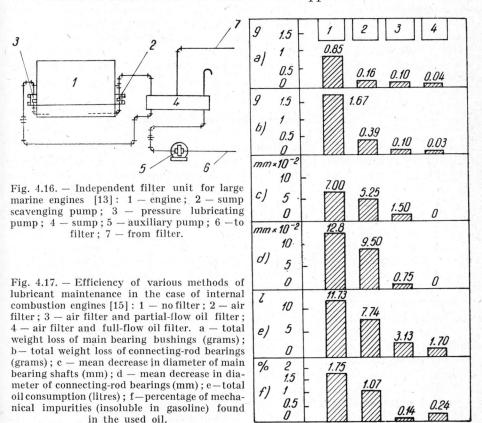

Fig. 4.16. — Independent filter unit for large marine engines [13] : 1 — engine ; 2 — sump scavenging pump ; 3 — pressure lubricating pump ; 4 — sump ; 5 — auxiliary pump ; 6 —to filter ; 7 — from filter.

Fig. 4.17. — Efficiency of various methods of lubricant maintenance in the case of internal combustion engines [15] : 1 — no filter ; 2 — air filter ; 3 — air filter and partial-flow oil filter ; 4 — air filter and full-flow oil filter. a — total weight loss of main bearing bushings (grams) ; b — total weight loss of connecting-rod bearings (grams) ; c — mean decrease in diameter of main bearing shafts (mm) ; d — mean decrease in diameter of connecting-rod bearings (mm) ; e—total oil consumption (litres) ; f—percentage of mechanical impurities (insoluble in gasoline) found in the used oil.

4.3.1.2. *Filters.* The design of the filtration equipment depends entirely upon the type of filtering circuit and the operating characteristics of the system it serves.

Many forms of filters are in current use, employing mechanical separation of the contaminating particles : adsorption and absorption, magnetic devices, centrifuges and settling tanks, etc. Mechanical filters with fine wire meshes and similar constructions are clearly the simplest type, but are usually only effective for the removal of coarse particles, absorption filters with felt, cotton or paper elements being used to achieve finer filtration with similar simplicity.

Magnetic filters are useful where the metallic nature of the contaminant is known to respond to such methods, being extremely simple and efficient even for fine particles and can often be used in conjunction with other types of filter. They absorb very little pressure energy (0.25 kg/cm² in their most complete form) and it is thus possible to distribute them at every intake duct without undue complication. Fig. 4—18 shows such a filter which can be used for a wide range of fluid viscosities, [16].

Centrifugal filters are generally the best solution for large scale applications, being both effective and efficient in terms of power losses, driven either by a separate power source, or using the energy of the circulating fluid. Fig. 4—15a shows a full flow centrifugal filter for engines, while Fig. 4—15b shows its partial flow variant, as already mentioned, [15].

4.3.2. Oil Recuperation and Regeneration

After an oil change the lubricant may be restored to its initial specification by filtration to finer limits than are convenient when the oil is actually in service and by various treatments that take too long to be employed continuously *in situ*.

Regeneration may also be carried out in parallel or series with the main lubrication system, but to justify this solution the system must be extremely large or use a large quantity of oil.

Because of the time available for the filtration process when used oil is being treated, settling tanks are particularly effective in solid particle removal and may be heated to accelerate the sedimentation. Fig. 4—19 shows a typical purification installation. The upper tank employs steam to heat and agitate the lubricant [14]. The purified oil is then led to the lower tank whence it is drawn off to the main system again.

Various means of heating the oil may be employed but its bulk temperature must not exceed 90°C and the surface temperature of the heating coils, be they supplied by steam, water or electricity, must not exceed 170°C, to avoid distillation or oxidation of the oil.

Fig. 4—20 shows a more complex system employing the combined action of condensed steam and an agitator pump to extract the water-soluble oxidation products. The oil is then passed through a centrifugal separator to remove the water and dissolved contaminants, [14].

Centrifugal separators can be divided into two classes :
a) With tubular rotor.
b) With disc rotor.

The latter is more widespread in use and an example is shown in Fig. 4—21. The liquid arrives through the supply-duct (1) and is distri-

buted to the discs (4) through feed holes (3) and thrown upwards through
ducts (5) to the upper part of the separator where the oil and the water
are segregated, due to their specific weights [17]. Clearly this last process
is very delicate since if the discs are too small the oil will be contaminated
with water again and if too large the oil will be expelled with the water.

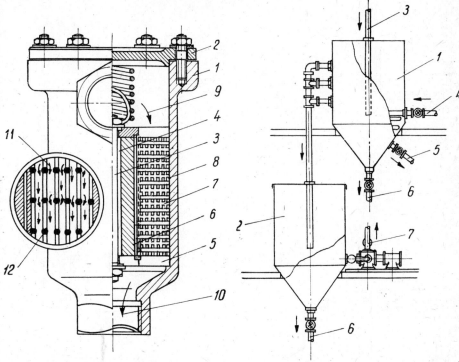

Fig. 4.18. — Magnetic filter : 1 — housing
of antimagnetic material; 2 — cover; 3 —
antimagnetic rod; 4 — permanent magnet;
5 — sliding blocks; 6 — antimagnetic
cover; 7 — iron rings; 8 — brass plates;
9 — oil inlet; 10 — oil outlet; 11 — contaminated oil flow through slots; 12 — magnetic impurities coated in the mesh.

Fig. 4.19. — Settling installation with two
tanks, [14] : 1 — upper tank; 2 — lower
tank; 3 — contaminated oil; 4 — steam;
5 — condensed water outlet; 6 — foul oil
outlet; 7 — purified oil back to lubrication
system.

For a given working temperature the dimensions of the separator
elements are given by

$$\varepsilon = \frac{e^2 - h^2}{e^2 - l^2} \qquad (4-19)$$

where e, h and l are shown in the figure and ε is the ratio of the
density of the heavy aqueous phase to that of the light oil phase at the
operating temperature, [17]. The water carries away with it a large
fraction of the solid impurities and the rest remain in the separator sump.

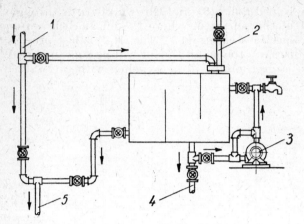

Fig. 4.20. — Complex installation with condensed steam and agitator pump, [14]: 1 — contaminated oil; 2 — condensate; 3 — agitator pump; 4 — to waste; 5 — to centrifugal separator.

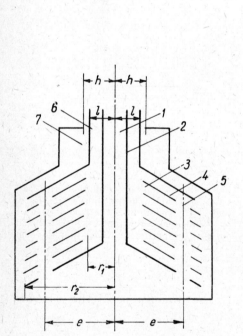

Fig. 4.21. — Disc rotor centrifuge, [17]: 1 — contaminated oil; 2 — shaft; 3 — inlet to discs; 4 — discs; 5 — feed holes; 6 — purified oil; 7 — water and impurities.

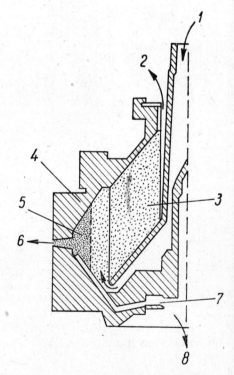

Fig. 4.22. — Centrifugal separator with continual removal of impurities, [17]: 1 — contaminated oil; 2 — purified oil; 3 — oil; 4 — interface; 5 — water phase; 6 — discharge of water and impurities; 7 — recirculating stream (water); 8 — reject.

Some separators are provided with the means of continual removal of the solid impurities (see Fig. 4—22).

Recent experiments have shown that chemical contamination of the oil as small as 0.001% (with acids, etc.) can increase the coefficient of friction sensibly when an installation operates in the regime of boundary lubrication [18]. Hence it needs hardly to be emphasized that chemical purification is of value when the oil supplies severely loaded bearing surfaces.

An example of a continuous regeneration system is shown in Fig. 4—23, [14]. The steam turbine works continuously, with the minimum

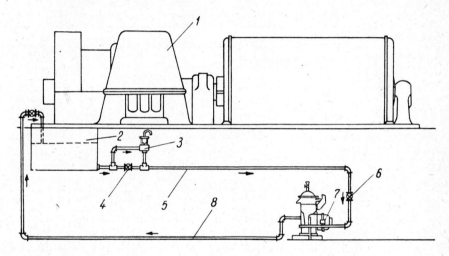

Fig. 4.23. — Continuous regenerating system for steam turbine, [14] : 1 — steam turbine ; 2 — oil sump ; 3 — level indicator ; 4 — valve ; 5 — contaminated oil duct ; 6 — place of settling tank ; 7 — centrifugal separator ; 8 — purified oil to oil sump.

of shut-down time for oil changes, and hence continuous oil treatment is economically justified. The system operates in two modes :

a) Most of the time with partial flow, valve (4) being closed so that only a fraction of the oil is drawn from the reservoir and processed.

b) Intermittently with full flow, the valve being opened to drain the reservoir completely through the purifying device. Besides the separator (7) the system can include one or several settling tanks with heating coils upstream of the separator (6).

In general the principle of partial flow filtration for the majority of the operating time and full flow when the contamination reaches a certain value, is a useful economy when applied to installations serving several machines.

An interesting use of separators is shown in Fig. 4—24 for purifying cutting fluids used by a number of machine tools, [19].

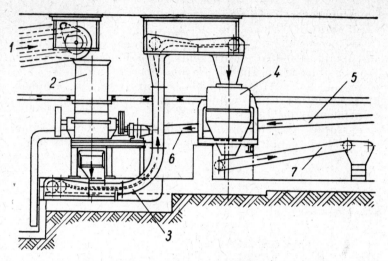

Fig. 4.24. — Separator for continuous recuperation of cutting fluids, [19] :
chip and cutting fluid mixture ; 2 — chip crusher ; 3 — chip conveyor ;
4 — centrifugal separator ; 5 — crushed chips and liquid duct ; 6 — purified liquid ; 7 — chip reject.

4.3.3. Oil Coolers

The load carrying capacity of a lubricant can be considerably
reduced and the contamination rate increased by internal or environmental heating, and in order to keep the steady state bearing temperatures to within safe limits, the oil must be cooled at some point in
its circuit through complicated machinery.

Usually the environmental cooling is insufficient and heat exchangers are added, using water or air as the cooling medium.

4.3.3.1. *Calculation Data*. Fig. 4—25 shows in a diagramatic form
the mechanism of heat transfer in the element of an oil cooler.

The heat transferred depends on the conductivity and thickness
of the intervening metal and the heat transfer coefficient of both
surfaces.

For ease of calculation an overall heat transfer coefficient is taken
for the interface thus

$$H = k A \, \Delta t \qquad\qquad (4{-}20)$$

where H is the rate of transfer, Δt the temperature difference between
the two fluids, A the area of contact between the two fluids and k an
overall transfer coefficient.

If T_1 is the initial oil temperature and T_2 its final temperature

$$T_1 - T_2 = \frac{H}{Q_l \, c} \qquad\qquad (4{-}21)$$

where Q_l is the lubricant flow and c its specific heat. For most oils $c = 0.5$ Kcal/h°C, and thus (4—21) can be written

$$T_1 - T_2 = \frac{2H}{Q_l} \qquad (4-22)$$

The cooling fluid temperature will vary similarly

$$t_2 - t_1 = \frac{H}{Q_c c'} \qquad (4-23)$$

Q_c being the flow of the cooling fluid. For water c' is 1, so that

$$t_2 - t_1 = \frac{H}{Q_c} \qquad (4-24)$$

while for air $c' = 0.24$, and

$$t_2 - t_1 = \frac{4H}{Q_c} \qquad (4-25)$$

These simplifications are no longer possible in special circumstances, such as aero-engine oil coolers where the coolant temperature is very low and its flow very large.

Coolers can be counter-flow or parallel-flow, the mean value of the temperature difference at any given point being Δt.

For counter-flow coolers (Fig. 4—26a), Δt results (Fig. 4—26 b) as

$$\Delta t = \frac{(T_1 - t_2) - (T_2 - t_1)}{\ln \dfrac{T_1 - t_2}{T_2 - t_1}} \qquad (4-26)$$

and for parallel-flow (Fig. 4—27a), Δt will be (Fig. 4—27b), [20]

$$\Delta t = \frac{(T_1 - t_1) - (T_2 - t_2)}{\ln \dfrac{T_1 - t_1}{T_2 - t_2}} \qquad (4-27)$$

The performance of these two types of heat exchanger can be represented on a single chart (Fig. 4—28), [20].

In practice yet another type of cooler is widely used, called a cross-flow heat exchanger (Fig. 4—29) and the performance of such a device can be represented in diagramatic form. The exact configuration of the unit can alter its performance considerably and Fig. 4—30 gives data for a cross-flow heat exchanger with complete separation of the fluid ducts [20].

Having gained some idea of the mean value of Δt, the coefficient k in (4—20) needs further clarification, being the net effect of three factors

$$k = \frac{1}{\dfrac{1}{\chi_i} + \dfrac{\delta}{\chi_m} + \dfrac{1}{\chi_c}} \qquad (4-28)$$

χ_i is the heat transfer coefficient at the oil-metal interface $\left(\dfrac{\mathrm{Kcal}}{m^2, h, °C}\right)$, δ the thickness of the metal dividing wall and χ_m its conductivity, and χ_c the heat transfer coefficient at the coolant-metal interface.

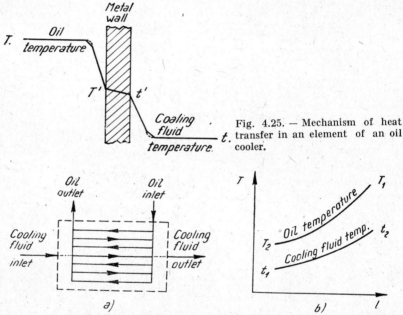

Fig. 4.25. — Mechanism of heat transfer in an element of an oil cooler.

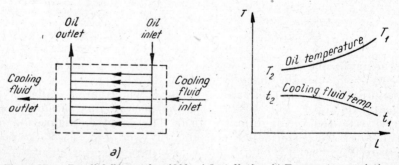

Fig. 4.26. — Counter-flow cooler [20] : a) Installation. b) Temperature variation.

Fig. 4.27. — Parallel-flow cooler, [20] : a) Installation. b) Temperature variation.

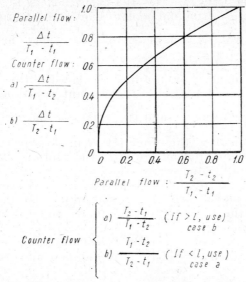

Parallel flow:

$$\frac{\Delta t}{T_1 - t_1}$$

Counter flow:

a) $\dfrac{\Delta t}{T_1 - t_2}$

b) $\dfrac{\Delta t}{T_2 - t_1}$

Parallel flow : $\dfrac{T_2 - t_2}{T_1 - t_1}$

Counter flow $\begin{cases} a)\ \dfrac{T_2 - t_1}{T_1 - t_2}\ \ \begin{array}{l}(\text{if} > 1,\ \text{use})\\ \quad\quad\text{case b}\end{array} \\[4ex] b)\ \dfrac{T_1 - t_2}{T_2 - t_1}\ \ \begin{array}{l}(\text{If} < 1,\ \text{use})\\ \quad\quad\text{case a}\end{array} \end{cases}$

Fig. 4.28. — Mean temperature difference for
counter-flow and parallel-flow coolers, [20].

Usually $\dfrac{\delta}{\chi_m}$ is small compared with $\dfrac{1}{\chi_i}$, $\dfrac{1}{\chi_c}$, and can be neglected.

In some cases the thermal resistances of the coolant and lubricant are very different as in the case of water and oil, and the surface area of the

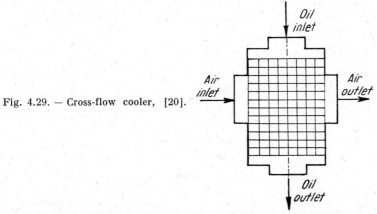

Fig. 4.29. — Cross-flow cooler, [20].

dividing wall on the lubricant side is increased with fins (Fig. 4—31), so changing the value of k

$$k = \frac{1}{\dfrac{1}{n\,\chi_i} + \dfrac{\delta'}{\chi_m} + \dfrac{1}{\chi_c}} \qquad\qquad (4-29)$$

where n is the ratio of oil and coolant contact areas and δ' the effective thickness of the wall, which in these cases may make the term $\dfrac{\delta'}{\chi_m}$ important.

When the coolant is air, the fins are placed in the air stream and the factor n is then associated with the coolant resistance.

In general the term $\dfrac{\delta}{\chi_m}$ and its variants is neglected and it therefore remains to calculate the other terms in the basic equation (4—28).

Both the coolant and oil are in forced motion, even in the case of air which is generally ducted to the oil cooler from a blower, and hence the coefficients of forced convection are required to be known. These coefficients depend to a large extent on whether the flow is laminar or turbulent, on the viscosity of the fluids and the internal geometry of the cooler.

For a given type of cooler the Nusselt number is thus a function of the Reynolds number, the Prandtl number and the viscosity ratio, thus

$$\mathbf{N_u} = f\left(\mathbf{R_e}, \mathbf{P_r}, \frac{\mu}{\mu_m}\right) \tag{4—30}$$

and experimental results presented in this form can be used for the design of any cooler of a similar construction. The viscosity ratio refers to the bulk viscosity μ and the viscosity at the temperature of the dividing wall μ_m.

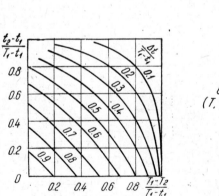

Fig. 4.30. — Mean temperature differences for cross-flow heat exchanger, [20].

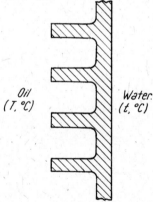

Fig. 4.31. — Heat-exchanger with additional cooling fins.

For design *ab initio*, McAdams recommends the use of the following relations

a). For water and air

$$\mathbf{N_u} = 0.023\,\mathbf{R_e^{0.8}}\,\mathbf{P_r^{0.4}}. \tag{4—31}$$

b). For oils and similar fluids :

$$\mathbf{N_u} = 0.027 \ \mathbf{R_e^{0.8}} \ \mathbf{P_r^{0.33}} \left(\frac{\mu}{\mu_m}\right)^{0.14}. \qquad (4-32)$$

Fig. 4—32 shows the value of the heat transfer coefficient for the special case of water flowing through straight circular pipes as a function of size and velocity, and Fig. 4—33 the same, for oils, [20].

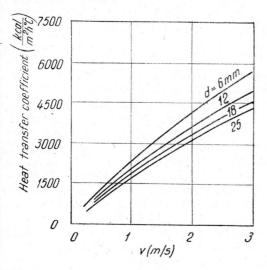

Fig. 4.32. — Values of heat-transfer coefficient for water flowing through straight circular pipes, as a function of velocity (v) and pipe diameter (d), [20].

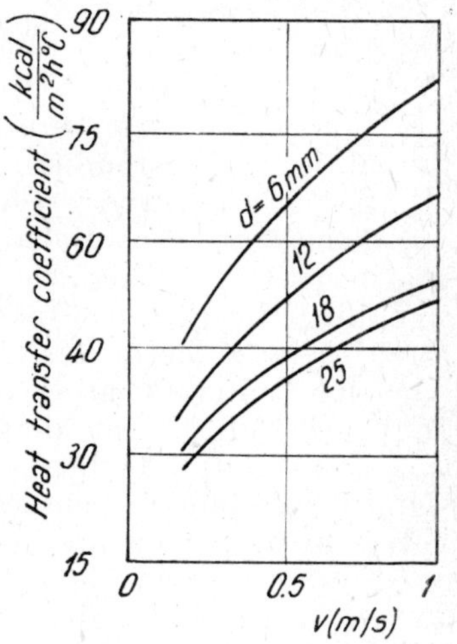

Fig. 4.33. — Values of heat-transfer coefficient for oil flowing through straight circular pipes, as a function of velocity (v) and pipe diameter (d), [20].

The effective diameter of non-circular pipes is given by the relation

$$d = \frac{4s}{p} \qquad (4-33)$$

s being the sectional area and p the perimeter.

4.3.3.2. *Design of Heat Exchangers.* Because of the different heat transfer coefficients of oil and water, a cooler using these fluids passes the water through pipes and the oil through the interspace between them. This allows simpler cleaning operations and the most efficient method of construction.

Fig. 4.34 shows possible solutions to the problem of bringing the coolant and oil into contact; the first two cases of "radial" and "segmented" flow provide the most efficient heat exchange. Fig. 4—35 shows a variant of the radial scheme with double flux for the coolant circulation.

The piping material can influence the performance of the cooler to a certain extent and it must be able to resist the chemical action of the oil and not be subject to corrosion by the coolant. Copper, aluminum, nickel and zinc based alloys are widely used.

Deposition of lime or other substances carried by the coolant has a considerable effect on the efficiency of the cooling device and the necessity for periodic cleaning is clearly shown in Fig. 4—36, [20].

4.4. Protection Devices

To protect the lubricated installations from catastrophic damage, the lubrication system must be provided with equipment to detect defects in its operation, and even to take curative action.

The dangerous defects can be pump failures, blocked supply-lines, bearing seizures, high levels of contamination, etc. Over and above signalling the presence of such faults in the installation, protection devices often include the means for starting auxiliary pumps and opening auxiliary feed circuits, as well as the more common facility of immediate shut-down of the installation.

The simplest means of protection are manometers and pressure signals, and similar temperature measuring and display devices. By-pass valves also protect the lubrication system itself from damage.

More complex systems include warning bells (used with turbines and rolling mills) and devices to pin-point the defective element with provision for automatically switching off the whole plant.

Infrared sensing units are used to measure the bearing temperatures on rolling stock for instance [12].

Another interesting device is used with diesel engines and air compressors for detecting the presence of oil fog in potentially explosive quantities, [21].

4.5. Lubrication System Testing

The increased performance required of lubrication systems in recent years has put more severe limits on the acceptable deterioration with usage.

One of the most effective methods of estimating the quality of a lubricant is to examine its colour, the shade deepening with age. In fact the sophisticated methods of chromatography can be used to produce quantitative measurements of oil contamination with acceptable rapidity. A test of this sort takes from 3 to 5 minutes and can yield a value for the iron content of the oil to an accuracy of 0.0001 grams, for example [22].

Electronic apparatus is used in conjunction with large industrial locomotive diesel engines for the continuous and direct measurement of the oil contamination. To this end, each cylinder is provided with a radioactive piston ring, and the oil in circuit is passed through a measuring chamber fitted with a Geiger counter.

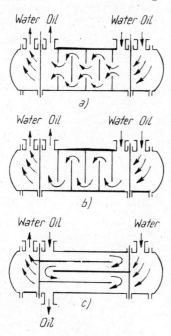

The results provided by this instrument give an idea of the wear rate, the lubricant contamination and the state of the system filters; a complete analysis of the results often requires the aid of a computer, [12].

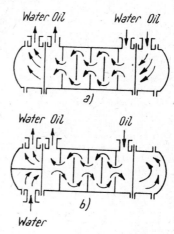

Fig. 4.34. — Design solutions for oil flow through heat-exchangers [20]: a) Radial flow. b) Segmented flow. c) Axial flow.

Fig. 4.35. — Design solutions for coolant flow through heat-exchangers [20]: a) Simple flux. b) Double flux.

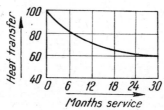

Fig. 4.36. — Drop in efficiency of oil-coolers due to deposition of impurities, [20].

References

1. N. TIPEI, V. N. CONSTANTINESCU, AL. NICA, O. BIȚĂ, *Lagăre cu alunecare* (Sliding Bearings), in Romanian. Editura Academiei R.P.R., Bucharest, 1961.
2. W. ERNST, *Oil Hydraulic Power and Its Industrial Applications.* McGraw-Hill Book Co., New York, 1949.
3. Tuthill Pump Company, Chicago, Illinois, U.S.A., *Catalog Section no. 100.*
4. A. F. BREWER, *Basic Lubrication Practice.* Reinhold Publishing Corporation, New York,1955.

5. T. P. BASHTA, *Dispozitive de acţionare şi agregate hidraulice pentru avioane* (Power Generation and Hydraulic Devices for Airplanes), in Romanian. Editura Tehnică, Bucharest, 1955.

6. O. E. TEICHMANN, L. A. VARGA, E. J. GYÖRY, *Experimental Techniques in Testing Liquid Sealing Face Seals*. Lubr. Eng., **20**, *9*, 1964.

7. D. F. DENNY, *Recent Research on Hydraulic Seals*, Sci. Lubr., **10**, *9*, 1958.

8. R. S. SHARPE, *Reducing Leakage from Hydraulic Systems*. Lubr. Eng., **16**, *1*, 1960.

9. L. A. PLUTALOVA, *Grafitovye uplotnenia vrashchioshchihsia valov*, in Russian. Vestnik Mashinostroenia, **37**, *2*, 1957.

10. E. T. JAGGER, *The Sealing of Antifriction Bearings*. Sci. Lubr., 1958 (Nov.), Special Issue.

11. N. A. SPITSIN, *Osnovy proektirovania uplotnenii dlia vysokoskorostnyh podshipnikov kachenia*, in Russian. Vestnik Mashinostroenia, **39**, *9*, 1959.

12. AL. NICA, *Sisteme noi de ungere a utilajelor industriale* (New Lubrication Systems for Industrial Equipment), in Romanian. I.D.T., Bucharest, 1960.

13. R. A. HOWLAND, *Lubricating Oil Filtration*. Lubr. Eng., **14**, *11*, 1958.

14. A. G. M. MICHELL, *Lubrication*. Blackie and Son, London, 1950.

15. E. A. STOKES, G. V. VOKES, *Methods of Testing Filter Performance and Characteristics of Some Types of Filters*. Sci. Lubr., **10**, *1*, 1958.

16. M. S. MINKOV, *Magnitnye filtry dlia ghidrovlicheskih i smazochnyh sistem*, in Russian. Vestnik Mashinostroenia, **39**, *9*, 1959.

17. CH. M. AMBLER, *Centrifugal Purification of Lubricating Oil*. Lubr. Eng., **17**, *1*, 1961.

18. I. ILIUC, *Effect of Lubricant Purity on the Reproducibility of Friction Coefficient Measurements*. Rev. Roum. Sci. Techn., Méc. Appl., **16**, *4*, 1968.

19. H. G. LENDER, *Schneidöl-Rückgewinnung durch Zentrifugen*. Schmiertechnik, **4**, *1*, 1937.

20. G. A. MONTGOMERY, *Oil Cooling and Oil Coolers*. Sci. Lubr., **9**, *3*, *4*, *5*, *6*, 1957.

21. — *Diesel Engine Crankcase Oil Mist Detector*. Sci. Lubr., **10**, *1*, 1958.

22. — *Használt olajok ellenörzése uj kémiaiés fiziko-kémia módszerekkel* (The Determination of the Oil Physical and Chemical Properties by Colour), in Hungarian. Muszaki elet, **11**, *16*, 1956.

CHAPTER V

Influence of Bearing Characteristics on their Lubricant Supply Systems

The operating parameters of moving load bearing devices (journal and axial sliding bearings, rolling bearings and gears) such as speed, load and operating temperature, determine the flow of oil required to ensure their effective performance.

In the case of sliding bearings the oil flow is effectively constrained by the geometry of the surfaces and the operating parameters, [1].

The oil supply for other types of bearings is generally determined by the thermal considerations, the critical thickness of the film and the possibilities of renewing the used lubricant, and the oil losses.

In the case of sliding bearings the general method of choosing the overall lubrication system parameters is as follows : the oil flow is established as a function of the operating characteristics of the bearing both fixed by its environment and allowed by the constructor ; the detail design construction is then completed to accord this quantity of oil flow, and the lubricant supply pressure and flow follow directly.

5.1. Sliding Bearings

5.1.1. Journal Bearings Operating Under Constant Loads and Speeds

The majority of oil passing through a given journal bearing Q, is thrown axially and this flow (Q_s) is therefore of greatest importance in establishing the characteristics of the oil supply. Using Gümbel's boundary conditions (see Fig. 5—1): $p = p_0$ for $\theta_1 = 0$ and $p = p_0$ for $\theta_2 = \pi$) and the axial limits of the bearing as : $x_3 = \dfrac{b}{2}, \ -\dfrac{b}{2}$, the axial oil flow becomes, [1], [2]

$$Q_s = (Q_{x_3})_{x_3 = \frac{b}{2}} - (Q_{x_3})_{x_3 = -\frac{b}{2}} =$$

$$= \frac{a_1 \, c^3 \, (1 + \varepsilon)^q \, \sqrt{\beta_{1q}} \, \tanh \lambda \sqrt{\beta_{1q}}}{3\mu_1} \left\{ 1 + \sum_{n=1}^{\infty} \frac{\varepsilon^{2n-1}}{2n+1} \cdot \right. \tag{5—1}$$

$$\cdot \left[\frac{(1 - q)(-q) \ldots (-q - 2n + 2)}{2n!} \, \varepsilon + \right.$$

$$\left. \left. + 2\bar{a} \, \frac{(1 - q)(-q) \ldots (-q - 2n + 3)}{(2n - 1)!} \right] \right\}$$

where c is the radial clearance, ε the eccentricity ratio ($\varepsilon = \dfrac{e}{c}$, e being the eccentricity of the bearing), μ_1 is the viscosity at entrance ($\theta = \theta_1$, $h = h_1$) and q is a parameter yielding the law of viscosity variation with temperature, [1], [2]:

$$\mu = \mu_1 \left(\frac{h}{h_1} \right)^q. \tag{5-2}$$

In relation (5—2) μ is the viscosity at any point in the film of thickness h.

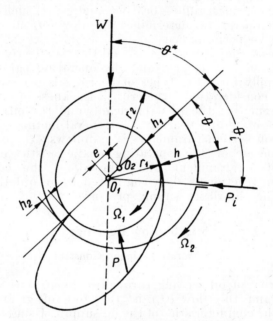

Fig. 5.1. — Journal bearing geometry.

The dimensionless parameters β_{1q}, $\bar{a}$ and a_1 from relation (5—1) have the form

$$\beta_{1q} = 0.83292 + 0.09828\, q + (0.7412 - 0.4992\, q)\, \varepsilon, \tag{5-3}$$

$$\bar{a} = \frac{A_{12q}}{A_{11q}} - \frac{1 - \dfrac{1}{\cosh 2\lambda}}{1 - \dfrac{1}{\cosh \lambda \sqrt{\beta_{1q}}}} \left(\frac{A_{12q}}{A_{11q}} - \frac{1 - \dfrac{1}{2}(1-q)\left[1 + \varepsilon^2 \left(1 - \dfrac{q}{2}\right)\right]}{1 - \dfrac{1}{2}\,\varepsilon^2 (1-q)\left(2 - \dfrac{q}{2}\right)} \frac{\varepsilon}{2} \right) \tag{5-4}$$

where

$$\frac{A_{12q}}{A_{11q}} = 0.05386 - 0.03816 + (0.6524 - 0.0254\, q)\, \varepsilon \tag{5-5}$$

and

$$a_1 = \frac{6\mu_1\,\omega\varepsilon\,r_1^2}{c^2\,(1+\varepsilon)\,q\,(1-\varepsilon^2)^{1-q}}\;\frac{1-\dfrac{1}{2}\,\varepsilon^2(1-q)\left(2-\dfrac{q}{2}\right)}{1+\dfrac{1}{2}\,\varepsilon^2(1-q)\left(1-\dfrac{q}{2}\right)} \qquad (5-6)$$

ω being the angular velocity and r_1 the radius of the journal.

These general relations will be simplified, in the first place by giving particular values ($q = 0$, i.e. constant viscosity in the bearing, common approximation for very lightly loaded bearings, or $q = 1$, the value for journal bearings subjected to medium loads).

Thus

$$Q_{s0} = \frac{4c\,\omega\varepsilon\,r_1^2\,\sqrt{\beta_{10}}\tanh\lambda\sqrt{\beta_{10}}}{2+\varepsilon^2}\left(1+\frac{2\varepsilon\bar{a}_0}{3}\right);\;\text{ for }q=0 \qquad (5-7)$$

β_{10} and $\bar{a}_0$ being the values of β_{1q} and $\bar{a}$ when $q = 0$

$$\beta_{10} = 0.83292 + 0.7412\,\varepsilon$$

$$\left.\begin{array}{c}\bar{a}_0 = \dfrac{A_{120}}{A_{110}} - \dfrac{1-\dfrac{1}{\cosh 2\lambda}}{1-\dfrac{1}{\cosh\lambda\sqrt{\beta_{10}}}}\left(\dfrac{A_{120}}{A_{110}}-\dfrac{\varepsilon}{4}\right)\\[2em]\dfrac{A_{120}}{A_{110}} = 0.6524\,\varepsilon - 0.03816\end{array}\right\} \qquad (5-8)$$

and

$$Q_{s1} = 2c\,\omega\varepsilon r_1^2\sqrt{\beta_{11}}\tanh\lambda\sqrt{\beta_{11}};\;\text{ for }q=1 \qquad (5-9)$$

where (for $q = 1$)

$$\beta_{11} = 0.9312 + 0.242\,\varepsilon. \qquad (5-10)$$

If the maximum temperature in the bearing is also known ($T = t_2$ to which corresponds $\mu = \mu_2$) besides the oil entry temperature ($T = t_1$; $\mu = \mu_1$), the parameter q can be easily deduced from the relation:

$$q = \frac{\ln\dfrac{\mu_1}{\mu_2}}{\ln\dfrac{1+\varepsilon}{1-\varepsilon}} \qquad (5-11)$$

and the value of Q_s for any given q

$$Q_s = Q_{s0} + (Q_{s1} - Q_{s0})\,q. \qquad (5-12)$$

The side-leakage can be expressed in the form of a dimensionless coefficient

$$C_{q_s} = \frac{Q_s}{c\,b\,V} \qquad (5-13)$$

the value of Q_s being given by relation $(5-12)$.

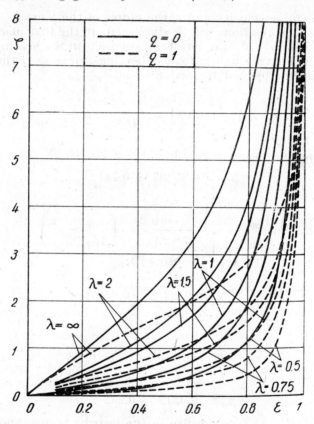

Fig. 5.2. — Variation of load-carrying coefficient ζ as a function of the eccentricity ratio ε for various λ and q.

The eccentricity ratio ε can be deduced from Fig. $5-2$, where the load-carrying coefficient ζ is represented as a function of ε and λ; $\lambda = \dfrac{b}{2r_1}$ is the slenderness of the bearing and ζ is yielded by relation

$$\zeta = \frac{p\,\psi^2}{\mu_1\,\omega} \qquad (5-14)$$

where p is the mean pressure on the projected area of the bearing $\left(p = \dfrac{W}{2 b r_1}, \text{ } W \text{ being the load}\right)$ and ψ is the clearance ratio : $\psi = \dfrac{c}{r_1}$.

By a method of trial-and-error one can determine ε and q from the above mentioned relations and chart, and thus Q_s.

These results only apply to a bearing supplied with a thin axial groove at $\theta = 0$, the oil supply pressure being atmospheric ($p_i = p_0$).

If the supply pressure is not atmospheric and the oil port is not positioned at the beginning of the positive pressure region, the resulting flow can differ greatly from the value predicted by (5 — 1). The shape and size of the supply groove also affect the oil flow, especially in the diverging region of the bearing geometry.

These various changes in the means of oil delivery have been found to leave the region of positive pressure largely unaffected, but to influence the axial oil flow considerably, hence the general lack of agreement between experimental values of Q_s and those predicted with the help of equations similar to (5—1).

In order to more accurately estimate side-leakage it is therefore necessary to add to relation (5—1) a more general relation, [3], [4], [5]. The extra flow due to a finite supply pressure can be allowed for, and the effect of the groove geometry can also be presented. Fig. 5—3 shows the bearing model with a thin axial groove of length $b_i = k_b b \, (k_b < 1)$ positioned at $\theta = \theta_i$.

The supply pressure is p_i, and in the diverging region before the oil port, the oil pressure will drop to zero, as shown in Fig. 5—4, pro-

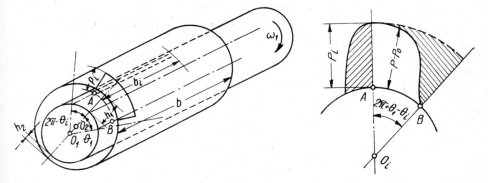

Fig. 5.3 — Geometry of oil-supply for journal bearings.   Fig. 5.4. — Variation of supply-pressure in the bearing.

ducing a certain amount of side flow. The oil pressure due only to the hydrostatic pressure will also drop to zero in the converging portion of the bearing and it is assumed that flow in both these directions are equal.

Thus the sectioned areas in Fig. 5—4 are equal since $\dfrac{\partial p}{\partial x_3} = \text{constant}$.

The extra side-leakage due to the pressurized port, length $k_b b$, can thus be considered as equivalent to the flow due to a constant pressure port (p_i) only effective over the arc AB. Hence the contributing pressure gradient over this arc will be

$$\frac{\partial p}{\partial x_3} = \frac{2p_i}{(1 - k_b)\, b} \qquad (5-15)$$

and using the film thickness

$$h = c\,(1 + \varepsilon \cos \theta) \qquad (5-16)$$

the extra side flow can be written as [2], [3]

$$\tilde{Q}_s = \frac{(1 + \varepsilon)\, p_i c^3}{6\mu_1 \lambda (1 - k_b)} \left[\left(1 + \frac{\varepsilon^2}{2} \right)(2\bar{a} + \theta_1 - \theta_i) + \right.$$
$$\left. + 2\varepsilon\,(\sin \theta_1 - \sin \theta_i) + \frac{\varepsilon^2}{4}\,(\sin 2\theta_1 - \sin 2\theta_i) \right] \qquad (5-17)$$

or non-dimensionally

$$\tilde{C}_{q_s} = \frac{\tilde{Q}_s}{c\,b\,V} = \frac{(1 + \varepsilon)\, p_i c^3}{6\mu_1 \lambda\,(1 - k_b)\, b\,V} \left[\left(1 + \frac{\varepsilon^2}{2} \right)(2\pi + \theta_1 - \theta_i) + \right.$$
$$\left. + 2\varepsilon\,(\sin \theta_1 - \sin \theta_i) + \frac{\varepsilon^2}{4}\,(\sin 2\theta_1 - \sin 2\theta_i) \right]. \qquad (5-18)$$

Consistent with the use of Gümbel's boundary conditions there is an additional side flow due to the discontinuity of pressure gradient at $\theta = \pi$. This term is only important in some cases when $\lambda > 1$ and is written thus [2], [3]

$$\tilde{\tilde{C}}_{q_s} = \frac{\varepsilon}{2}\,(1 - 2\bar{a}) \left(1 - \frac{\tanh \lambda \sqrt{\beta_{1q}}}{\lambda \sqrt{\beta_{1q}}} \right). \qquad (5-19)$$

The total side flow becomes

$$\varrho_{q_s} = C_{q_s} + \tilde{C}_{q_s} + \tilde{\tilde{C}}_{q_s} \qquad (5-20)$$

where C_{q_s} is the dimensionless flow yielded by relation (5-1).

It was found that this theoretical relation for the side flow agrees with the experimental values when k_b is 0.5, [3], and that the value of the side flow is practically proportional to k_b over a wide range of values $(0.05 < k_b < 0.75)$. It is obvious that for excessive values of $k_b (k_b > 0.75)$, the oil flow will be artificially increased, without increasing its cooling effect in proportion.

In general, it can be said that the amount of side-leakage determines the extent of the load-carrying zone and the degree of cooling of the bearing.

By admitting a linear relationship between the side flow C_{q_s}, and the value k_b, and of the part $\widetilde{C}_{q_s}$ with $(1-k_b)^{-1}$, and putting

$$\frac{1}{1-k_b} = 1 + k_b + k_b^2 + \ldots \tag{5—21}$$

it results for $k_b \ll 1$ (the practical situation) that this term is also linearly connected with k_b. In consequence, the real side flow from a bearing can be deduced from the theoretical value of $\mathcal{C}_{q_s}$ calculated for $k_b = 0.5$, by assuming its proportionality with k_b

$$\mathcal{C}_{q_{s\,real}} = 2 k_b\, \mathcal{C}_{q_s\,;\,(k_b=0.5)}. \tag{5—22}$$

From the above, the dimensionless side flow coefficient can be written [1], [2]

$$\mathcal{C}_{q_s} = \frac{2 k_b c^2 (1+\varepsilon)^q}{3 \mu_1 \omega\, r_1 b} \Bigg\{ a_1 \sqrt{\beta_{1q}}\, \tanh \lambda \sqrt{\beta_{1q}}.$$

$$\cdot \left[1 + \sum_{n=1}^{\infty} \frac{\varepsilon^{2n-1}}{2n+1} \left(\frac{(1-q)(-q)\ldots(-q-2n+3)}{(2n-1)!} \frac{-q-n+2}{2n}\, \varepsilon + 2\bar{a} \right) \right] +$$

$$+ \frac{p_i}{\lambda} \sum_{n=1}^{\infty} \left\{ \left[\binom{2n}{n} \left(\frac{1}{2} \right)^{2n} \varepsilon^{2n} \left(\frac{3-q}{2n} \right) + 1 \right] (2\pi - \theta_i) - \right.$$

$$\left. \frac{1}{n} \sin n\,\theta_i \sum_{k=0}^{\infty} \left[\binom{n+2k}{k} \left(\frac{1}{2} \right)^{n+2k-1} \cdot \varepsilon^{n+2k} \left(\frac{3-q}{n+2k} \right) \right] \right\} \Bigg\} \tag{5—23}$$

where β_{1q}, $\bar{a}$ and a_1 are given by relations (5—3), (5—4) and (5—6).

For $q = 0$ and $q = 1$, relation (5—23) takes the more simple forms

$$\mathcal{C}_{q_{s\theta}} = \frac{2 k_b c^2}{3 \mu_1 \omega r_1 b} \Bigg\{ \frac{6\left(1 + \frac{2\varepsilon\bar{a}}{3}\right) \mu_1 \omega\, r_1^2 \varepsilon}{c^2 \left(1 + \frac{\varepsilon^2}{2} \right)} \sqrt{\beta_{10}}$$

$$\cdot \tanh \lambda \sqrt{\beta_{10}} + \frac{p_i}{\lambda} \left[\left(1 + \frac{3\varepsilon^2}{2} \right)(2\pi - \theta_i) - 3\varepsilon \left(1 + \frac{\varepsilon^2}{4} \right) \sin \theta_i - \right.$$

$$\left. - \frac{3}{4}\, \varepsilon^2 \sin 2\theta_i - \frac{\varepsilon^3}{12} \sin 3\theta_i \right] \Bigg\} \tag{5—24}$$

and

$$\varrho_{q_{s_1}} = \frac{2\,k_b\,c^2\,(1\,+\,\varepsilon)}{3\mu_1\,\omega\,r_1\,b} \left\{ \frac{6\mu_1\,\omega\,r_1^2\,\varepsilon}{c^2\,(1\,+\,\varepsilon)}\,\sqrt{\beta_{11}}\,\tanh\,\lambda\sqrt{\beta_{11}}\, + \right.$$

$$\left. +\,\frac{p_i}{\lambda}\left[\left(1\,+\,\frac{\varepsilon^2}{2}\right)(2\pi\,-\,\theta_i)\,-\,2\,\varepsilon\,\sin\,\theta_i\,-\,\frac{1}{4}\,\varepsilon^2\,\sin\,2\,\theta_i\right]\right\} \tag{5—25}$$

where $\bar{a}_0$, β_{10} and β_{11} are yielded by relations (5—8) and (5—10).
The value of ϱ_{q_s} for any q can be deduced from relation

$$\varrho_{q_s} = \varrho_{q_{s_0}} + (\varrho_{q_{s_0}} - \varrho_{q_{s_0}})\,q\,. \tag{5—26}$$

The influence of the supply-pressure p_i can be shown by considering separately the side flow in the initial low pressure region of angle θ_1 (Fig. 5—3), and the flow corresponding to load-carrying region

$$\varrho_{q_s} = p_i\,\tilde{\varrho}_{q_s} + 2k_b\,C_{q_s}^* \tag{5—27}$$

where

$$\tilde{\varrho}_{q_{s_0}} = \frac{2k_b\,c^2}{3\,\lambda\,\mu_1\,\omega\,b\,r_1}\left[\left(1\,+\,\frac{3\,\varepsilon^2}{2}\right)(2\pi\,-\,\theta_1)\,-\,3\,\varepsilon\cdot\right.$$

$$\left.\cdot\left(1\,+\,\frac{\varepsilon^2}{4}\right)\sin\,\theta_1\,-\,\frac{3}{4}\,\varepsilon^2\,\sin\,2\,\theta_1\,-\,\frac{\varepsilon^2}{12}\,\sin\,3\,\theta_1\right]\; ;\; \text{for } q = 0$$

$$\left.\tilde{\varrho}_{q_{s_1}} = \frac{2k_b\,c^2\,(1\,+\,\varepsilon)}{3\,\lambda\,\mu_1\,\omega\,b\,r_1}\left[\left(1\,+\,\frac{\varepsilon^2}{2}\right)(2\pi\,-\,\theta_1)\,-\,\right.\right.$$

$$\left.-\,2\,\varepsilon\,\sin\,\theta_1\,-\,\frac{1}{4}\,\varepsilon^2\,\sin\,2\,\theta_1\right]\; ;\; \text{for } q = 1 \qquad\qquad \Biggr\} \tag{5—28}$$

and

$$C_{q_{s_0}}^* = \sqrt{\beta_{10}}\cdot\tanh\,\lambda\sqrt{\beta_{10}}\cdot\frac{\varepsilon\left(1\,+\,\dfrac{2\,\varepsilon\,\bar{a}_0}{3}\right)}{\lambda\left(1\,+\,\dfrac{\varepsilon^2}{2}\right)}\; ;\; \text{for } q = 0$$

$$\Biggr\} \tag{5—29}$$

$$C_{q_{s_1}}^* = \frac{\varepsilon}{\lambda}\,\sqrt{\beta_{11}}\cdot\tanh\,\lambda\,\sqrt{\beta_{11}}\; ;\; \text{for } q = 1.$$

It was found that the values $\tilde{\varrho}_{q_s}$ are small compared with the values of $C_{q_s}^*$ for normal supply-pressures, so that one can re-write (5—27) thus [1], [2]:

$$\varrho_{q_s} \cong 2k_b\,C_{q_s}^*. \tag{5—30}$$

For practical calculations the values of $C_{q_s}^*$ for $q = 0$ and $q = 1$ are represented in Figs. 5—5a and 5—5b, respectively, as a function of the eccentricity ratio ε and the slenderness of the bearing λ, [2], [3].

From these diagrams it is seen that the necessary coefficient of flow $C_{q_s}^*$ can be deduced from the operating parameters and geometry of the bearing (load, speed, radial clearance, width, radius and slenderness) as a function of the eccentricity ratio ε, through the intermedium of the load-carrying coefficient ζ (using Fig. 5—2), [1]. The flow coefficient ϱ_{q_s} which determines the oil flow required of the supply system, is then given by relation (5—30).

If, however, the oil supply system is already in existence and ϱ_{q_s} is thus fixed as well as $C_{q_s}^*$, the coefficient k_b can be changed to accomodate the difference

$$k_b = \frac{\varrho_{q_s}}{2C_{q_s}^*} \tag{5—31}$$

k_b is changed by enlarging the axial length of the supply groove (of depth 2 — 4 mm) and its most efficient value is 0.5, providing $p_i > 1$ atm. Changing k_b cannot correct for deficiencies in the oil supply which determine its value to be greater than 1.

In this case, if k_b given by (5—31) is greater than or almost equal to 1, and the oil supply cannot be increased, the operating parameters, or the geometry of the bearing must be altered. This means that k_b can be chosen directly as 0.5, giving the value of $C_{q_s}^*$ required by equation (5—30). The charts in Figs. 5—5 can then be used to choose some new combination of the bearing construction and operating parameters.

The position of the supply groove has an enormous effect on the flow of oil through a bearing, and it must be remembered that the port is best placed in the diverging regions of the steady state bearing geometry (Fig. 5—6), [5]. It can be seen that the angle between the oil port and the line of centres (θ_i), produces a maximum flow coefficient (ϱ_{q_s}) at around 0° (or 360°).

In hydrodynamic regime the material of which the rubbing surfaces are made has no effect on oil flow, [3].

Since the geometry of the supply-hole is of particular importance in determining the flow in the bearing, that is to say in the design of the lubrication system, a summary of the possible situations and of the correct values for k_b is presented in Table 5—1, [1]. By examining this table, a direct correlation between the characteristics of the lubrication system and the real flow in the bearing can be observed.

Thus, it is seen that in the case of low pressure systems very small values must be considered for k_b; this means that only small values of ϱ_{q_s} can be achieved and that the bearing loads and speeds must be low.

The ring-feeding permits a tolerably correct estimation of the parameter k_b, by considering the dimensions and number of rings.

For high pressure systems it can be observed that any practical value of k_b can be achieved, a remarkable fact being that in special

Table 5—1

Feed	Bearing	Equivalent value of k_b
Low pressure systems	Gravity fed journal bearings	$k_b \leqslant 0.1$
	Capillarity fed journal bearings	$k_b \leqslant 0.1$
	Ring-fed journal bearings (n = number of rings; b_{in} = ring width)	$k_b = \dfrac{nb_{in}}{b}$
High pressure systems	Bearings fed through an oil-hole of diameter d_i	$k_b = \dfrac{d_i}{b}$
	Bearings fed through an oil oil-hole and an axial groove of width b_i	$k_b = \dfrac{b_i}{b}$
	Split-cylindrical bearings with two axial grooves, situated at 180°	$k_b = 0.8 \div 1.5$
	Bearings fed through a circumferential groove	$k_b = 1 \div 2$

cases, an equivalent value of k_b, higher than unity, can be obtained. Split cylindrical bearings and circumferential grooved bearings (which can be considered as two united bearings) are examples of this, [6].

In the light of the data presented above, the flow required by a bearing can be found as a function of its operation and design, and the design of the bearing itself can be optimized.

5.1.2. Bearings with Varying Loads and Speeds

In the case of bearings with rotary loads, the general method of calculation for bearings with constant loads can be successfully applied, especially for the flow calculations, since the eccentricity is constant and the line of centres rotates with the same angular velocity as the load.

The most general case, when both the loads and the velocities vary, cannot be calculated directly, due to the complexity of the problem, so that usually only a check is possible, after the dimensions of the bearing have been selected. The dimensions can be obtained by a method of trial-and-error, considering the mean load over a cycle and a mean angular velocity. In this way it is possible to calculate the mean temperature of the bearing, the mean eccentricity, the mean thickness of the film and the real clearance by taking into account the expansion [22]; it is possible then to check its performance by comparison with a bearing under constant load and running at a fixed speed, [1], [7], [8].

Lubricant flow in these bearings is very complicated and it is particularly difficult to establish accurate design formulae. The remarks

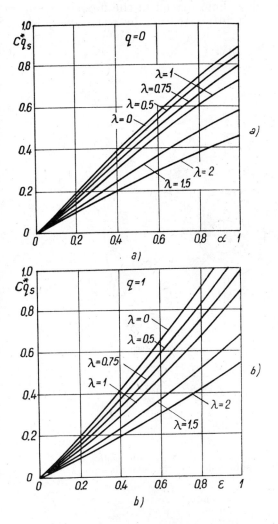

a)

b)

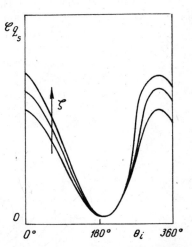

Fig. 5.6. — Influence of the supply-hole positioning on the side-flow, for various operating conditions (ζ).

Fig. 5.5. — Variation of flow coefficient $C_{q_s}^*$ as a function of the eccentricity ratio ε for various λ and q: a) $q = 0$; b) $q = 1$.

regarding the influence of the relative position of the supply-hole to the direction of the load (§ 5.1.1.) apply fully in this case, since the direction of the load changes continuously.

Experimental work carried out with connecting-rod bearings showed the variation of the rate of flow with the positions of the vectorial diagram of the load and with the position of the oil-hole. In Fig. 5—7 the variation in side-leakage is presented for various positions of the oil-hole (positions 1—13) for the specified mean values of the supply-pressures, runs per minute, and viscosity; the polar diagram of the load is also shown in the figure, [7].

The oil was supplied through a hole placed in the median plane of the bearing. These results show an intimate link between the position

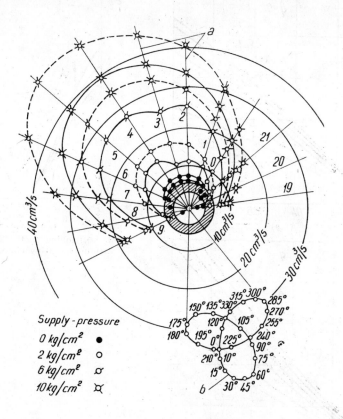

Supply - pressure

0 kg/cm²	●
2 kg/cm²	○
6 kg/cm²	⌀
10 kg/cm²	⌀

Fig. 5.7.— a) Oil flow in bearing subject to periodic loading, for various positions of the supply-hole ; b) the polar diagram of the load.

$$\mu = 2.10^{-3} \text{ kgs/m}^2 ;$$
$$\underline{\hspace{2cm}} = 1500 \text{ rpm} ;$$
$$- - - - = 1.820 \text{ rpm}.$$

of the oil-hole and the flow of lubricant ; it is possible to discern a position for the oil-hole with respect to the vectorial diagram of the force for which the oil flow has a maximum value. This position is termed "favourable" and is determined by the pattern of the load diagram.

The value of the oil flow varies inversely with viscosity and is largely influenced by the value of the supply-pressure (in this instance it varies between 0 and 10 atm.).

For efficient cooling of bearings with variable loads and velocities with the lubricant, it is seen that the position of the oil-hole must coincide if possible with the "favourable" position. Investigations regarding the variation of lubricant temperature with the rate of flow, showed that the differences between the maximum and minimum temperatures of the oil in the bearing ($t_2 - t_1$) vary inversely with the flow (see Fig. 5—8), [7].

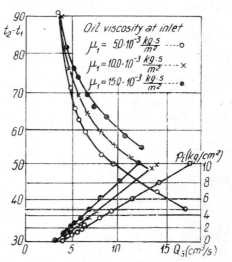

By examining this diagram it can be seen that when a low viscosity lubricant is used, low values of supply-pressure must be avoided, otherwise very high temperatures can arise. The necessity of taking into consideration the position of the oil-hole is thus obvious. The method of determining the optimum position of the oil-hole is based on the correlation between the side flow in the unloaded region of the bearing for

Fig. 5.8. — Variation of the temperature and of the oil flow in the bearing.

various positions of the oil-hole and the thickness of the lubricant film. It is found in this way that the position of the oil-hole must coincide with the mean position of the line of centres considered during one complete cycle. The mean position during a cycle can be found by determining the successive instantaneous positions; but this operation is very difficult and not always possible, so that it is more practical to use values from Table 5—2, yielding the angle of deviation between the favourable position of the oil-hole and the mean direction of the external forces working on the bearing. These results have been deduced for certain operating conditions [7].

This data is used by considering the angle between the favourable position of the oil-hole and the mean direction of the external forces. This is taken to be equal to the mean angle of the instantaneous positions of the centre and the directions of the instantaneous forces. The polar diagram of the forces with respect to the journal is cosidered, since the oil-supply is through the journal. If the oil-hole is placed in the bushing, the polar force diagram will be relative to a point in the housing.

Another method of finding an advantageous position for the oil-hole is to discover the region of lowest mean load. This can be achieved by examination of the polar force diagram referred to the journal or the housing, as the case may be. The forces at every 10°, say, are added

Table 5—2, [7]

Type of load and speeds		Angles of deviation		
		Mean viscosity of the oil in the film $\left(\dfrac{\text{kgsec}}{\text{m}^2}\right)$		
		2×10^{-3}	4×10^{-3}	6×10^{-3}
The variation of the instantaneous loads in magnitude and direction is small (the oscillation angle of the load vector is 40°, and the ratio $\dfrac{W_{max}}{W_{min}} = 1.78$; $n = 1,500$ rpm)	For maximum flow For optimum cooling Mean values	14.5 16 15.2	19 21 20	21 25 23
Same load as above; $n = 1,820$ rpm.	For maximum flow For optimum cooling Mean values	20 16 18	14 17 15.5	24 22 23
The variation of the instantaneous loads in magnitude and direction is large; the vector of the load rotates 360°, the maximum load 180°, and the ratio $\dfrac{W_{max}}{W_{min}} = 7.56$; $n = 1,820$ rpm.	For maximum flow For optimum cooling Mean values	7 10 8.5	0 5 2.5	0 0 0
The load vector rotates 118°, and ratio $\dfrac{W_{max}}{W_{min}} = 7.56$; $n = 1,820$ rpm.	For maximum flow For optimum cooling Mean values	16 23 19.5	13 23 18	10 12 11

for each successive position, and the best position for the oil-hole will be in the region of lowest total load, [8].

A commonly used oil distribution arrangement consists of a central hole with circumferential groove, since it is not always possible to locate the oil-hole with sufficient accuracy to assure an abundent oil-supply. This solution splits the bearing into two distinct zones, each one laterally supplied. The pressure diagram is modified in this case, and in consequence a check is required of the new load-carrying capacity of the bearing, since the total capacity of two bearings is not the same as for an equivalent single bearing having the same length and similar geometry.

The oil flow is considerably higher than the flow through a bearing supplied by a single oil-hole, under similar operating conditions (some authors found it up to four times as much).

Fig. 5—9 shows the variation of the side flow Q_s and the film thickness h for the same bearing when supplied through an oil-hole

(Fig. 5—9a) and through an oil-hole and a circumferential groove
(Fig. 5—9b), [8].

It is seen that the side-leakage increases considerably in the unloaded region of the bearing, and it is considerably higher for the grooved
bearing. Comparison of the film thickness is pessimistic for the grooved

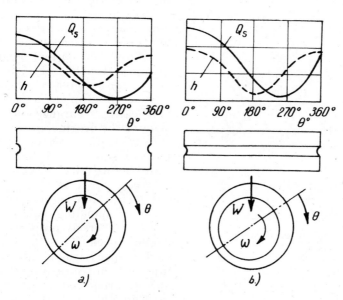

Fig. 5.9. — Relation between side flow Q_s and film thickness
for unloaded bearings with [8] : a) central oil hole ; c) circumferential groove.

bearing, but it must be pointed out that the viscosity was considered
constant. In reality, the higher flow through the bearing with a central
groove produces a lower bearing temperature, an increase in viscosity, and
hence a corresponding increase in the load-carrying capacity.

Since the maximum loads act upon the bearing for only a very
short time, the resulting thickness of the lubricant film which corresponds
practically to boundary lubrication values, is not generally considered
to be dangerous. However, in some circumstances the operating conditions of internal combustion engine bearings require improvement in the
lubricant supply during the application of the maximum force in order
to avoid film breakdown.

Even when the oil-hole was placed in the optimum position, it was
found that the short periods of high loading led to fatigue damage of
the bearing.

Methods of improving the lubrication during this critical period
include the "Ramrod" method which seems to be efficient and is widely
used. This method consists of injecting small quantities of lubricant

under high pressure into the bearing, during the compression stroke, shortly before ignition (Fig. 5—10), [9].

The injection of lubricant is effected with a piston pump of relatively simple construction, placed between the supply-duct and the main bearing oil-hole. The pumps are equipped with non-return valves, so that after the necessary quantity of oil is injected just before the maximum load, the pumping stops and for the rest of the cycle the bearing is fed by the normal engine lubricating system (see Fig. 5—11).

The amount of injected lubricant is determined as a function of the bearing clearance and the dimensions of the bearing, in order to make sure that the space between the moving surfaces will be full of lubricant before the maximum load is applied.

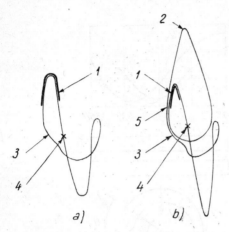

Fig. 5.10. — Polar diagram of the load in an engine bearing and the timing of oil injection in the case of "Ramrod" lubricant supply [9]: a) two-stroke engines; b) four-stroke engines: 1 — oil injection period; 2 — beginning of admission; 3 — beginning of compression; 4 — ignition; 5 — beginning of exhaust.

The time necessary to inject the corresponding volume of lubricant is inversely proportional to the engine speed. Thus, the higher the engine speed, the higher must be the injection pressure in order to introduce the required quantity of lubricant in the shortest time available. For instance, for a large industrial engine the injection pressure is 35 atm at 500 rpm, and for a car engine the injection pressure is 175 atm at 5,000 rpm.

It has been established that the lubricant injection pumps absorb about 0.3% of the total power output; however, this is recovered by reduction of friction in the bearings and a considerable improvement in wear rate. The use of this method of lubrication also allows the use of a wider range of bearing materials, and a higher specific bearing load.

The lubrication system of an engine (for the crankshaft, connecting-rods and camshaft) must also be able to deal with timing gears and the lubrication of pistons in their cylinders, etc.

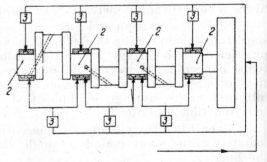

Fig. 5.11. — Lay-out scheme of the lubrication system for a three-cylinder engine using the "Ramrod" method, [9]: 1 — conventional oil-supply system; 2 — main bearings; 3 — Ramrod pumps.

Among the many solutions to this complex problem, the most common are [9]:

a). Pressure feed with wet sump.

b). Pressure feed with dry pump.

c). Mixed feed: pressure and splash.

Fig. 5—12 shows schematically an example of the first type constructed for a diesel vehicle engine. With the help of this system the lubrication of the bearings, and indeed of the motor in general, is assured in the following manner: the oil pump removes oil from the sump and transmits it through a series of ducts machined in the cylinder block to the main bearings, and thence to the big ends. The front and rear main bearings are provided with oil seals to deflect the oil back to the sump. Some of the oil fed to the big end bearings is transmitted through the connecting-rods to the little end, to the inside of the piston, and to the cylinder walls, thus providing two functions, of lubrication and cooling.

A second lubrication circuit supplied from the main circuit (sometimes even with its own oil pump) provides the camshaft with lubricant as well as the tappets and timing gears. A small derivative from this circuit directs oil to the valves and tappet levers. The oil which is not burnt or lost is then returned to the sump.

A crankcase breather system avoids loss of oil due to excess internal pressure forcing it past the end seals.

It is very important with this type of lubrication system to design for the correct quantity of oil in the sump: too much leads to unnecessary friction and oil heating which in turn leads to a higher oil consumption, while too little risks the starvation of bearings and consequent seizure. The filters are placed in series or parallel with the rest of the circuit, as discussed in Chapter IV.

Experimental work on a test bench especially designed to observe the performance of the lubrication system of an automobile engine makes it possible to measure variation of the sump temperature, feed line oil temperature and oil flow as functions of the operating parameters of the engine, [10].

The oil flow was measured with a special electric flow-meter through the main bearings, the big ends and the rest of the bearings separately, with the aid of valves [11]. The oil flow through the main bearings increases with the supply-pressure and engine speed (Fig. 5—13), and the big ends may take as much as 30—50% of the main bearing oil flow.

A pressure fed dry sump system is represented in Fig. 5—14 which shows certain differences in comparison with the wet sump system [9].

Thus it can be seen that the oil is no longer left in the sump, which now merely serves as a collector for the oil returning from the various lubrication points, but is returned to a separate oil tank through a filter and sometimes a de-emulsifier. It is also possible to include an oil cooler in the circuit if necessary (see § 4.3.3.). A second pump

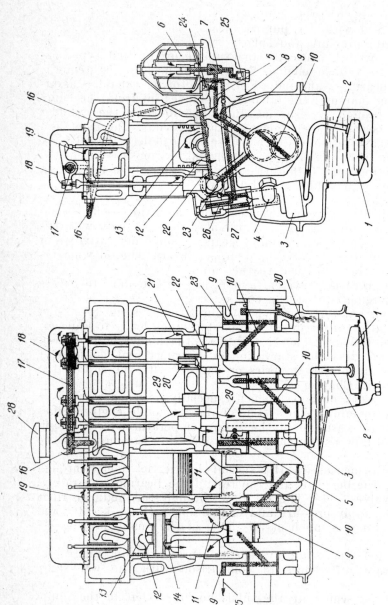

Fig. 5.12. — Wet sump pressurized lubrication system for engines, [9] : 1 — inlet filter ; 2 — intake ; 3 — oil pump ; 4 — pressure relief valve ; 5 — piping to filter ; 6 — oil filter ; 7 — piping from filter ; 8 — main lubricating ducts ; 9 — ducts to crank-shaft bearings ; 10 — con-rod feed ; 11 — splash lubrication of cylinders ; 12 — oil wiped by the scraper rings ; 13 — lubrication of gudgeon-pin bearings with oil vapour ; 14 — oil from the gudgeon-pin bearings ; 15 — piping for timing gears ; 16 — piping to tappets ; 17 — channel in the rocker axis ; 18 — lubrication of the upper part of tappet lever by oil return ; 19 — lubrication of valves by oil recovered from rocker actuators ; 20 — lubrication of push rod joint by oil return ; 21 — lubrication of push rods ; 22 — lubrication of cams ; 23 — lubrication of the camshaft bearings ; 24 — filter by-pass valve ; 25 — stopper ; 26 — lubrication of oil pump main bearing ; 27 — lubrication of oil pump driving gears ; 28 — crankcase breather ; 29 — oil return from overflow ; 30 — oil return to the sump from the rear main bearing.

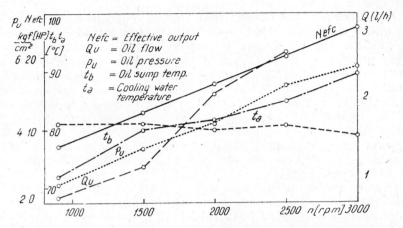

Fig. 5.13. — Oil flow in the main bearings of an engine and the sump oil temperature variation as a function of speed, power output and supplypressure.

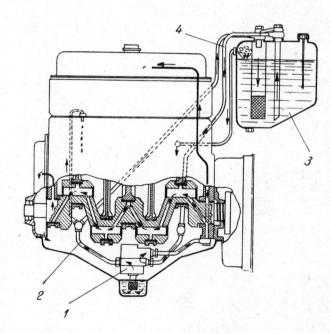

Fig. 5.14. — Dry sump pressurized lubrication system for a vehicle engine [9]: 1 — scavenge pump; 2 — oil return to reservoir; 3 — separate oil reservoir; 4 — delivery line from reservoir to pump.

delivers the oil to the distribution circuit, eventually through yet another filter. The scavange pump has a larger capacity than the delivery pump so that the reservoir can never be pumped dry while there is still oil in the engine.

Unfortunately this means that the scavenge pump is always operating under starvation conditions, and this can introduce air and other gases into the oil. To remove this effect, anti-foam additives are used, or other methods of gas removal. This type of lubrication circuit is generally used for motor vehicles where it cannot be guaranteed that the inclination of the engine will always remain sufficiently steady to ensure that the delivery pump in a wet sump system is always supplied with oil.

The mixed lubrication system with pressure and splash feed is generally used for monocylinder stationary engines with low speeds and low power outputs. The design is far simpler than the previous examples, being without the complex system of internal ducts in the crankshaft, etc.

Usually the main bearings and big ends are supplied by pump, as are the other accessible moving parts ; the cylinders and pistons are however lubricated by splash, with the aid of a scoop fixed to the bottom of the connecting-rod (see Fig. 5—15) [9].

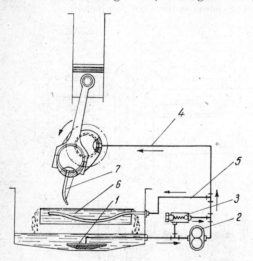

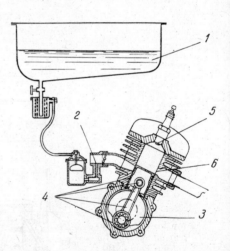

Fig. 5.15. — Mixed lubrication system (pressurized main bearings and splash lubrication for connecting-rod and piston-cylinder), [9] : 1—pump suction ; 2 — oil pump ; 3 — by-pass ; 4—pressure line to main bearings ; 5 — splash tray supply line ; 6 — splash tray ; 7 — scoop on the connecting-rod for splash effect.

Fig. 5.16. — Lubrication system for small two-stroke engines with oil pre-mixed with the petrol, [9] : 1 — reservoir for petrol-oil mixture ; 2—air-petrol-oil mixture ; 3—crankcase ; 4 — lubrication points of the engine ; 5 — deposits on the plugs ; 6 — coke at the exhaust-port.

In order to ensure that the scoop produces a constant supply of lubricant, the sump is provided with a subsidiary tray maintained at a constant level by the main supply pump and the returning oil.

Depending on the operating conditions and environment of a particular engine, extra filtration, oil cooling and warning systems can be provided, as outlined in Chapter IV.

The lubrication of two-stroke engines provides several special problems because of their particular construction. Various solutions are possible [9] :

a). Total loss with oil pre-mixed with the petrol.

b). The same, plus a separate supply of undiluted oil.

c). Total loss with a separate oil reservoir ; the undiluted oil is continuously metered into the fuel under low pressure.

d). Pressure feed with undiluted oil directly to the cylinder.

The first method is the most effective, being used almost without exception in small low output two-stroke engines. Fig. 5—16 shows such a system and the principle of operation can be clearly seen, the oil being burnt rather than accumulating in the small volume of the crankcase.

Fig. 5—17 illustrates the second method, using a supplimentary oil supply direct to the crankshaft bearings. The oil supply may eventually reach the cylinder walls, being driven from the bearings by crankcase pressure to the combustion chamber. This method is used in larger engines producing more power.

The third variant is illustrated in Fig. 5—18 and is the latest attempt at two-stroke lubrication, avoiding the pre-mixing of fuel and oil, which

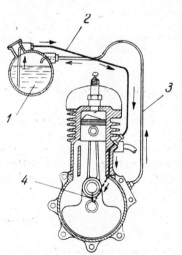

Fig. 5.17. — Lubricating system for two-stroke engines with oil pre-mixed with petrol and separate supply of un-diluted oil, [9] : 1 — oil reservoir ; 2 — separate supply of undiluted oil ; 3 — pressurized air duct ;4 — undiluted oil to the main bearings.

is now started at the carburetter and completed in the crankcase. This system is generally employed in motor vehicles.

Whichever way the oil is introduced into the fuel, the quantity should lie between 3 and 8% of the fuel consumption, depending on load. The usual ratio is however 4 to 5%, while the tendency is now to reduce this to 2 to 3%. While running-in, the oil content is doubled.

These ratios are independent of the lubricant viscosity, depending mainly on the detail construction of the particular motor.

The final type of two-stroke lubrication system, with oil injected directly into the cylinders, is met with in large industrial diesel engines and is usually complemented with a completely separate system supply-

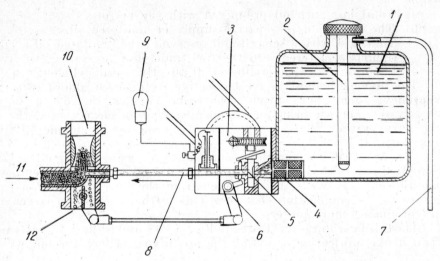

Fig. 5.18. — Lubrication system for two-stroke engines with undiluted oil continuously metered into the fuel; 1 — oil reservoir; 2 — level indicator; 3 — oil pump; 4 — pump suction with filter; 5 — pump piston; 6 — actuating lever; 7 — breather pipe; 8 — oil-supply; 9 — alarm lamp; 10 — carburettor; 11 — petrol duct; 12 — throttle (fully open).

ing sometimes a different type of oil form that used for other bearing surfaces.

The oil injected into the cylinders is burnt, and the other oil is circulated through all the usually ancillary recuperation equipment.

The viscosity and other properties of lubricants used in two-stroke internal combustion engines differ from those used for four-stroke applications and must be established for each particular case.

5.1.3. Partial Journal Bearings

This type of bearing is used in circumstances where the loads are small and the direction of load application is fixed or is known to lie between close limits. The advantage of this method of construction lies in its simplicity and in its reduced friction compared with that of a complete journal. This is due to limiting the extent of the mating surfaces to the region of maximum pressures, thus eliminating unnecessary fluid shearing, (Fig. 5—19).

One type of partial bearing with a large range of current application is the fitted bearing, having the bush diameter equal to the shaft diameter. These bearings are used where there is repeated starting and stopping because, although operating in the semi-fluid lubrication regime, they have a large area of contact. Among the technical applications of this principle, one is notable, that of axle bearings of railway rolling stock where, even if the initial fit is not perfect, after the running-in period the axle and journal take on the same curvature due to wear and plastic deformation of the bearing, (see Fig. 5—20).

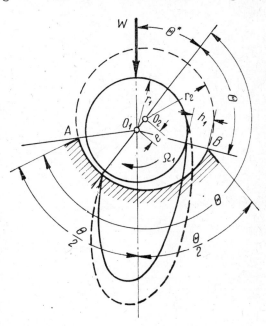

It is easily found out that for hydrodynamic regime the angular extent of the bearing, Θ, must be less than 180°. To estimate the oil flow through a partial bearing, the circumferential flow must be taken into account, as well as the axial flow.

The total leakage Q_s is made dimensionless as before:

$$C_{q_s} = \frac{Q_s}{e\,b\,V} \qquad (5-32)$$

Fig. 5.19. — Partial journal bearing.

and varies with the angle Θ^*, the exit angle coefficient $\beta = \dfrac{\theta_2}{\Theta}$, (Fig. 5—20), and λ, the length ratio, as shown in Fig. 5—21.

This diagram demonstrates that C_{q_s} drops with Θ^*: for a given β, $\theta_1 = -(1-\beta)\,\Theta^*$ increases, whereas the entrance section $b h_1 = b e \cos\theta_1$ decreases.

In general this type of bearing is supplied with oil by wick feed, for which the value of k_b is given in Table 5—1.

5.1.4. Axial Bearings

The various forms and applications for axial bearings include rotating thrust washers for hydroelectric installations, propeller shafts, plane translatory motion bearings on lathe beds, large reciprocating engine crossheads and many low load variants, such as mating plane surfaces.

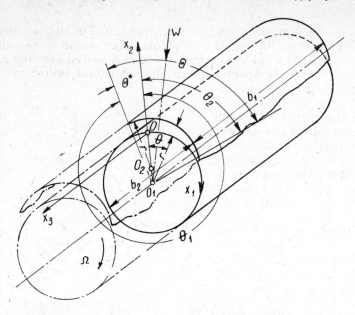

Fig. 5.20 — Fitted bearing.

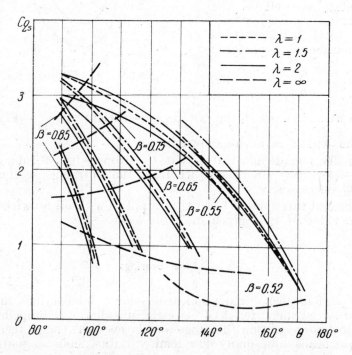

Fig. 5.21. — Variation of flow coefficient C_{qs} as a function of
angular extent of the bearing Θ for various values of λ and β.

Whether the sliding surfaces are circular or flat makes no differ- ence to the mode of pressure generation, since the latter can be considered a special case of the former in which the mean radius of the bearing tends to infinity. Hence, an axial sliding bearing consists of a plane

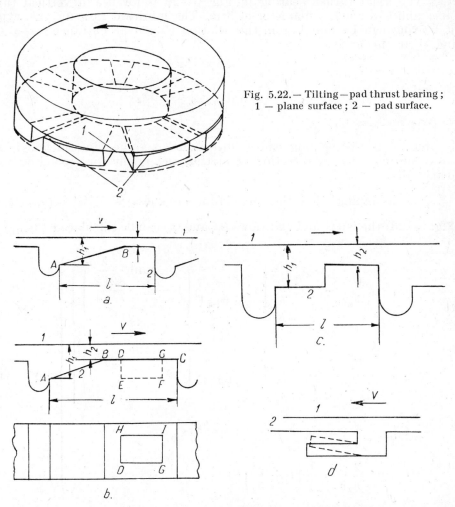

Fig. 5.22.— Tilting—pad thrust bearing ; 1 — plane surface ; 2 — pad surface.

Fig. 5.23. — Step thrust bearings : a) step bearing ; b) step bearing with oil pocket ; c) parallel step bearing ; d) thermal distortion bearing ; 1—plane surface ; 2—step surface.

surface in relative motion with respect to a segmented surface. The form of the segmented surface may differ considerably, sometimes even in- cluding hinged sliders, but more generally with steps or inclined planes, with grooves through which oil is supplied to the load bearing regions (see Figs. 5—22 and 5—23).

Geometric variation of one surface can also be obtained by elastic or thermal distortion which may sometimes simplify the manufacture of this type of bearing which, because of its close running clearances, must be finished to a high degree of precision.

The axial thrust bearing in Fig. 5—22 is for use in vertical turbines and can reach a diameter of 3 m. The lubricant flow for this type of bearing can be found from the relation (Q_i at the entrance: $x_1 = 0$, and Q_e at the exit: $x_1 = l$)

$$Q_{i,e} = \int_{-\frac{b}{2}}^{\frac{b}{2}} \int_0^h (v_1)_{\substack{x_1=0, \\ x_1=l}} \, \mathrm{d}x_3 \, \mathrm{d}x_2 \tag{5—33}$$

in which b is the bearing width (direction x_3) h the film thickness, x_1 the co-ordinate in the direction of motion and v_1 the corresponding velocity (Fig. 5—23).

By assuming that the mean film thickness is $h_m = \dfrac{1}{2}(h_1 + h_2)$, (Fig. 5—23) the entry and exit flows (Q_i and Q_e) can be calculated thus [1]

$$\left.\begin{array}{l} C_{q_i} = \dfrac{Q_i}{V h_m b} = \dfrac{1}{1+\dfrac{h_2}{h_1}}\left[1 - \dfrac{\mathcal{A} h_1^2}{6\mu_m V}\left(1 - \dfrac{\tanh\dfrac{\lambda}{2\sqrt{2}}}{\dfrac{\lambda}{2\sqrt{2}}}\right)\right] \\[4ex] C_{q_e} = \dfrac{Q_e}{V h_m b} = \dfrac{1}{1+\dfrac{h_1}{h_2}}\left[1 + \dfrac{\mathcal{A} h_2^2}{6\mu_m V}\left(1 - \dfrac{\tanh\dfrac{\lambda}{2\sqrt{2}}}{\dfrac{\lambda}{2\sqrt{2}}}\right)\right] \\[4ex] \bar{C}_{q_i} = \dfrac{Q_i}{V h_2 b} = C_{q_i}\dfrac{h_m}{h_2} = \dfrac{1}{2}\left(1 + \dfrac{h_1}{h_2}\right)C_{q_i} \\[3ex] \bar{C}_{q_e} = \dfrac{Q_e}{V h_2 b} = \dfrac{1}{2}\left(1 + \dfrac{h_1}{h_2}\right)C_{q_e} \end{array}\right\} \tag{5—34}$$

where

$$\mathcal{A} = \dfrac{6\mu_m V}{h_1^2}\dfrac{\dfrac{h_1}{h_2} - 1}{\dfrac{h_1}{h_2} + 1}\left[1 + \dfrac{3.7}{0.1 + \lambda} + 16\left(\dfrac{\dfrac{h_1}{h_2} - 1}{\dfrac{h_1}{h_2} + 1}\right)^{\frac{1}{4}} e^{-0.65\,\lambda^{\frac{5}{4}}}\right]. \tag{5—35}$$

The leakage flow $\left(\text{on sides } x_3 = \pm \dfrac{b}{2}\right)$ results as

$$Q_s = Q_i - Q_e\,; \quad C_{q_s} = C_{q_i} - C_{q_e}\,; \quad \overline{C}_{q_s} = \overline{C}_{q_i} - \overline{C}_{q_e}$$

$$C_{q_s} = \frac{Q_s}{V h_m b} = \frac{1 - \dfrac{h_2}{h_1}}{1 + \dfrac{h_2}{h_1}} - \frac{\mathcal{A}\, h_1^2}{6\,\mu_m\,V}\left(1 - \frac{\tanh \dfrac{\lambda}{2\sqrt{2}}}{\dfrac{\lambda}{2\sqrt{2}}}\right)\left(1 + \frac{h_2^3}{h_1^3}\right) \qquad (5\text{--}36)$$

$$\overline{C}_{q_s} = \frac{Q_s}{V h_2 b} = \frac{1}{2}\left(1 + \frac{h_1}{h_2}\right) C_{q_s}\,.$$

Diagrams in Figs. 5—24, 5—25 and 5—26 give the values of $\overline{C}_{q_i}$, $\overline{C}_{q_e}$ and $\overline{C}_{q_s}$ as functions of $\dfrac{h_1}{h_2}$ and λ. For $\dfrac{h_1}{h_2} = 1$, $\overline{C}_{q_i} = \overline{C}_{q_e} = \dfrac{1}{2}$, $\overline{C}_{q_s} = 0$, but as $\dfrac{h_1}{h_2} \to \infty$ asymptotic relations are found

$$(C_{q_i})_{\frac{h_1}{h_2} \to \infty} = 1 - \left(1 + \frac{3.7}{0.1 + \lambda} + 16\, e^{-0.65\,\lambda^{\frac{5}{4}}}\right)\left(1 - \frac{\tanh \dfrac{\lambda}{2\sqrt{2}}}{\dfrac{\lambda}{2\sqrt{2}}}\right) \qquad (5\text{--}37)$$

$$(C_{q_e})_{\frac{h_1}{h_2} \to \infty} = 0$$

and, when $\lambda \to \infty$, $(C_{q_i})_{\lambda \to \infty} = (C_{q_e})_{\lambda \to \infty} = 0$ or, for $\lambda = 0$ it results

$$(C_{q_i})_{\lambda=0} = \frac{1}{1 + \dfrac{h_2}{h_1}}\,; \qquad (C_{q_e})_{\lambda=0} = \frac{1}{\dfrac{h_1}{h_2} + 1}\,;$$

$$(C_{q_s})_{\lambda=0} = \frac{1 - \dfrac{h_2}{h_1}}{1 + \dfrac{h_2}{h_1}}\,. \qquad (5\text{--}38)$$

Thus C_{q_i} increases with $\dfrac{h_1}{h_2}$ if λ is small and decreases when the length ratio is much larger; at the same time C_{q_e} decreases in each case, while the side leakage coefficient increases with $\dfrac{h_1}{h_2}$.

Design problems of high speed axial thrust bearings for use in gas or steam turbines, compressors, centrifugal pumps etc., are often resolved by constructing a full scale model. In this way, using certain theoretical guiding principles, the specific loading of such bearings has been increased to values of 400 kgf/cm² which already allows the construction of a smaller bearing with less friction.

The complete study of the oil flow in segmented bearings has enabled their design to be optimised by improving the coolant effect of the oil flow under the same conditions of load and speed. Fig. 5—27 shows the result of such an optimisation of the heat dissipation by improving the oil flow at the segment limits by judiciously rounding off their plane and profile sections, and by a general improvement of their geometry, [12].

The lubricant supply system for linear sliding bearings is one of the simplest, being normally by drip feed. Lightly loaded axial bearings of small size can be operated actually inside an oil bath, but heavier loads and larger bearings need pressure fed oil, the supply systems being comparatively simple.

Water turbines present a special problem, since they must be well sealed to avoid the emulsification of the oil with leaking water.

5.1.5. Water Lubricated Bearings

Lubrication with grease or oil of bearings operating either semi or fully submersed in water presents a very complicated sealing problem. In fact in such conditions there will always be a certain amount of water contamination of the lubricant. Consequently the simplest solution to the problem is to use the water itself as lubricant, and this can produce perfectly satisfactory results.

The bearing material most commonly used in this situation is rubber, which completely covers the material surface of the journal and is found to perform well even with abrasive particle contamination. The applications in which this system is currently used with success include water turbines, pumps, excavators, dredgers, etc. The problem of deep drilling was eased with the utilisation of these bearings.

Yet another material, used particularly in marine drives, is wood. It is worth mentioning that metal bearing surfaces can sustain the corrosive action of water when used as a lubricant. One of the best alloys for this application is a bronze with lead and tin additions (BzSnPb 20) and this is used for the journals of submersible water pumps, with reasonable resistance to wear [13].

It has been established that water lubricated bearings, be they axial or radial, can operate in the hydrodynamic regime. The operating and construction parameters must however remain between close limits because of the small film thickness involved, due to the low viscosity of water.

Fig. 5.24. — Variation of flow coefficient $\bar{C}_{q_i}$ as a function of $\dfrac{h_1}{h_2}$ ratio for various values of λ.

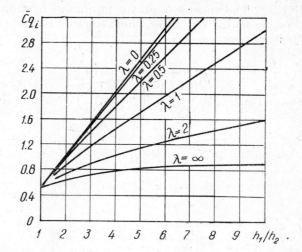

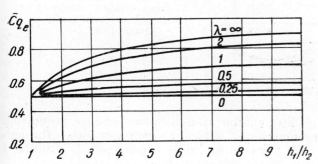

Fig. 5.25. — Variation of flow coefficient $\bar{C}_{q_e}$ as a function of $\dfrac{h_1}{h_2}$ for various values of λ.

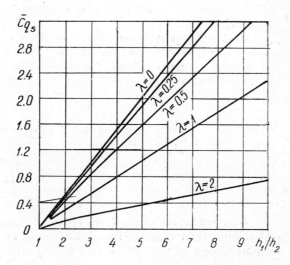

Fig. 5.26. — Variation of flow coefficient $\bar{C}_{q_s}$ as a function of ratio $\dfrac{h_1}{h_2}$, for various values of λ.

The specific load for minimum friction has been found to be of the order 60 kgf/cm² after which the film is liable to rupture with a consequent sharp friction rise (Fig. 5—28), [14].

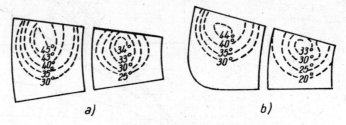

a)   b)

Fig. 5.27. — Temperature distribution in a segmented thrust bearing : a) original pads ; b) modified pads.

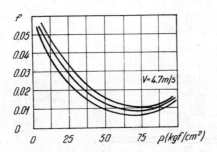

Fig. 5.28. — Variation of friction with load for rubber bearing surfaces with water lubrication.

Plane water bearings also exhibit an additional pressure generating mechanism called the "thermal wedge" effect : as the water passes through the converging geometry its temperature rises because of the frictional energy losses and thus expands to an extent which can sensibly improve the load-carrying capability of a bearing. This effect increases as the film gets thinner.

It must be remembered that because of the close clearances at which water bearings work, not only must the manufacturing tolerances be high but also the surface finish, to avoid the existence of asperities of film thickness dimensions.

Fig. 5.29. — Optimum profile for plane, water lubricated bearings.

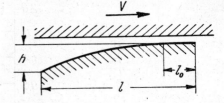

The entry of fluid into the close clearances met with in water bearings is particularly critical. In the case of axial, or linear bearings this is a question of design as well as surface finish, and Fig. 5—29 shows the smooth

entry profile to the load-carrying region, which reduces friction and increases specific loading to a surprising degree [14].

Lubricant supply is clearly not a problem with these bearings, since
they usually work immersed.

5.1.6. Hydrostatic Bearings

In contrast with hydrodynamic bearings, the load-carrying capacity
of hydrostatic bearings does not depend on the relative motion of the surfaces but rather on the lubricant supply pressure in the load zone.

The load carrying capacity and rigidity of these bearings depends
to a considerable extent on the restrictors used in the supply circuit.
In general these restrictors are fixed and external to the bearing, being
usually in the form of capillary tubes, or fine orifices. Fig. 5—30 shows
the restrictors and pressure pockets of a hydrostatic journal bearing.

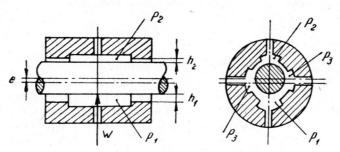

Fig. 5.30. — Externally pressurized journal bearing with four
inlet ports, [15].

When a load (W) is applied to the shaft, the side leakage from the
pressure pocket towards which the shaft is deflected is reduced, because
of a drop in the clearance (from h_1 to h_2). This has the effect of increasing the respective pocket pressure (from p_1 to p_2) since the pressure
drop in the restrictor is proportional to the flow. Thus the load is supplied
just so long as the eccentricity is not too great for the pocket size restrictors, since the pressure points are all connected in parallel to the same
source.

On some large size hydrostatic bearings (the Mount Palomar tele-
scope cradle for example) the pressure points are fed from separate positive displacement pumps where the supply pressure is independently
linked to the film thickness and can provide an almost rigid bearing.

In certain cases, such as rolling mill bearings when the radial stiffness
of the bearing must be high, the provision of variable restrictors can produce an effectively rigid bearing.

The variable restrictor (Fig. 5—31) can either be actuated by shaft
deflection, or by the pocket pressures. This method is clearly a more
efficient way of assuring the stability of a bearing than the use of fixed

restrictors, and can increase the radial stiffness of a simple hydrostatic bearing 25 times [15].

In fact the restrictor in Fig. 5—31 is controlled by pocket pressure with a load sensing device. The difference between p_1 and p_2 deflects

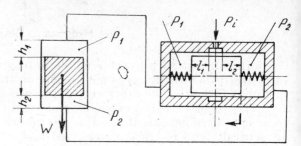

Fig. 5.31. — Externally pressurized journal bearing supplied through variable flow restrictors wiht load sensing device, [15].

the piston and the consequent difference between l_1 and l_2 produces a different pressure drop and flow in both directions from the central pressure p_i to balance $p_1 + p_2$.

5.2. Rolling Bearing Lubrication

Any type of rolling bearing requires much less lubricant for its hydrodynamic operation than a sliding bearing of similar size. This is because of the much smaller area of effective contact between the moving elements. Thus the supply of too much lubricant can raise friction unnecessarily, although it may have some overall cooling effect, especially in high speed bearings of this type.

Lubricant is thus sparingly supplied to rolling bearings, being deposited in a thin film on moving surfaces and race ways. The thickness of this film is determined, for the most part, by the balance between surface tension and centrifugal force.

The geometry of the region of contact between a rolling element and its race way is sketched in Fig. 5—32.

The film thickness can thus be written down as

$$h = r_1 \left(1 + \frac{1}{1 + \left(\dfrac{h_2}{r_1} \right)} \cos \Theta \right) \tag{5—39}$$

with an error of less than 5% for $\nu\Theta < 18°$, and in fact the extent of the oil film will usually be much smaller, for the reasons expressed above [2].

Centrifugal force tends to expel the fluid from the rotating surfaces and its value per unit area can be expressed thus

$$p = \rho h \frac{V^2}{r} = \frac{\rho h}{r} \frac{\Omega^2}{4} r_m^2 \left(\sec \nu\Theta + \frac{r_1}{r_m} \operatorname{tg} \nu\Theta \right)^2 \tag{5—40}$$

where ρ is the lubricant density, V the surface velocity at a point on a rolling element and Ω the angular speed, r_m being the centre distance between the shaft and the ball or roller.

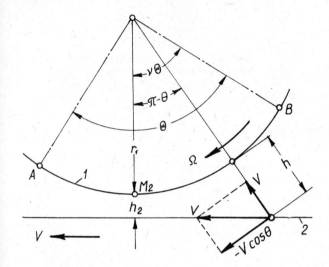

Fig. 5.32. — Geometry of the lubricating film of a rolling bearing.

The surface tension force on a cylindrical surface can be similarly expressed as a pressure

$$p = \frac{\gamma}{r} \qquad (5-41)$$

where γ is the surface tension of the fluid, which leads to

$$h = \frac{\gamma}{\rho V^2} \qquad (5-42)$$

by combination with (5—40).

In the case of a ball bearing the surface tension forces are twice as large and hence the thickness of the oil film is twice as large

$$h' = 2\,h = \frac{2\gamma}{\rho V^2}. \qquad (5-43)$$

The oil film thickness on the outer race (if stationary) tends to be greater than these values, whereas the inner race of radial ball bearings and the revolving race of thrust ball bearings cannot usually retain more than a molecularly thin film of lubricant, because the surface forces tend to expel the fluid : their total curvatures are in almost all cases negative.

The film of lubricant that remains on the inner race of a roller bearing is equal to that on the roller surface and hence the total thickness is

$$\bar{h} = \frac{2\gamma}{\rho V^2} \qquad\qquad (5-44)$$

which is clearly the same for the inner race of a ball bearing, since the inner race carries no film and the ball twice as much as a roller.

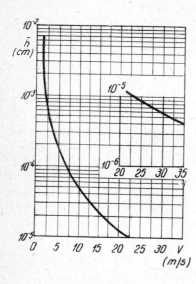

Fig. 5.33. — Variation of the minimum film thickness with speed in roller and ball bearings, [16].

The total oil film based on relation (5—44) is shown calculated for various surface speeds in Fig. 5—33; γ is assumed 25 dynes/cm and $\rho = 0.9$ g/cm³, which are reasonable values for all mineral oils, [16].

The value of h can give some idea of the minimum film thickness between rolling elements and races, and it is clearly much less than the values met with in sliding bearings.

At high speeds, even this estimate of film thickness, which errs on the big side, reaches high surface finish asperity size. As well as the provision of an elastohydrodynamic film between the moving elements of a rolling bearing, the oil film clearly helps to cool the surfaces and inhibits their softening due to high temperatures. The film also isolates the surfaces from the atmosphere, thus avoiding oxidation.

However, to achieve all these ends the film need not be too thick, and the oil supply to a rolling element bearing is thus generally very much smaller than that for sliding bearings and can be as effective with even smaller quantities than those calculated above.

5.2.1. Low Speed Bearings

Low speed rolling bearings are best pre-packed with grease, since the grease also acts as a very effective seal and can remain in the bearing body for long periods without replacement.

These greases are usually made from mineral oils and sodium or calcium soaps. The latter type of grease melts at around 100°C while the former between 150 and 180°C. Both types of grease tend to separate into oil and soap with time and temperature, which after all is their mechanism of supplying lubricant to the loaded surfaces, but this must not occur too rapidly because rolling bearings do not require a high rate of oil supply and also because the accumulation of soap in the bearing needs to be cleaned out rather than simply replenished, and this is clearly better done as seldom as possible.

An estimate of the separation rate at a given temperature is achieved simply by leaving the grease in a receptacle and measuring the oil it gives up. These greases can both be used in temperature environments of down to −20°C, but the calcium based greases are only recommended for temperatures up to 45°C and the sodium based grades up to 100°C.

If the running temperature of a bearing is high, then oil is suitable. Great attention must be paid to the lubricant supply since too much grease can produce overheating due to generation of excess friction. The lower limit is fixed rather by the criterion of effective sealing than by the necessity of a complete oil film.

The supply of grease is usually provided manually, or by means of a semi-automatic greaser with provision for indicating the completion of a dose.

For large systems a complete semi- or automatic circuit is used to provide periodic grease shots as described in Chapter III.

5.2.2. High Speed Bearings

At speeds of over 3,000 rpm, the use of grease produces overheating because of excess friction and its poor cooling properties. In these cases mineral oil is used as the lubricant and is generally the same as used in the rest of the installation, the only special requirements for rolling bearings being a high vaporisation temperature and a good viscosity index.

At extremely high speeds it is no longer possible to partially immerse the bearing in oil, and the oil must be fed by drops, oil mist, or wicks.

In fact oil mist is a very appropriate means of lubricating high speed rolling bearings (§ 3.2.3) both for cooling and reduced friction. An overall view of the lubrication of anti-friction bearings is presented in [17].

5.3. Lubrication of Gears

The relative motion of the mating surfaces between gear teeth is compounded of both rolling and sliding. Hence fresh lubricant is continuously entrained in the loaded region because of sliding motion. Recent research (Cameron, [18]) has shown that the film thicknesses encountered between gear tooth surfaces are sufficiently large to be due to hydrodynamic, rather than boundary lubrication. On the other hand, the difficulty of obtaining a high surface finish on the gear teeth makes this type of load transmitting contact inferior to that of a rolling bearing contact. Because of the difficulty of taking the surface microgeometry into account and predicting the elastic deformation of the highly loaded metal surfaces, the majority of research into this problem has been experimental in character.

One of the most successful experiments in this field used two discs whose relative motion could be altered continuously from pure rolling to pure sliding [16]. The different disc materials and lubricants provided data of great interest.

In this way, for the similar performance of cylindrical, conical and helicoidal gears, it is possible to draw the following conclusions :

 a). The more viscous the oil the better is its anti-scuffing potential. An addition of lead naphthenate or other lead soaps can increase the scuffing load by 10 to 20%.

 b). Extreme pressure additives (see § 6.1.1) can raise the transmission loads by 200% without failure.

 c). The scuffing load depends on the disc or gear materials, the amount of sliding or rolling motion, and the speed, for a given constant temperature.

 d). For any given slide-roll ratio, pair of materials, and lubricant, the surface-stress σ_s and the sliding velocity V for scuffing are found to be related in the following way

$$\sigma_s V^n = K \qquad\qquad (5-45)$$

n and K being constants, within a range of sliding velocities usually encountered in practice. This means that, keeping the other parameters constant, there will be a certain optimum sliding speed for the largest scuffing load. The oil additives change n and the other parameters alter K.

The conclusions reached from experiments with different materials, oils and slip ratios encountered in worm-gears were as follows :

 a). The coefficient of friction falls with increasing velocity for any slide-roll ratio, or base lubricant. Additives in the oil may either increase, or lower the coefficient of friction.

 b). Oils which yield a mean coefficient of friction greater than 0.03, produce rapid abrasive wear.

 c). Additives which do not improve the load transmission under gear-wheel (steel-to-steel) conditions can work in the case of worm-gearing.

d). Some anti-scuffing additives increase abrasive wear, a fact which is also met with in normal spur gearing.

e). A higher oil viscosity improves the scuffing load, as before.

f). The friction coefficient met with in worm-gearing is 10 times as large as that in fully hydrodynamic bearings, and is comparable to the friction of a sliding bearing operating in the boundary lubrication regime.

g). The load which can be safely carried without risk of failure by scuffing is dependent to a large extent on the mating materials, especially on the composition and hardness of the bronze member.

The form of the lubricant supply is determined firstly by the speed of the gears in question, this parameter being the critical one determining the ease with which oil can be transported into the contact regions.

The required quantity of lubricant is small because of the thin film of lubricant necessary between the mating teeth. The lubricant is also a coolant and it is in this capacity that the oil is supplied in greater quantities.

5.3.1. Low Speed Gears

For peripheral speeds of less than 15 m/sec the gear train in a sealed housing is usually provided with an oil sump whose level reaches the teeth of one or two of the pinions which then transfer the oil around the whole system (see Fig. 5—34), [16].

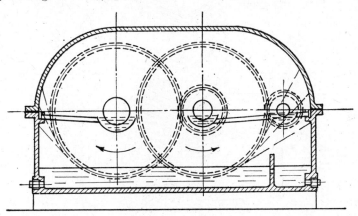

Fig. 5.34. — Lubrication of low speed gears, [16].

The subsidiary oil baths are kept full by the spray of droplets from the housing lid.

The most important consideration is that the oil must be directed to the inner faces or roots of the driven teeth. The flow need not be excessive for the additional reason that excess oil is trapped between the teeth and thus gives rise to extra loads and vibration, especially in the case of very wide, or close-fitting teeth, [16]. Because of this fact, large heavy duty gear trains have separate circuits for the cooling and lubricating oil.

The cleanliness of oil is of extreme importance in gear lubricants.

The oil sump method of lubricant supply is suitable for fixed installations, but in certain instances it is more convenient and trustworthy to use a low pressure pump to circulate the oil to the important loaded contacts.

5.3.2. High Speed Gears

For peripheral speeds of over 12 m/sec a system is used delivering pressurized lubricant in a jet directed into the contact zone, from the entry side (Fig. 5—35), [16].

The velocity of the oil jet need not be greater than the peripheral gear speed, in fact it is generally recommended to be slightly slower, in order to provide better covering of leading tooth faces.

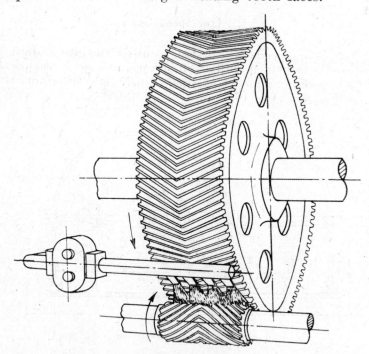

Fig. 5.35. — Lubrication of high speed gears, [16].

For particularly wide gear teeth it is necessary to provide several oil jets to cover the whole tooth face. For extremely high speed gears (10,000 to 30,000 rpm) it is also necessary to remove the oil after use as well as to replace it, in order that the cooling oil flow may be maintained in the regions of major importance, without over-filling the tooth spaces. This over-filling can produce extremely high loads, and in some cases has led to tooth breakage. The manner in which both cooling and lubrication are provided by the oil in such a high speed gear set is shown in Fig. 5—36, [19].

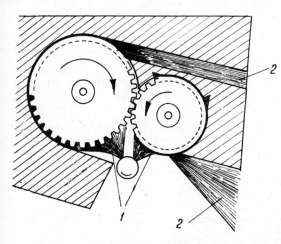

Fig. 5.36. — Lubrication of very high speed gears.

It is to be noted that the oil supply in this case is placed at the exit from the contact zone and fed through one or more orifices of 1 to 1.2 mm diameter. The removal of excess lubricant is effected merely by allowing the oil to leave due to its kinetic energy.

The oils to be used in these cases of extremely high speeds must be of low viscosity and not prone to foaming. This usually means that a synthetic oil must be used.

Again, oil mist is a very useful method of oil supply to large high speed units and the sprays should be arranged in the same manner as in Fig. 5—35 and designed in accordance with the data supplied in § 3.2.3.

Recently attention has been drawn to the high temperature operation of gear trains, and considerable research has been carried out on this question. The problem lies mainly in the selection of a suitable lubricant that will maintain its properties with time and resist oxidation. The best results were achieved with silicones and diphenyl chlorates and it was also found that certain surface treatment of the gear teeth (nitrating) also added to the efficacy of their lubrication [20].

Other data on the performance of synthetic oils and high temperature lubrication will be presented in Chapter VI; data of practical interest on gear lubricants both for high and for low temperature applications is to be found in [21].

References

1. N. Tipei, V. N. Constantinescu, Al. Nica, O. Biţă, *Lagăre cu alunecare* (Sliding Bearings), in Romanian. Editura Academiei R.P.R., Bucharest, 1961.
2. N. Tipei, *Theory of Lubrication*. Stanford University Press, Stanford, 1962.
3. N. Tipei, Al. Nica, *On the Boundary Conditions and Oil Flow in Complete Journal Bearings*. Rev. Méc. Appl., **2**, *1*, Bucharest, 1957.
4. J. A. Cole, C. J. Hughes, *Oil Flow and Film Extent in Complete Journal Bearings*. The Engineer, **201**, *5225, 5226*, 1956.
5. N. Tipei, Al. Nica, *Influenţa condiţiilor de alimentare cu lubrifiant asupra funcţionării lagărelor cu aluncare* (The Influence of Oil Supply Conditions on the Performance of Journal Bearings), in Romanian. Metalurgia şi Construcţia de Maşini, **9**, *10*, 1959.
6. D. F. Wilcock, E. R. Booser, *Bearing Design and Application*. McGraw-Hill Book Company, New York, 1957.
7. A. K. Diachikov, *Issledovania v oblasti dinamiceski nagrujenîh podşipnikov*, in Russian. Trenie i iznos v maşinah, Sbornik IV, Izdatelistvo Akademii Nauk SSSR, 1949.
8. M. C. Shaw, E. F. Macks, *Analysis and Lubrication of Bearings*. McGraw-Hill Book Co., New York, 1949.
9. A. Schilling, *Les huiles pour moteurs et le graissage des moteurs* II, Editions Technip, Paris, 1962. (English Edition, 1968 : Motor Oils and Engine Lubrication. Scientific Publications, Broseley, Shropshire).
10. Gh. Vasilca, Al. Nica, *Contributions to the Experimental Determination of the Operating Parameters of Bearings in Internal Combustion Engines*. Rev. Méc. Appl., **8**, *5*, 1963.
11. Gh. Marin, *Instalaţie de laborator pentru măsurarea debitelor şi temperaturilor uleiului la lagărele arborilor cotiţi de la motoarele cu ardere internă* (Experimental Installations for Measuring Oil Flows and Temperatures in the Bearings of Internal Combustion Engines), in Romanian. St. Cerc. Mec. Apl., **12**, *3*, Bucharest, 1961.
12. N. I. Letkov, *Naturnîe ispîtania podpiatnika ghidrogheneratora Voljskoi g.e.s. V. I. Lenina. Razvitie ghidrodinamiceskoi teorii smazki primenitelino k upornîm podşipnikam skolijenia*, in Russian. Izdatelistvo Akademii Nauk SSSR, Moskva, 1959.
13. Gh. Vasilca, Al. Nica, *Studiul comportării la alunecare a aliajului antifricţiune de tipul BzSnPb 20, la lagărele lubrificate cu apă* (The Sliding Behaviour of an Antifriction Alloy of the BzSnPb 20 Type, in Water Lubricated Journal Bearings), in Romanian. Internal Paper, The Institute of Fluid Mechanics, Bucharest, 1963.
14. A. V. Kolcenko, A. A. Silin, *Despre unele particularităţi ale funcţionării lagărelor metalice cu cauciuc* (Operating Characteristics of Metallic Journal Bearings with Rubber Surfaces), in Romanian. Bul. Constr. Maşini, *10*, Bucharest, 1957.
15. E. J. Mayer, M. C. Shaw, *Characteristics of an Externally Pressurized Bearing Having Variable External Flow Restrictors*. Journ. Basic Eng., **85**, *2*, 1963.
16. A. G. M. Michell, *Lubrication*. Blackie and Son, London, 1950.
17. —   *Some Practical Notes on the Lubrication of Antifriction Bearings*. Sci. Lubr., **10**, November (Special Extra Issue), 1958.
18. A. Cameron, *Principles of Lubrication*. Longmans, London, 1966.
19. J. W. Dern, *Lubrication Problems in High Speed Gears*. Lubr. Eng., **15**, *1*, 1959.
20. E. E. Shipley, *Investigations of Factors Affecting High-Temperature Gear Operation*. Lubr. Eng., **15**, *3*, 1959.
21. H. J. Watson, *The Choice of Gear Lubricants*. Sci. Lubr., **10**, *10*, 1958.
22. Al. Nica, *Contributions to the Determination of the Real Clearance in Sliding Bearings*. Journ. Basic Eng., **87**, *3*, 1965.

CHAPTER VI

Lubricants, Materials and Particular Antifriction Methods

The conditions under which modern machines and industrial installations are required to operate, has made necessary extensive research into the choice of appropriate lubricants, capable of sustaining high speeds and loads, as well as extreme temperatures.

Progress in the development of more effective lubricants has had a parallel effect on the design of bearings and lubricant supply systems. In situations where fluid lubricants are still impractical it has been necessary to develop suitable antifriction materials and coatings.

6.1. Fluid Lubricants

The development of fluid lubricants has been made in several directions : oil additives, synthetic oils, and oils treated in various other ways

6.1.1. Oils with Additives

As has been stated, one of the ways of improving the quality of fluid lubricants is by the addition of small controlled quantities of certain substances capable of changing their properties in the desired manner. These substances are generally called "additives". While their beneficial effect has been recognised for many years, additives have only been widely used for the past ten to fifteen years.

Additives may be chosen for various functions which improve the oil's properties and include detergents, antioxidants, defoamants, antiseizure agents, viscosity index improvers, but their importance and efficiency must not be over-estimated and generalized without due investigation. The side effects of some additives may be detrimental to performance of the lubricant in other directions and thus they must be very carefully selected and their quality and quantity precisely controlled.

Other additives include a series of chemical compounds which may be mixed with the oil to react with the metallic surfaces involved. Thus,

some products containing sulphur and chlorine are used in the metal working industry to modify the frictional characteristics and to improve the
life of the cutting tool and the resulting surface finish, [1].

6.1.1.1. *Extreme Pressure Additives.* The high speeds and pressures encountered in certain devices (especially in hypoid gears which
were impractical until adequate lubricants were available) have necessi-
tated extensive experimental work aimed at finding suitable ameliora-
ting additives.

Table 6—1 compares the effects of various additives on the performance of oils used to lubricate gears, and it can be seen that the extreme
pressure (antiseizure) additives are efficient either under heavy loads
or at high speeds.

Table 6 — 1

Chemical nature of additive	Utilisation in hypoid gears in the case of	
	High speeds	High loads
Chlorine based	E	O . . . (E)
Active sulphur in non-carboxylic com-pounds	E	D
Relatively inactive sulphur in non-car-boxylic compounds	E	(D)
Relatively inactive sulphur in carboxylic esters	(D) . . . (E)	E
Relatively inactive sulphur in carboxylic acids	E	E
Carboxylic esters	D	E
Carboxylic acids	(D) . . . D	E
Oxiphosphite acid esters	E	E
Oxiphosphite neutral esters	O	O
Oxiphosphate neutral esters	O	O
Thiophosphate neutral esters	E	E

Symbols : E = very efficient
(E) = relatively efficient
O = inefficient but not detrimental
(D) = slightly detrimental
D = very detrimental

The chemical nature of lubrication at high pressures has been the
subject of considerable research and it has been established that the
chemical reactions with the lubricated surfaces are stimulated by the pressures involved. Additives with good antiseizure properties are adsorbed
on the rubbing surfaces, the resulting compounds having a beneficial
effect on friction, by both reducing the asperity heights and by filling
the spaces between the asperities.

Although many chlorine-containing compounds have been suggested
as extreme pressure additives, only a few are available in commercial
form. When selecting EP additives containing chlorine it is important
that the material does not contain free hydrochloric acid, nor hydrolize

readily to form this acid; chlorinated paraffin wax, for instance, can be secured without these defects, while chlorinated naphthalene in spite of being more stable against hydrolysis is also more toxic, [2].

The sulphur or sulphur compounds must react with the ferrous metal to form iron sulphide, in order to be efficient as EP additives; sulphur compounds are most satisfactory in gear oils if they have controlled activity. It is considered that sulphides and disulphides are efficient EP agents, while mercaptans are not, [2].

In order to combine the advantages of both chlorinated and sulphurized oils, chlorosulphurized additives have been realised. Such products may be prepared either by mixing sulphurised and chlorinated additives in the required proportions, or by chemical combination of the two. Their efficiency in reducing seizure failure is remarkable: for the inclusion of 5% additive in oil the seizure load is about 10 times greater than that obtained with the pure oil [3].

Phosphorous-containing compounds also can be efficient extreme pressure additives, but their chemical structure influences in a large measure their usefulness. It was found that phosphites are superior to phosphates and that aliphatic esters are better than aryl ones. It is also believed that for EP efficiency a molecule must contain, in addition to a phosphorous atom, another active group such as chlorine or hydroxyl for attachment to the metal surfaces and at least one aryl or alkyl group. Later work showed that the phosphoric acid itself was not an active EP additive, [2].

Lead soaps were among the first to be suggested as ingredients for hypoid gear oils, since they resist the wiping action of gears under combined sliding and rolling motion and they act as corrosion inhibitors; the widest usage, in gear oils, employs lead naphthenate, in the form of a concentrate in lubricating oil. It seems that complex lead soaps made from a combination of naphtenic acid and lactic acid are superior to lead naphthenate alone. When gear oils containing these soaps operate in the presence of water, troublesome emulsions can result, so that due measures must be taken.

Very good results can be obtained by introducing some organometallic compounds to the oil, [3].

Temperature is an important factor in the prediction of oil behaviour at high pressures, some authors stating that the temperature plays a more important part than pressure and suggesting that these additives be called "high temperature additives", instead of "high pressure additives". Since in almost every case both high pressures and high temperatures are met with together, it is hardly necessary to differentiate between the particular mode of operation of the benefitial additives. However, it is to be noted that in general at low temperatures the lubricating properties of the chlorine based additives are superior to those of sulphur based compounds.

6.1.1.2. *Antioxidant Additives*. These additives retard the oxidation process, their action consisting of the extension of the induction period and the inhibition of chain reactions. The effect of these additives can also be explained by the formation on the metallic surface of an insulating layer which prevents its contact with the surrounding oil.

Since some additives are multi-functional, a separate antioxidant is not always required : many extreme pressure additives act as antioxidants, and the reverse is also true since phosphorous- and/or sulphur-containing antioxidants and corrosion inhibitors may increase the strength of the oil film at the same time, [2].

The effective oxidation inhibitors can be grouped as follows :
  a) Oxydrilic compounds (phenols, naphthols).
  b) Nitrogen compounds (amines, etc.).
  c) Organo-metallic compounds.
  d) Halogenated compounds.
  e) Sulphur compounds (disulphides, thioethers).
  f) Compounds containing the upper terms of the groups with nitrogen and oxygen from the periodic system of elements, such as phosphorus, arsenic, antimony, selenium and tellurium.

It has been established that the following compounds (enumerated in order of increasing efficiency) are the best oxidation inhibitors : diphenylguanidine, β-naphthylamine, ethyl-α-naphthylamine, para-aminophenol, diphenylamine, phenyl-α-naphthylamine and asymmetrical diphenylhydrazide.

6.1.1.3. *Corrosion and Rust Preventives*. Among the substances most frequently used as anticorrosion additives are the derivatives of phosphorus and sulphur, the phenols and the amines.

The first two groups inhibit corrosion by the formation of protective films, while the latter two work directly, by reducing the degree of oil oxidation. The majority of antioxidants are also effective as corrosion preventives.

Lately a new class of rust inhibitor has been discovered, i.e. volatile corrosion preventives. These compounds consist of organic amine nitrites and related compounds such as urea plus sodium nitrite, dicyclohexylamine nitrite and di-isopropylamine nitrite. All these products contain the nitrite ion which is the active constituent that inhibits corrosion, [4].

6.1.1.4. *Detergents*. These additives are used to avoid the deposition of the various products which appear in the oil in the course of its utilisation, on warm oil-wetted metallic surfaces.

In general these additives are organo-metallic compound,s their behaviour differing widely from one oil to another, and when used for the same oil their efficacity also differs widely. The mechanism of their action is not yet completely understood and they also are subject to some disadvantages, e.g. the emulsification of water when present, which thus increases the corrosive potential of the oil.

Among the chemical compounds used as detergents there are: calcium sulphonates based on petroleum products, calcium cethylphosphate, calcium octyl-salicylate, calcium phenylstearate, barium compounds of sulphonic acids obtained by the sulphonation of the substituted alkyl derivatives of benzene, etc.

Detergents and/or dispersants may also act as corrosion inhibitors, as do the barium and the mixed barium-calcium salts of di-isobutyl phenol sulphide or the same salts treated with phosphorous sulphide, [2].

6.1.1.5. *Antiwear Additives.* Since wear is the result of friction, it is logical to expect that any additive capable of reducing friction under conditions of boundary lubrication is also capable of diminishing the rate of wear. However, research work in this direction has shown that no direct correlation can be established between the effect of additives on both friction and wear.

Thus, some additives are inefficient in reducing wear, in spite of their antifriction properties, and vice-versa. The lack of a connection between these two phenomena is due, probably, to the fact that wear takes place during a short space of time and on limited areas of the metallic surfaces subjected to friction; on the other hand, corrosion phenomena play an important part in wear extent.

It has been observed that the polar compounds (oleic acid, palmitic acid, etc) are more efficient in reducing corrosion wear than abrasive wear; corrosion wear can also be reduced with the help of graphite additions to the oils: 1% of colloidal graphite in oil leads to a considerable reduction in the wear of piston rings and engine cylinders, [5]. Important reductions in wear were reported by the addition in oils of methyldichlorostearate; this beneficial effect was found both during starting tests (conducive to corrosive wear) and during hot running (when abrasive rather than corrosive wear predominates).

The additives enumerated in § 6.1.1.3. are very efficient in preventing corrosion wear.

6.1.1.6. *Antiseizure Additives.* These additives are used to eliminate dry friction and its consequences. They are usually polar compounds with low acidity, containing oxygen, sulphur, phosphorus, halogens, etc. As examples there are the alkyl-phosphates, the sulphurised animal oils, etc.

While preventing the seizure of surfaces under normal working conditions, these additives can stimulate high rates of wear, so that they must be used with discretion.

Experimental work in this field has established the properties required of these additives :

a) They must be strongly adherent to the metallic surfaces or to the oxides of the metallic surfaces.

b) When necessary, the adsorbed film must react rapidly with the surface in order to produce the antiseizure inorganic layer.

c) The resulting films must be easily sheared in order to keep the coefficient of friction to a minimum.

6.1.1.7. *Antiemulsion and Antifoam Additives.* The emulsions of oil with water or other liquids must be broken up; in steam turbines one of the main lubrication problems is to avoid oil emulsions with water leakages. The basic quality of water separability (demulsibility) of lubricants is obtained by careful selection and refining of the base stocks, which also ensure a good oxidation stability, [1]; defoamants can be included.

Among the most common defoamants are the substituted amines and the silicones; the latter exhibit a spectacular efficiency, some authors stating that only 5 parts per million are sufficient to obtain the necessary antifoam effect, [1]. However, these additives must be carefully selected, since some of them may impart side effects which result in reduced demulsibility or other characteristics of the finished oil blend.

Foam inhibition is also an important problem in gears, since some of the gear oils tend to form a dense foam during circulation or by the action of gear teeth which pull air into the fluid.

In this case too, very small proportions of additives are used : silicone fluids, in concentrations of 0.01 to 0.001% have been the most widely used antifoam agents, [2]. Since the silicones used are insoluble in petroleum oils, it was suggested that chemical inhomogeneity in the film is a very efficient mechanism of film instability, hence of foam inhibition.

A great variety of other compounds have been proposed as foam inhibitors : calcium soaps of wool olean and sodium alkyl esters of sulphonic acid, potassium oleate, various fluorinated compounds, organosilicone phosphorous condensation products, esters of sulphonated ricinoleic acid, etc., [2].

While it is recommended to include antifoam additives in any gear oil, it is necessary to check its efficiency by actual tests ; at the same time, after eventual storage a recheck of the foaming tendency of the oil must be made and due attention must be paid to the fact that foam inhibitors usually have only limited solubility in oil.

6.1.1.8. *Antifreeze Additives.* The freezing point of an oil can be lowered in several ways ; e.g. by adding some chemical compounds to the oil. The best known antifreeze agent is a polyalkylnaphthalene obtained by the condensation of chlorinated paraffin in the presence of aluminum chlorinate, [6]. This product known as "Paragel" can lower the freezing point of an oil by 28°C for a concentration of 1 to 2%.

Investigations performed in countries where vehicular transportation at low temperatures constitutes a real problem have shown that the engine oil pump is no longer efficient even at temperatures slightly above the freezing point, and the design of the engine sump can be an important factor in the prevention of oil freezing.

6.1.1.9. *Viscosity Index Improvers.* As is well known, viscosity index defines the quality of a lubricant by comparison with two typical oils : a paraffinic Pennsylvania oil which has a gradual variation of viscosity with temperature and whose V. I. = 100, and a Gulf Coast oil with a steep variation of viscosity with temperature and whose V. I. = 0.

Recently it has been found however, that there exist oils with a V. I. > 100. For this, and other reasons, there has been a recent move to abandon this somewhat subjective classification of the viscosity-temperature quality of oils, and to replace it with other criteria, such as the viscosity ratio [7].

There is some doubt also as to the fundamental value of artificially raising the viscosity index, since the long chain polymers involved have a limited life, and are subject to physical damage under conditions of high shear. This latter fault may lead to the inefficient operation of lubricant systems, since the delivery pipe viscosity of the oil may be considerably higher than its working value in thin lubricating films. The practical solution today is the use of a thin fluid and of a very viscous polymer, [8].

6.1.2. Synthetic Oils

The group of "synthetic oils" include a variety of fluids derived from other sources than mineral, animal or vegetable oils, and have been produced to satisfy the special conditions under which some modern machinery operates : very high or very low temperatures or both, high bearing loads, resistance to ignition, resistance to chemical attack and so on.

Thus, in spite of the fact that modern petroleum oils are prepared very carefully and their qualities are in consequence very well controlled, their comparatively limited useful temperature range necessitates the use of other lubricants among which synthetic oils play an important part. The special characteristics of synthetic lubricants, which cannot be provided by mineral oils, are as follows : fire resistance, thermal stability, resistance to oxidation and to nuclear radiation. It is possible either chemically, or by the use of additives to obtain "tailor-made lubricants", specifically designed to provide the properties necessary in particular operating conditions. Properties which can be modified in a more or less important degree are : viscosity range and index, stability to oxidation, corrosion resistance, foaming tendency, pour point, and extreme-pressure resistance.

The main types of currently available lubricants are as follows [9], [10] : dibasic acid esters, phosphate esters, neopentyl polyol esters, silicate and borate esters, polyphenyl ethers, fluoroesters, polyglycols and their derivatives, chlorofluorocarbon polymers and silicones. Their most important properties are shown in Table 6—2, so that comparisons may be easily made, [9].

Fig. 6—1 shows viscosity variation with temperature for several synthetic oils compared with a typical mineral oil (SAE 10), [11].

Table

Characteristics	Lubricant	Diesters	Phosphate esters	Neopentyl polyol esters	Polyphenyl ethers
Density		1.0	0.9/1.2	—	1.2
Pour point (°C)		—72/—38	—70/+30	—60/—30	—6/20
Flash point (°C)		205/240	200/500	235/260	205/335
Viscosity index		140/175	—18/150	80/135	140
Lubricity		very good	very good	very good	very good
Fire resistance		poor	very good	poor	poor
Thermal stability		good	good	good	very good
Odixation resistance		good	very good	moderate	very good
Hydrolytic stability		good	good	—	very good
Volatility		moderate	low-moderate	low	moderate

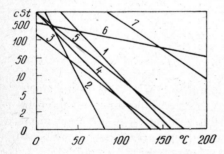

Fig. 6.1. — Variation of the viscosity of synthetic oils with temperature, in comparison with a mineral oil ; 1 — mineral oil (SAE 10) ; 2 — fluorocarbon compounds ; 3 — silicate esters ; 4 — polyglycols ; 5 — diesters ; 6 — methyl silicones ; 7 — phenyl methyl silicones.

6.1.2.1. *Dibasic Acid Esters (Diesters)*, are obtained by reacting straight chain aliphatic acids (adipic, azelaic or sebacic) with branched chain primary alcohols, such as 2-ethylhexanol or iso-octanol, [9].

Complex esters are synthesized by linking dibasic acid half-esters through a glycol, thus creating a single long-chain molecule, [10]

$$\underset{\substack{\text{Branched} \\ \text{Primary Alcohol}}}{C_8H_{17}-O-}\underset{\substack{\text{Dibasic} \\ \text{Acid}}}{\overset{\overset{\text{O}}{\|}}{C}-(CH_2)_8-\overset{\overset{\text{O}}{\|}}{C}-O-}\left[\underset{\substack{\text{Polyalkylene} \\ \text{Glycol}}}{(CH_2-CH_2-O)_n-}\underset{\substack{\text{Dibasic} \\ \text{Acid}}}{\overset{\overset{\text{O}}{\|}}{C}-(CH_2)_8-\overset{\overset{\text{O}}{\|}}{C}-O-}\right]_x \underset{\substack{\text{Branched} \\ \text{Primary} \\ \text{Alcohol}}}{C_8H_{17}}$$

Long-chain complex esters can also be made by linking monobasic acid glycol half-esters through a dibasic acid bridge, [10]

$$C_8H_{17}-\overset{\overset{\text{O}}{\|}}{C}-(O-CH_2-CH_2)_n \left[-O-\overset{\overset{\text{O}}{\|}}{C}-(CH_2)_8-\overset{\overset{\text{O}}{\|}}{C}-O-(CH_2-CH_2-O)_n \right]_x -\overset{\overset{\text{O}}{\|}}{C}-C_8H_{17}$$

| Monobasic Acid | Polyalkylene Glycol | | Dibasic Acid | Polyalkylene Glycol | Monobasic Acid |

Esters of tribasic acids (aconitic and tricarballylic) have also been investigated, but they showed poorer viscosity temperature characteristics than the esters of complex diesters.

6—2, [9]

Silicate and borate esters	Fluoroesters	Polyglycols	Chlorofluoro-carbon polymers	Silicones	Petroleum oils
0.9	1.6	0.9	1.8	0.9	0.9
−72/−45	−60/30	−24/20	−60/30	−72/−6	0
95/205	−150/260	150/260	—	95/335	220
140/200	−75/−45	100/200	−165	175	100
moderate	good	good	very good	moderate	very good
moderate	moderate	poor	very good	moderate	poor
good	good	good	good	very good	moderate
very good	good	poor	very good	very good	moderate
very poor	poor	very good	good	good	good
low	moderate	low	high	low	moderate

These fluids present good lubricating properties at very low and very high temperatures so that they have been widely used, both in equipment operating in rigorous winters, and in prop-jet engines and gas turbines.

6.1.2.2. *Phosphate Esters* are termed the trialkyl, triaryl and alkyl aryl esters of orthophosphoric acid, of the following general structure

$$O=\overset{\overset{\text{OR}'}{|}}{\underset{\underset{\text{OR}'''}{|}}{P}}-OR''$$

where R′, R″, R‴ may be alkyl or aryl groups, [9].

All these esters have good lubricating properties and fire-resistance, but their viscosity is influenced by the type and proportion of alcohol and/or phenol, cresol or xylenol used in their production. In this way several classes of phosphate esters are available, each serving a definite temperature range.

Phosphate esters are used as lubricants for compressors, vacuum pumps etc., transmission fluids, fire-resistant hydraulic fluids; they have been used also as additives for mineral oils.

Among the commercial products of phosphate ester-type synthetic lubricants and hydraulic fluids, there are [10]:

a) The "Skydrol" series of fire-resistant fluids, developed for use aboard transport aircraft; these fluids were designed to overcome the hazards of flammable hydraulic fluids coming in contact with hot brakes, exhaust manifolds, or other ignition sources, if a leakage occurred.

b) The "Pydraul" fluids designed to fulfil the need for fire-resistant hydraulic fluids and lubricants for industrial machinery.

c) The "Cellulube" fluids recommended as air-compressor lubricants.

6.1.2.3. *Neopentyl Polyol Esters.* These products are obtained by reacting certain monobasic acids (usually within the range C_7 to C_{10}) with a polyhydric alcohol containing the neopentane structure

$$H_3C - \underset{\underset{CH_3}{|}}{\overset{\overset{CH_3}{|}}{C}} - CH_3$$

Also included in this group are such polyols as neopentyl-glycol, trimethylolpropane and pentaerythritol, [9]

$$H_3C - \underset{\underset{CH_2OH}{|}}{\overset{\overset{CH_2OH}{|}}{C}} - CH_3 \qquad\qquad H_3CH_2C - \underset{\underset{CH_2OH}{|}}{\overset{\overset{CH_2OH}{|}}{C}} - CH_2OH$$

Neopentyl Glycol   Trimethylolpropane

$$HOH_2C - \underset{\underset{CH_2OH}{|}}{\overset{\overset{CH_2OH}{|}}{C}} - CH_2OH$$

Pentaerythritol

These esters have good lubricity, good viscosity-temperature characteristics and an excellent resistance to oxidation.

The number of hydroxyl groups available for esterification has a bearing on viscosity of the ester; the difunctional polyols gives the lowest viscosity esters for any given acids, the trifunctional polyols give heavier esters and the tetrafunctional polyols give the heaviest ones. While the length of the hydrocarbon side chains on a neopentyl polyol also has some effect on viscosity, the functionality is of far greater importance, which is graphically shown in Fig. 6—2, where approximate viscosities are shown versus acid carbon chain lengths, [10].

The neopentyl polyol esters were used in gas turbine engines when the temperatures (above 250°C) prohibited the utilisation of diesters.

Their properties make them particularly suitable also in other situations where extreme temperatures are encountered, as in some hydraulic circuits, or lubricants for instruments operating in such conditions.

6.1.2.4. *Silicate and Borate Esters.* First of all there are the orthosilicates, that is to say the silicic acid derivatives of alcohols and

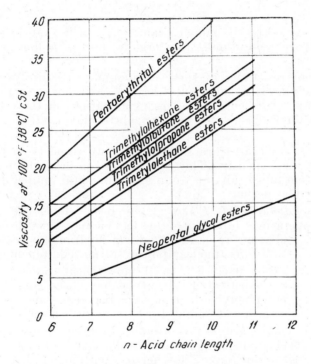

Fig. 6.2.— Viscosity variation of neopentyl polyol esters as a function of acid chain length and polyol functionality, [10].

phenols; they are in fact tetra-alkoxy or tetra-aryloxy silanes of structure

$$R_4\text{—}O\text{—}Si\begin{matrix} O\text{—}R_1 \\ | \\ | \\ O\text{—}R_3 \end{matrix}O\text{—}R_2$$

where R_1, R_2, R_3 and R_4 are alkyl or aryl groups, identical or dissimilar, and which may have chloro, fluoro, nitro, alkoxy or thio-alkoxy substituent groups; these materials contain carbon-oxygen-silicon bonds while the tetra-aryl or tetra-alkyl silanes contain carbon-silicon bonds so that confusion between them must be avoided, [9].

In addition to orthosilicates, there are a group of compounds sometimes called "dimer silicates" whose structural formula is — [10]

$$
\begin{array}{ccc}
 & O-R_2 & O-R_4 \\
 & | & | \\
R_1-O-\;Si- & O-\;Si- & O-R_6 \\
 & | & | \\
 & O-R_3 & O-R_5
\end{array}
$$

These are correctly named hexaalkoxy- or hexaaryloxy-disiloxanes. The R groups can be almost any organic radical and may be identical or dissimilar.

The poor resistance of these compounds to hydrolysis limits their potential usefulness as lubricants despite their low volatility and good viscosity-temperature characteristics. Applications of these fluids include heat transfer fluids, electronic coolants, lubricants for refrigerators, hydraulic fluids.

The triaryl borates are similar in many respects to the tetra-aryl silicates, but less expensive. They can be used in properly designed equipment (free from moist air) up to an environmental temperature of 300°C, for considerable periods.

6.1.2.5. *Polyphenyl Ethers* have been developed to serve as extreme temperature lubricants (in jet engines for instance) and as thermal and radiation resistant fluids in hydraulic systems operating under special conditions (nuclear power station equipment and rockets).

Diphenyl ether itself is a well-known heat-transfer medium and certain of its alkyl substituted derivatives have been considered as lubricants, but the polyphenyl ethers in an advanced stage of development as lubricants are those containing three or more benzene rings.

The compounds are named around the group present in the centre of the main ether chain; a polyphenyl ether containing an even number of benzene rings would have an ether oxygen molecule at the centre of the chain and hence would be named an ether, [10]

Bis (p-phenoxyphenyl) Ether

while a compound having an odd number of benzene rings would be named as for the centre benzene ring

p-Bis (p-phenoxyphenoxy) Benzene

However, the nomenclature becomes complex when the number of benzene rings is increased and when the molecule is unsymmetrical with respect to linkage of substituents; it is often necessary in such cases to use numbers as well as the ortho-meta-para designations.

Polyphenyl ethers are generally prepared by the Ullman synthesis (an alkali phenate is reacted with an aromatic halogen compound — usually a bromide — in the presence of a suitable copper catalyst), [9].

The position of the ether linkages, the type and position of any substituent groups and the molecular weight of the ether has considerable influence on the physical properties of these lubricants : meta-linked ethers have the lowest melting points and a strong tendency to supercool, medium molecular weight ethers have increased viscosities, mono-alkyl substituents tend to lower the melting point and also unfortunately the excellent oxidation resistance and thermal stability.

6.1.2.6. *Fluoroesters*. The various esters containing fluorine developed for good oxidation resistance and efficiency over a wide range of temperature are classified under this name. Their typical structure is

$$H(CF_2)_x CH_2 OOC(CF_2)_y H$$

Their production is a compromise between low flammibility of the perfluorocarbons and improved viscosity characteristics and lower volatility of the esters [9]. The need for lubricants with an operating range up to 250°C (in gas turbine engines for instance) was the motive for their development. Their disadvantages include a tendency to hydrolyse and a high freezing point. However, esters derived from organic carboxylic acids and fluoroalcohols are much more resistant to hydrolysis than esters derived from fluorinated acids and alkanols [10]. Carboxylic acid esters of fluoroalcohols are more viscous, have larger temperature coefficients of viscosity and lower boiling points than their unflorinated counter parts. Since the fluoroesters are comparatively new products, further development is possible.

6.1.2.7. *Polyglycols and Derivatives*, are linear polymers of the following general formula, [9]

$$RO\!-\!\left[CH_2\!-\!\underset{\underset{R'}{|}}{CH}\!-\!O\right]_n\!\!-\!R''$$

where R and R'' can be hydrogen, or alkyl, aryl, or ester group, and R' hydrogen and or an alkyl.

They differ widely, and their uses are also varied ; cost limits their application to fire-resistant hydraulic fluids, dispersed in water (which provides very good fire-resistant properties). Anti-corrosion additives are necessary.

6.1.2.8. *Chlorofluorocarbon Polymers* ; the demand for fluids with a high-chemical stability has led to the development of low molecular weight chlorofluoroethylene polymers as lubricants. The commercially available chlorofluorocarbon lubricants are based on chlorotrifluoroethylene (CTFE).

This unsaturated monomer can be solution polymerised to yield low molecular weight polymers

$$
\begin{array}{c}
\text{F} \quad \text{F} \\
| \quad | \\
\text{C}{=}\text{C} \longrightarrow \text{X} \left[-\text{C}-\text{C}- \right] \text{Y} \\
| \quad | \\
\text{F} \quad \text{Cl}
\end{array}
$$

Monomer   Polymer

The nature of the end groups, X and Y depends upon the type of initiatior and chain transfer agent employed, [9].

Various grades of chlorofluorocarbon lubricants are obtained by fractional distillation of mixtures of polymers of different molecular weights. These fluids are used as lubricants in atomic energy installations, space craft (rockets), gyro systems and chemical plants.

6.1.2.9. *Silicones*. These lubricants are semi-organic polymers or co-polymers containing an inorganic backbone of repeating silicon-oxygen units with organic side groups substituted on the silicone atom along the polymer-chain, free from cross-linking and of much lower molecular weight than silicone rubbers.

The structure of the silicone fluids can be represented by [10]

$$
\begin{array}{c}
\text{R} \quad\quad \text{R} \quad\quad \text{R} \\
| \quad\quad | \quad\quad | \\
\text{R SiO} - \left(-\text{SiO} \right)_n -\text{SiR} \\
| \quad\quad | \quad\quad | \\
\text{R} \quad\quad \text{R} \quad\quad \text{R}
\end{array}
$$

where the R's may be the same or different organic groups. By adjusting the polymer size and by varying the average molecular weight these fluids can be varied from grade to grade to meet specific requirements.

The viscosity-temperature slopes of the silicones are shown in Fig. 6—3 ; the methyl group allows the polymer to retain most of its flexibility and therefore the dimethyl fluids have the flattest slope of the stable silicone fluids. If other organic groups are substituted for methyl in the chain, the flexibility of the silicone polymer is reduced and the viscosity-temperature slope is steeper. Comparison is made with a typical mineral oil (SAE 30), [10].

Whilst known to chemists for a long time, they have only recently been used as lubricants for high-temperature applications. Silicones have proved themselves to be good lubricants for antifriction bearings ; they are also satisfactory lubricants for gears designed to have primarily rolling contact.

A certain inability of dimethyl silicones to satisfactorily lubricate steel sliding on steel was found both from laboratory tests and from experience with certain gear and piston-type pumps. When one of the bearing surfaces was changed to a nonferrous metal, such as bronze, lubrication was significantly improved. In studies with unilaterally loaded journal bearings it was shown that bearings of copper-lead, bronze, tin-base, babitt, cast iron, brass, aluminum, copper and alfin metal were adequately lubricated by silicones when used in conjunction with a chrome-plated steel shaft [10].

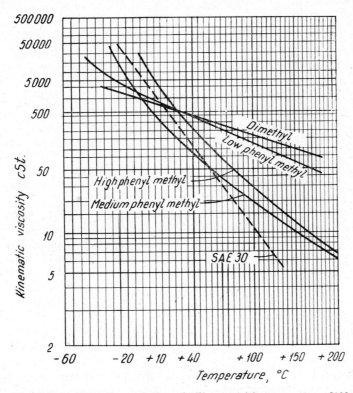

Fig. 6.3. — Viscosity variation of silicones with temperature [10].

Further developments may increase their field of applications.
6.1.2.10. *Synthetic Oils with Additives.* The use of additives to improve performance properties of synthetic lubricants for particular applications is considerable. For example, if a diester lubricant is used where a high viscosity index is desirable and a non-oxidizing condition prevails, a viscosity index improver might be the only additive required; when improved lubrication is necessary and an oxidizing environment exists, an antioxidant plus an extreme-pressure additive would be required.

The extreme-pressure additives, corrosion inhibitors, and viscosity index improvers utilized with synthetic lubricants can be similar in structure to those employed in mineral oils. A different situation is found for

the antioxidants; extensive research has been devoted to the development of suitable chemicals, for inhibiting antioxidative degradation. As
newer, more thermally stable lubricants are developed, the stability of
additives increases in importance. For example, phenothiazine is a highly
efficient antioxidant in diesters but proved to be unsatisfactory at the
higher useful temperatures of the more recent neopentyl polyol esters;
this resulted in the development of 5-ethyl-10, 10-diphenylphenazasiline
[10].

In addition to research on antioxidants, considerable effort is expen-
ded to develop additives to improve other characteristics of synthetic
lubricants, and certain marginal properties of the base fluids can undoub-
tedly be improved.

6.1.2.11. *New Synthetic Lubricants.* Among the newly developed
synthetic lubricants still under investigation, are [10]:

a) Tetraalkylsilanes, studied as base stocks for high-temperature
applications (−20 to 325°C); they are organosilicone compounds essentially hydrocarbon in composition (unlike the polymeric silicones) and
possess many of the physical and chemical properties of the long chain
paraffinic compounds. Antiwear additives and oxidation inhibitors are
necessary for industrial applications.

b) Ferrocene derivatives, first characterized in 1951; they are unusual organometallic compounds possessing the configuration of two parallel
cyclopentadienyl rings symmetrical about a central iron atom. The relationship between their physical properties and composition is not yet
clearly established. However, it has been found that their trialkylsilyl-
substituted derivatives possess many of the designed properties of a
lubricant.

c) Tetrasubstituted urea derivatives prepared by a reaction with
phosgene and an appropriate secondary amine; they are resistant to alkaline hydrolysis, but further synthesis is required to develop derivatives
thermally stable up to 400°C.

d) Heterocyclic derivatives (as tetra-kis-trifluoromethylpyrazine)
and hexafluorobenzene have been found to be stable up to 650°C thus pro-
mising to be useful as lubricants in the very high temperature regions.

6.1.3. Special Methods of Oil Improvement

Quality of oils may be improved not only by inclusion of foreign
matter (additives) but also my modifying their physical and chemical
characteristics in bulk. One of the methods of doing this is to expose the
oil to the action of silent electrical discharge in specially designed installations. The effect on the lubricating properties is remarkable: viscosity is
raised considerably, oiliness is improved and the detergent properties are
enhanced, [12]. An addition of only 7% of oil treated in this way is sufficient to improve oil quality considerably.

The mechanism of molecule ionisation at high electric tension is known, but the detailed physico-chemical process of improving the lubricating qualities of the oil by silent electrical discharges is not yet fully understood.

Oils treated in this way are used with particular efficiency in the lubrication of steam engines and industrial automotive engines. Up to the present it is the only known method of producing oils which do not leave deposits in the combustion chambers, even under the most difficult working conditions. This property is maintained even in the case of diesel engines running with residual fuels.

Another remarkable property of these oils is their ability to produce stable water emulsions, which makes them suitable for the lubrication of overheated steam engines and large diesel engines.

6.2. Greases

As in the case of fluid lubricants, there are numerous methods of improving semi-fluid lubricants. Besides the utilization of additives, quite new greases have been obtained from synthetic oils or using special thickeners : synthetic, inorganic, microgels, etc. In addition, there are cases in which synthetic products and additives are used together.

The so called "multipurpose" greases are being used in increasing quantities since they are capable of replacing two or three specific greases, and this constitutes an important advantage in the operation of complex machines and installations.

6.2.1. Greases with Additives

6.2.1.1. *Antioxidant Additives*. The oxidation of greases is a problem of particular importance, due to [13] : a) the higher operating temperature ; b) the requirement that the same grease should last the working life of some machines and mechanisms (electric motors, certain mechanisms of vehicles, etc.) ; c) the necessity of stock piling greases as well as the storing of automotive and other equipment protected with grease.

Thus it is natural to list antioxidants among the most important additives used in greases, and in fact practically all greases contain such additives.

The natural inhibitors found in petroleum oils were first used, then came phenolic derivatives or amines, phosphorous compounds, metal salts of phenols, compounds of silicone, selenium and tellurium.

Recent extensive research work [13] has proved that dithiocarbamates, amino-phenyl ethers, phenilene-diamines, methane derivatives, certain phenols and di-substituted amines make good antioxidants.

The lubricants used in the tests were greases of the following types : lithium soap, calcium soap and mixed lithium-calcium soaps in mineral oil, and lithium soap in various ester fluids. The antioxidant ability of the additive was evaluated by the Norma-Hoffman method, ASTM D 942—50, at 210°F and 250°F, the criterion being the rate of pressure drop (a maximum of 5 psi per 100 hours or 20 psi for 400 hours).

In addition, the worked penetration, the acidity and the ability of greases to pass the copper corrosion test ASTM D 1261—55 were also checked. No correlation between the structure and the antioxidant characteristics was established in spite of efforts directed to prove this.

Fig. 6—4 shows the general structure classification and a typical example of each of the various classes of additives considered.

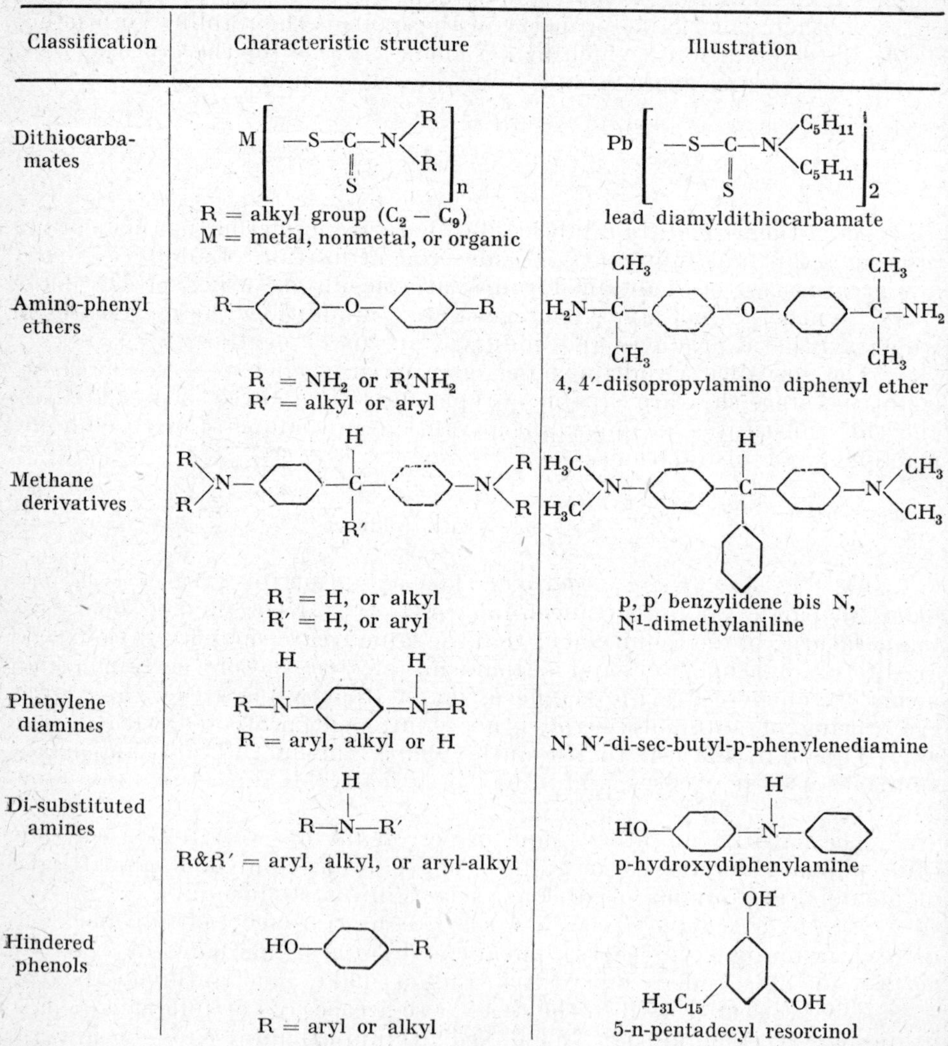

Classification	Characteristic structure	Illustration
Dithiocarbamates	$M\left[-S-\underset{\underset{S}{\|\|}}{C}-N\underset{R}{\overset{R}{<}}\right]_n$ R = alkyl group ($C_2 - C_9$) M = metal, nonmetal, or organic	$Pb\left[-S-\underset{\underset{S}{\|\|}}{C}-N\underset{C_5H_{11}}{\overset{C_5H_{11}}{<}}\right]_2$ lead diamyldithiocarbamate
Amino-phenyl ethers	R—⬡—O—⬡—R R = NH_2 or R'NH_2 R' = alkyl or aryl	$H_2N-\underset{CH_3}{\overset{CH_3}{C}}$—⬡—O—⬡—$\underset{CH_3}{\overset{CH_3}{C}}-NH_2$ 4, 4'-diisopropylamino diphenyl ether
Methane derivatives	$\underset{R}{\overset{R}{>}}N$—⬡—$\underset{R'}{\overset{H}{C}}$—⬡—$N\underset{R}{\overset{R}{<}}$ R = H, or alkyl R' = H, or aryl	$\underset{H_3C}{\overset{H_3C}{>}}N$—⬡—$\overset{H}{\underset{⬡}{C}}$—⬡—$N\underset{CH_3}{\overset{CH_3}{<}}$ p, p' benzylidene bis N, N¹-dimethylaniline
Phenylene diamines	R—$\overset{H}{N}$—⬡—$\overset{H}{N}$—R R = aryl, alkyl or H	N, N'-di-sec-butyl-p-phenylenediamine
Di-substituted amines	R—$\overset{H}{N}$—R' R&R' = aryl, alkyl, or aryl-alkyl	HO—⬡—$\overset{H}{N}$—⬡ p-hydroxydiphenylamine
Hindered phenols	HO—⬡—R R = aryl or alkyl	$H_{31}C_{15}$—⬡(OH)(OH) 5-n-pentadecyl resorcinol

Fig. 6-4. — Antioxidant additives [13].

   All dithiocarbamates proved to be good antioxidants at 210°F, except where M (see Fig. 6—4) was an organic group or a nonmetal (selenium for instance); when M was a di- or tri-valent metal the compounds were not only very effective antioxidants but in some cases were also good extreme pressure additives.

   In the same way, all amino-phenyl ethers were also found to be good antioxidants at 210°F and most of them even to 250°F, while the methane derivatives were generally good at 210°F but none were effective at 250°F. It should be mentioned that the temperature barrier seems to be the major obstacle for antioxidants, since only 9 out of about 100 which were effective at 210°F were equally effective at 250°F. Several of the phenylenediamines were quite effective even at 250°F; the di-substituted amines were poor antioxidants considered as a group, but some of them were excellent even at 250°F. The difficulty in judging the antioxidant ability by the structure of the considered compound is obvious. Further investigation in this direction appears necessary.

   6.2.1.2. *Extreme Pressure and Antiwear Additives*. It is clear that greases may be called upon to replace oils in any of their roles, by reason of their own specific advantages and particularly for the sake of simplicity.

   Thus it is natural that extreme pressure antiwear, oiliness and lubricity additives are necessary for greases too.

   It is to be noted that the diversity of opinions about the comparison of additive effectiveness for both oils and greases is mainly due to the numerous experimental devices used to determine the efficiency of these additives, each of them leading to differing results.

   In the following table some results obtained with Four-ball, Falex and Timken testers using various extreme pressure additives in lithium soap mineral oil greases can be examined [13]. Table 6—3 includes the most representative extreme pressure additives tested, together with their percentage in phosphorus, sulphur, chlorine and lead.

Table 6—3, [13]

Additive	Composition (%)			
	P	S	Cl	Pb
Chloronaphta xanthate		10.8	34	
Commercial gear lube additive	4.7	13.1		
Commercial gear lube additive	0.31	8.25	20.5	
Chlorinated wax			4.1	
Phosphite ester of alkylated phenol	5.75			
Tricresyl phosphate	8.4			
Cutting oil concentrate		19	23	
Lead di-2-ethyl-hexyl-dithiocarbamate		15.3		24.8
Molybdenum disulphide		40.2		
2-Mercaptobenzothiazol		38.3		
Lead diamyldithiocarbamate		18.5÷19		31÷32
EP gear lube additive		4.7	4.3	7.5

The evaluation of these additives under the specified conditions leads to various conclusions. The chlorine-based additives add nothing to the performance of the base grease in the four-ball machine (wear test), while the Falex and Timken tests show clearly a higher extreme pressure load-carrying capacity. The same conclusion is reached for sulphur-containing additives.

The phosphorous-based additives show the opposite effect : they improve the wear resistance, while the extreme-pressure capacity is not significantly changed. It is thus to be expected that optimum results are to be obtained by combining phosphorous with chlorine or sulphur. Phosphorous-sulphur additives exhibit both wear resistance and extreme pressure performance, as expected.

Combinations of sulphur and chlorine additives lead to spectacular rises in extreme pressure capacity, but wear is increased sensibly, which seems to suggest that these extreme pressure additives work by chemical reaction ; it must be noted that wear values increase as the additive concentration increases.

Lead-based additives show moderate improvements in some cases, both in wear resistance and extreme pressure properties ; however, the influence of the lead is not wholly certain since the considered additives contained also sulphur, phosphorus or chlorine.

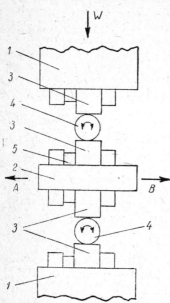

Fig. 6.5. — Layout of the fretting corrosive tester [13] : 1 — fixed parts of the machine ; 2 — oscillating arm ; 3—test blocks ; 4 — test cylinders ; 5 — wedges.

Is is concluded from these results that the efficiency of an additive is a function of its chemical action rather than of its component elements and that, in general, good extreme pressure behaviour is followed by a drop in wear resistance [13].

6.2.1.3. *Additives to Reduce Fretting Corrosion.* Some of the above mentioned extreme pressure and wear additives have been tested for their efficacy in reducing fretting corrosion. The special testing machine required for these experiments is shown in Fig. 6—5, [13].

As can be seen in the figure, arm (2) reciprocates along the line AB causing fretting to occur between the test cylinders (4) and test blocks (3). The test conditions were as follows : load = 450 lb, amplitude of oscillation = 0.025 in, speed = 600 cycles per minute, time = 50 hours.

The total loss of weight of the four test blocks and two test cylinders was used to judge the extent of fretting wear.

It was found that the sulphur-based additives reduced fretting wear, while phosphorous-based additives behaved to the contrary. Sperm oil without additives or with sulphur-phosphorous additives always produces less fretting damage. Molybdenum disulphide led to deceptive results, while remaining an efficient extreme pressure additive [13]. Calhoun and Murphy draw the conclusion that when molybdenum disulphide is mixed with a grease, each particle is coated with a layer of grease and is thus isolated. In these conditions the particles of molybdenum disulphide cannot contact each other or the bearing metal until sufficient pressure expels the grease. Thus under ordinary pressure — temperature conditions lubrication is effected by the grease alone, the molybdenum disulphide being inefficient through lack of direct contact with the rubbing surfaces.

6.2.1.4. *Rust Preventives*. In addition to lubrication, greases are used to protect the friction surfaces from rust; this condition must be fulfilled particularly in the case of outdoor operating equipment.

Experimental observations in this direction have shown the following additives to be efficient rust inhibitors [13]: nonylphenoxy acetic acid, ethylene diamine sulphonate, lead dinonyl naphthylene sulphonate, barium sulphonate, basic barium sulphonate, ammonium sulphonate.

The additive percentage is a function of the base grease and varies between 0.5 and 2.

In this case, due attention must also be paid to the selection of the right additive, since there are cases where the use of an incorrect one can lead to the deterioration of some physical or chemical property of the grease.

For example, it has been observed that molybdenum disulphide tends to induce the formation of rust. This tendency can be counteracted by the use of a suitable rust preventive compound (1.0% nonylphenoxy acetic acid, for instance), [13].

6.2.2. Synthetic Greases

As was specified in § 6.1.2, synthetic oils can also be used to produce synthetic greases. The dibasic acid esters (diesters) are used as low-temperature greases; the neopentyl polyol esters, the polyphenyl ethers and the fluoroesters as high-temperature greases, while the chlorofluorocarbon polymers show very good anti-corrosion and lubricating qualities.

Silicones have found a growing field of application in the form of greases, especially for high-temperature requirements, [9], [10].

6.2.3. Multipurpose Greases

Multipurpose greases are new products, based particularly on the action of various synthetic thickeners, and their superior lubricating qualities enable them to cover a large range of operating conditions, as already specified.

A group of greases with a variety of applications is obtained from inorganic microgels; as opposed to the typical lithium-, sodium-, or calcium-soap based greases, these new greases are based on silica, Fuller's

Table 6–4, [14]

Industry	Equipment	Grease application point	Operating characteristics		Previous grease		Service results with new inorganic microgel grease
			Temperature °C	Other specifications	Type	Performance	
				Dry applications			
Chemical	Gear drive flexible couplings for chlorine compressors	Gears	Moderate	Peripheral velocity: 6.8 m/min	Lithium base multipurpose	After 6 months grease showed considerable hardening	After same 6 months little change in consistency, lubrication excellent and ample margin of safety
Metal working	Tungsten wire drawing machine	Various bearings	150	Continuous service.	Lithium base multipurpose	Daily lubrication cycle.	Lubrication cycle extended to 7 days
Steel	Ingot bogies	Tilt bronze bearings	High temperature	Shock loads, continuous service	Clay base and high melting point calcium base	On 8-hour lubrication cycle deterioration of grease resulted in high rate of bearing failure	On same lubrication cycle bearing failures were completely eliminated
Cement	White clinker drier	Grate eccentrics and support wheels (bronze bushings)	120/220	Continuous service in very dusty medium	Lithium base multipurpose	Frequent lubrication	Grease consumption reduced, better lubrication and ability to form grease seal
				Wet applications			
Chemical	Pumps	Bearings	Ambient to 80	Continuous and intermittent service	Lithium base multipurpose	Various lubrication schedules, usually 3–4 month cycle	Lubrication cycle extended to 6 months with large margin of safety
Textile	Ager	Roll Support Bearings	100	Continuous service in contaminating medium	Lithium base multipurpose	Weekly lubrication cycle	Lubrication cycle extended to 3 weeks
Automotive	Pallets (Auto-body assembly and finishing)	Castor and wheel bearings	100/180	Operations include detergent wash, baking of prime and finishing coats	High melting point calcium base	7 to 30 day lubrication cycle	Same lubrication cycle, but more economical

earth, etc. Experimental observation as well as utilization in industry shows that they provide remarkable lubricating qualities. The results of some of these experiments are presented in a condensed form in Table 6—4, compared with the results obtained with conventional greases, [14].

From examination of this table it is observed that the multipurpose inorganic microgel greases yield very good results in practice, being economically attractive as well as efficient.

Other classes of multipurpose greases can be formed with organic thickeners. One of these thickeners can be obtained by reacting an isocyanate with an amine in a suitable mineral oil [15]. The resultant greases have a low thickener content in which the fibres resemble those of lithium soap ; they have good lubricating qualities, high drop points, and very good resistance to oxidation, water, leakage and working.

Practical experience has proved their efficiency under conditions of extreme temperature, and in the presence of water and corrosive agents. They thus broaden the field of applications for multipurpose greases.

6.3. Solid Lubricants, Coatings and Special Antifriction Materials

The special operating conditions (extreme temperatures, high-loading and speeds), imposed on the friction parts of modern machinery, the requirements of modern technological processes and the impossibility in certain cases of using a conventional lubricant (oil or grease) have led to the development of a new class of lubricants, i.e. antifriction materials, capable of assuming the function of a lubricant.

6.3.1. Solid Lubricants

The mechanism of dry friction and of lubrication with solid lubricants has been discussed in some detail in Chapter 1. Thus some typical practical applications of solid lubricants can now be examined.

6.3.1.1. *Molybdenum Disulphide* (MoS_2) is a widely known solid lubricant and is used in various forms : additive for oils and greases, superficial coatings, dry powder and so on.

The importance of problems solved with the help of this lubricant is considerable, but its advantages as well as its disadvantages need continuous consideration. Extensive research has been made into the pros and cons of using this substance as a solid lubricant, thus making possible a sober evaluation of its real value.

Chemically pure molybdenum disulphide is a brown coloured mineral, resembling graphite in its lamellar structure and low hardness (1 to 1.5 on the Moh's scale). Its melting point is 1,185°C in air ; an inert atmosphere raises it to 1,427°C, while if heated in absolute vacuum it decomposes into its basic components at 1,100°C. It is thermally stable between −50°C and 400°C in usual atmospheric conditions. Between 420 and 450°C its oxidation is slow, but at temperatures in excess of 455°C the lubricating properties disappear as a result of the advanced process of oxidation. Under vacuum or inert atmospheres its lubricating properties are conserved up to 1,000°C.

Molybdenum disulphide is also chemically stable : it does not decompose in water at any temperature, and it is not influenced by solvents ; it is affected only by chlorine, fluorine, hydrochloric acid and nitric acid at the boiling point. It has no electric conductibility or magnetic properties.

The internal friction of MoS_2 is particularly low, the coefficient being usually between 0.04 and 0.09. In the case of high speed its friction characteristics are comparable with those of oleic acid, one of the best boundary lubricants. The coefficient of friction of MoS_2 as a function of pressure is given in Table 6−5, [11].

Table 6−5

Pressure	Coefficient of Friction
700 Kgf/cm²	0.070
3,500 ,,	0.030
15,000 ,,	0.045
30,000 ,,	0.022

Molybdenum disulphide is an efficient antifriction additive : only 1% added to turbine oil, reduces the coefficient of friction from 0.108 to 0.068.

In order to obtain molybdenum disulphide suitable for lubrication purposes, it has been found that it must not only have a high degree of purity, but also the grain size must be between 1 and 3 microns, or even less than 1. Methods of application for MoS_2 are various : by rubbing the cleaned metallic surfaces with MoS_2 in powder, by spraying the metallic surfaces with solvents or oils containing colloidal MoS_2, by lubricating the surfaces with grease containing MoS_2. The metallic surfaces can be chemically or thermochemically treated (phosphating, sulphurization, etc.) before the application of MoS_2 in dry powder form.

The lubricant action of MoS_2 is due, as was shown in § 1.3.1, to its molecular structure with weak bonds. Clean metallic surfaces can absorb a layer of MoS_2 several molecules thick.

The lubricant properties of MoS_2 have also been investigated in connection with other substances (resins and other additives with bonding properties) with encouraging results [16]. Films bonded with organic binders were shown to exhibit good wear life and low friction coefficients ; MoS_2 appeared superior to the other lamellar solid lubricants (graphite, boron nitride, etc.) when used in bonded coatings. Experiments with inorganic films also proved its efficiency, though not to the same extent as with organic films.

The use of MoS_2 presents many advantages :

— MoS_2 films on steel retards corrosion (up to 2.81^7 cycles for balls and 10^7 for plane surfaces, in comparison with less than 10^2 cycles without MoS_2) ;

— it can prevent seizure at high speeds, in conditions which make graphite behave as an abrasive;

— it has good lubricating qualities at high pressures (up to 23,000 kgf/cm^2, some authors quoting up to 29,000 kgf/cm^2) and low speeds;

— it prevents the seizing of slow moving parts or immobile parts subject to high pressures and temperatures and that must be subsequently dismantled.

These properties lead to the widespread utilization of molybdenum disulphide, for example:

— lubrication of mechanical worked parts in deep drawing, pressing, hot stamping, since the MoS$_2$ films reduce considerably wear of expensive tools (dies, punchs, etc.); waste is also reduced and the technological process is accelerated, since the number of passes is diminished and some times expensive thermal treatments can be avoided;

— lubrication of cutting tools in order to improve their durability and to reduce the high speed stresses;

— lubrication during tube milling;

— gear lubrication;

— solves the problem of: lubrication during assembly of valves stud bolts, etc., of steam or gas turbines with a view to their subsequent dismantling; lubrication of valves in chemical installations; since it is the only lubricant for extreme pressure at very slow speeds, MoS$_2$ is used in the running-in of large industrial diesel engines, where the loads are very high and the speeds low;

— it can be successfully used in the case of high working temperatures: glass producing machines, mills, conveyors of furnaces and kilns, die casting installations, etc.;

— lubrication of antifriction bearings on assembly, when useless friction can be avoided, as well as during running-in and usual operation.

The utilization of MoS$_2$ for running-in is generally accepted as beneficial; thus, in Fig. 6—6 the efficiency of MoS$_2$ in run-in bearings is clearly reflected in the drop of friction as a function of the working characteristics of the bearing: viscosity η, speed n, and load W [11].

Investigations regarding the behaviour of MoS$_2$ as a lubricant have been lately extended to tungsten disulphide (WS$_2$) and it has been found that in vacuum both materials present the same characteristics [17]. The coefficient of friction of WS$_2$ at ambient temperature is nearly constant and equal to 0.065.

6.3.1.2. *Other Solid Lubricants.* The excellent sliding behaviour of lead films impregnated with MoS$_2$ has permitted their use as bearing coatings. Lead presents the advantage of not welding with the majority of metals used in machine construction, and of good running-in characteristics. The ability of lead films to assimilate MoS$_2$ particles is the explanation of the success of this combination of materials. The resulting film is capable of resisting high pressures, and can be considered as a solid lubricant for extreme pressures.

This method is inexpensive and can reduce wear of sliding parts considerably; it can be successfully applied also to metal working tools.

Solid lubricant layers on stainless steel have been obtained in the same way with lead monoxide (PbO), their lubricating efficiency being maintained up to a temperature of 600°C, [18]. Film thickness has a great influence on the lubricating properties of the film: if the thickness is under 0.025 mm friction is low and similarly the wear, and film life is longer than for thicker films. If the temperature is high, the formation of PbO is encouraged, so that lubrication is improved, and small quantities of silicone dioxide (SiO_2) and of magnetite (Fe_3O_4) prevent the volatilization of the lead monoxide and its transformation to red lead oxide (Pb_3O_4).

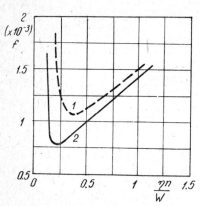

Fig. 6.6. — Friction drop in MoS_2-treated bearings: 1 — bearings without MoS_2; 2 — MoS_2-treated bearings.

The results obtained with stainless steels, either austenitic or martensitic, are very satisfactory up to 600°C and for speeds of up to 50 m/sec.

The utilization of thin metallic layers as solid lubricants has been discussed in detail in § 1.5.2.

In conclusion it can be seen that the development of lubrication with different lubricating media is becoming extremely diverse, and draws inspiration from a wide range of disciplines.

A systematic presentation of its various aspects is thus not an easy task; thus some lubricants are also bearing materials and vice versa, some bearing materials can also assume the role of lubricants.

6.3.2. Antifriction Coatings and Treatments

Under this heading lie methods of confering good antifriction properties on sliding surfaces by modifying their superficial physical and chemical composition. While these methods differ in their mode of action and technology or application, they can be grouped together for the simple reason that they achieve the same end : the reduction of friction and wear. The most efficient and widely used techniques of surface treatment are sulphur coatings and phosphating.

6.3.2.1. *Sulphur Coatings*. Elemental sulphur and sulphur compounds were among the earliest additives to be discovered. Due to their increased efficiency as extreme pressure additives, the sulphur compounds are used in association with lead soaps. It was assumed, and this assumption was confirmed by electron diffraction studies, that this combination gives rise to films containing lead sulphide under heavy load conditions [19]. This compound, however, does not exhibit a structure with weak interlayer cohesion as one would expect from an anti-friction addition, its hardness is rather high (2.5 on the Moh scale) and it melts at 1,100°C. In spite of this characteristic, lead sulphide films provide good frictional properties in the presence of mineral oils.

Extensive research work, some of it with the help of a crossed-cylinder machine [19], has helped to clarify the mechanisms of these sulphur-based additives.

The appearance of a brownish antiwear film on the rubbing surfaces was observed during experiments with lead sulphide, and an interesting fact was that the reaction zone seemed to exceed the actual area of contact between the specimens.

Autoradiographs of the wear tracks were obtained by using radioactive sulphur (S—35). Mechanical and chemical methods of removing the lead sulphide coatings proved ineffective, the films it formed adhering strongly to the metal surfaces. The most efficient method of obtaining adherent films was found to be by deposition of the lead sulphide in the form of a paste with an adhesive consisting of cellulose acetate dissolved in acetone. After a certain working time a protective film is formed, characterized by a low friction coefficient (0.06 to 0.21) and a high seizure resistance.

Experiments with radioactive sulphur confirmed the existence of a protective coating, both on the cylinder on which the paste was deposited, and on the other cylinder ; the thickness of the protective film was found to lie between 200 and 2,000 Å.

It was found that metallic sulphide coatings are most efficient in redu cing friction, when the thickness is above 1,500 Å (Bowden and Tabor, 1950)-

The extreme pressure performance of these sulphide coatings is considerably increased by a previous period of running-in, [19].

6.3.2.2. *Phosphating.* The wear-protective action produced by phosphating steel has been known for a relatively long time (Mansion, 1943 ; Barwell, 1951), but some details of the mechanism by which the phosphate crystals contribute to the wear protection have been disclosed more recently [20].

Experiments were performed with a machine with an annulus bearing rubbing against three discs, or with two annuli rubbing together.

The bearing was completely immersed in a liquid paraffin lubricant. The steel specimens were degreased, pre-heated and phosphated by two methods : either in an accelerated iron-phosphate bath, or in an accelerated iron-manganese phosphate bath, at an operating temperature of 96°C, 20 minutes in the first bath, 12 minutes in the second.

It was found that the phosphate crystals lie flat on the metallic surface, their diameter being about 10 to 30 μ and their thickness 1/10 of the diameter. The profile of the metallic surface was undulatory, with the phosphate crystals situated on the high spots ; the channels were 10—20 μ deep and 30—50 μ wide. The phosphating process is an electrolytic one, the phosphate crystals being deposited on the cathodic areas, which polarizes the local cell action, so that when 75% of the surface is covered, the reaction ceases. The nature of the process does not allow a progressive build-up of the coating thickness, the "surface-roughness" being a better measure of the degree of phosphating achieved. In action the phosphate

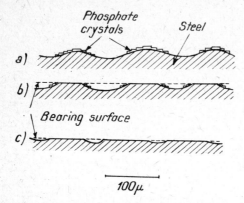

Fig. 6.7. — Wear of phosphated steel surfaces, [20] : a) unworn phosphated steel surface ; b) phosphated steel surface after 0.15 m use as a bearing ; c) same surface after 300 m run ; the phosphate layer has been removed but the metallic surface is very smooth.

crystals are rapidly worn away from the high spots on which they are initially deposited, and very few survive the running-in period, as seen both microscopically and by electron diffraction (Fig. 6—7).

Fig. 6—8 represents the friction and wear curves for the phosphated discs rubbing against a phosphated annulus as functions of the dis-

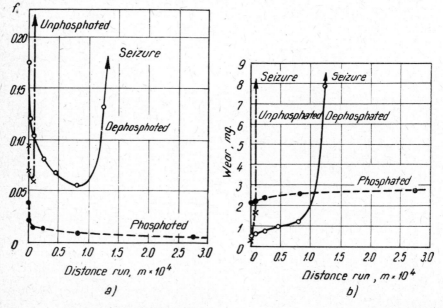

Fig. 6.8. — Variation of friction and wear as a function of the distance run, for phosphated, dephosphated and unphosphated lathe-turned mild steel surfaces, [20] : a) coefficient of friction ; b) wear (in milligrammes).

tance run with a mean pressure of 100 kgf/cm² ; these results are compared
with performance of unphosphated and dephosphated specimens of lathe-
turned mild steel. The phosphate crystals are rapidly removed, but at the
same time the friction and wear rate fall to very low values. Midgley and
Wilman [20] think that this is due to the condition of fluid lubrication
then attained. It was found that the friction and wear depend very much
on the surface finish, decreasing as the surfaces are made smoother, which

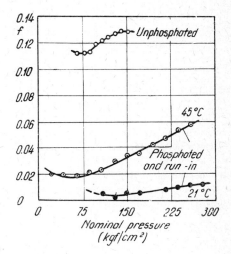

Fig. 6.9. — Variation of friction with
pressure for phosphated and unphosphated lathe-turned mild steel surfaces [20].

is best achieved by etching the surfaces with nitric acid, which are then
phosphated and polished.

It follows that the phosphate crystals do not act as a solid lubricant
in the same way as molybdenum disulphide or graphite, but they contribute to a rapid levelling of the surface asperities and thus encourage the
growth of fully hydrodynamic lubrication. Thus the friction decreases
from $f = 0.2$ to $f = 0.05$ as films of MoS_2 are built up on sliding steel surfaces, while in the case of phosphated specimens it drops from 0.3 to 0.005,
that is to say it is decreased by a factor of 60, which means that the quali-
tative character of the lubrication is changed.

The variation of friction with pressure and temperature for phosphated and unphosphated lathe-turned mild steel is shown in Fig.
6—9, [20].

It can be seen that friction increases with temperature (the viscosity
decreases) while with pressure the rise in friction is moderate. However,
the curves in Fig. 6—9 were both reversible and repeatable, which seems
to indicate a stable state corresponding rather to thin film lubrication than
to boundary lubrication.

6.3.3. Antifriction Materials with Intrinsic Lubrication

6.3.3.1. *Plastic Materials.* Valuable experience has been accumulated with plastic antifriction materials with or without fluid lubricants, in recent years.

Since plastic materials necessitating the support of fluid lubricants are not the object of the present section, details with respect to this problem are given only to the extent to which they refer to plastic materials which do not require additional lubrication.

Thus, it is to be noted that a characteristic common to all antifriction plastics is their resistance to catastrophic damage in the event of seizure; after due cooling of a bearing its re-use is possible without re-polishing the surfaces [21].

Plastic materials, in general, also present the advantage of coping easily with abrasive particles in the lubricant or in the surrounding medium (they have a good embeddability) and in this way a potent source of shaft wear is eliminated.

Some plastics (based on textile materials or wood) allow water to be used for lubrication and cooling and thus are particularly convenient for hydraulic turbine applications, mill bearings, naval applications, etc. They are also very elastic so that dynamic loads are more easily accepted.

The materials also present a remarkable resistance to fatigue, and work satisfactorily with very small amounts of lubricant, or non-existent external lubrication. Plastics are also very economical in use: in the case of a rolling mill, speed was increased by 40% after replacing the metallic bearings by plastics (textile waste based) bearings, due to the reduced friction, [22].

Plastic materials for bearings are also constructed from cellulose fibres as well as cotton and card fibres which are more expensive to produce. Rubber wastes have also been used producing a plastic material

Table 6—6

Plastic material	Maximum contact pressure (kgf/cm²)	
	Periphereal velocity V = 1m/s	Periphereal velocity V = 2.8 m/s
Hlopcovolocnite	100	—
Cordovolocnite	55	112
Textolite	120	190

named "cordovolocnite" (with 6% rubber), while "hlopcovolocnite" is obtained from degreased cotton wastes, with help of a rezolic resin. These materials can be successfully used in water-lubricated bearings. Table 6—6 shows some experimental characteristics of the materials mentioned above [23].

The use of mineral oils as lubricants worsens the performance of these materials.

The polyamides (nylon, capron, etc.) either homogenous or combined, are widely used as journal bearing materials.

Experimental investigation has led to the conclusion that nylon bearings, for instance, possess load-carrying capacity and temperature limitations comparable to those of the tin-based antifriction materials, while their wear resistance is much superior to that of metallic bearings. In addition, nylon manifests a reduced friction coefficient : $f = 0.17$ to 0.20 in the case of friction on steel without lubricant, in the presence of a mineral oil $f = 0.014$ to 0.02, and for water lubrication $f = 0.02$ to 0.05. Since friction is reduced, the heat developed between the friction surfaces is not excessive.

For light loads, the lubricating properties of nylon are sufficient to remove the need for a lubricant. In the case of heavy loads, it is possible to use oils, water, or emulsions. Nylon is not chemically sensible to mineral oils, up to 150°C it is not soluble in common organic solvents, and it is chemically inert to the action of alkalyne substances, of weak acid solutions and to salt water.

It was found that the optimum economic design is obtained by applying a thin nylon layer to a bearing housing of steel or cast iron. Utilization of segmented bushings makes possible the necessary compensation for thermal expansion, or for the geometrical modifications due to absorbtion of water. The thickness of such nylon layers is standardized; it lies between 0.2 and 0.5 mm, and sometimes can be limited to 0.08 mm.

There are some plastic materials (for instance the so-called "capron", [24]) which are particularly inexpensive, their cost being one sixth that of an equal volume of bronze, but they cannot be used at temperatures greater than 85°C; on the other hand they offer coefficients of friction as low as those of the best metallic antifriction materials and a wear rate 10 to 100 times smaller. In the case of dry lubrication it can be used in combination with graphite.

A widely used plastic material is polytetrafluoroethylene (PTFE) known commercially as "Teflon" or "Fluon". A large amount of experimental work has been carried out with this material, in order to determine its properties. Particularly low values for its coefficient of friction were found, especially at low speeds when the temperature rise is not important. It was found that shearing takes place only at the surface of this material and not in the bulk of it, but the bulk properties naturally influence the value of its shear strength [25]. This property renders seizure impossible.

When the rubbing speed is increased and the temperature rises, the usual dry friction mechanism becomes predominant, so that its material properties will be similar to those of any plastic material, but it conserves a particularly low value of friction and remains insensible to water, solvents and chemical attack.

In table 6—7 the mean values of the friction coefficients of some plastics are presented in comparison with other solid lubricants, in the absence of a fluid lubricant [26].

Table 6—7, [26]

Material	Coefficient of friction
Dense wood (lignum vitae)	0.70
Polyethylene	0.60
Nylon	0.52
Processed graphite composition	0.33
Soap impregnated woven cotton	0.33
Polytetrafluoroethylene	0.21

Polytetrafluoroethylene can be used as an efficient antifriction material in various forms : thin layers on metallic surfaces, fibres, etc. In its basic form Teflon presents disadvantages, due to its unsatisfactory mechanical strength, low thermal conductivity, and large thermal expansion, thus it is advisable to try out combinations with other materials to obtain the desired overall mechanical properties.

A remarkable unlubricated bearing material is obtained by depositing a thin lining of sintered bronze (89% Cu and 11% Sn), impregnated with a mixture of PTFE and lead on a thin steel backing; the bronze surfaces are covered with a thin layer of the same PTFE and lead mixture [27]. The combination is known by the commercial name of "DU" and is produced in strip form and made into bearings which do not require machining before use.

The mechanical and physical properties of the DU material are comparable to those of the metals used as bearing materials, so that its utilization with steel housing or shafts is perfectly acceptable : its yield strength is 3,680 kgf/cm², its coefficient of linear expansion is $15 \times \times 10^{-6}$/°C, and its thermal conductivity 0.1 cal/sec cm°C [27]. Wear is comparable to that of antifriction metals with fluid lubrication and its coefficient of friction is practically constant with load and speed, its mean value being 0.13. However, reports about industrial applications indicate a variation between 0.01 and 0.20.

When misalignment exists between the shaft and bushing, DU bearings (like all plastic bearings) perform less satisfactorily, since the consequent excess heating results in detrimental thermal expansion and eventually to seizure. The operational temperature range of this material is large : from — 200°C to 280°C and the same relationships betwen pressure and speed can be safely used in this range. It is also to be noted that these bearings operate satisfactorily even when subjected to sudden and large temperature variations. Since the DU bearings need no fluid lubrication, no special precautions are necessary to prevent contamination with dirt and grit. However, when large quantities of abrasive material are present, it is admissible to use some type of rotating seal. They have been successfully used in cement- and concrete-mixing machinery, in roller conveyors in foundries and in belt conveyors in mines.

DU bearings can be used submersed in water or other liquids, even under the most adverse conditions, the bearings being treated in the same way as if they were operating dry. Naturally, if a hydrodynamic film is induced in the bearing, significant improvements in the load-carrying capacity will result. Applications of submersed DU bearings include their use in gear and other pumps for petrol, paraffin and other solvents, as well as for rollers operating below the level of an acid plating solution; for this last application they were first plated with lead before assembly, and no trace of bearing corrosion was observed.

In general, DU bearings have a wide range of applications in all cases where oil-lubrication is impractical or undesirable (domestic equipment, textile industry, food industry, etc.). In addition to the above mentioned applications, their use is possible in automobile accessories (starter-motors, generators, distributors, pumps, fans, etc.) and cabin equipment for aircraft (air-pressurizing equipment, etc.).

Table 6—8 shows the limiting values $p_m.n$ (the mean pressure in the bearing multiplied by speed) of this material, as a function of the operating conditions and the type of bearing.

Table 6—8, [27]

Shaft material	Mild—steel		Hardened steel		Very hard steel	
Operating period (hours)	1,000	10,000	1,000	10,000	1,000	10,000
Bearing type	Values (kgf/cm² × rpm)					
Bearing with oscillating shaft	14,000	12,000	15,000	13,000	16,000	13,500
Bearing with rotating load	11,000	10,000	13,000	10,500	14,000	13,000
Bearing with unidirectional load	7,500	5,700	9,000	6,500	11,000	8,500
Flat annular thrust washers	5,700	3,000	6,000	3,500	7,000	4,500

6.3.3.2. *Graphite and Carbon*. Among the more efficient antifriction materials that have come into use recently are graphite and carbon compounds used in various forms and combinations. The properties of these antifriction compounds depend largely on the base material and on the technological methods used to obtain the desired molecular structure.

The friction mechanism of these materials was discussed to some extent in § 1.5.1., so that in the following section only their development and application will be discussed. Carbon compounds can be separated into categories by their widely differing physical properties:

— hard, amorphous carbon based materials;
— electrographited materials;
— impregnated gas-proof materials.

The basic materials are natural graphite, retort graphite, coal- and petroleum-coke, carbon black. As a binder, petroleum, vegetal or synthetic (polymerized) tar are used. Recently finely dispersed carbon dust has been used exclusively, because it was found that large grained samples were not efficient. In addition to the various types of tar, graphite, bakelite, colloidal solutions of polytetrafluoroethylene and other synthetic resins can be used as binders.

One of the latest methods of obtaining antifriction surfaces from graphite or carbon materials consists in their impregnation under high pressure with liquid metals (copper, lead, bronze and tin, silver or cadmium based white-metals, etc.).

Among the most interesting properties of graphite and carbon based materials is their exceptional thermal stability, due to a low linear expansion coefficient $(2-5 \times 10^{-6})$ and to their good thermal conductivity. The comparison made with refractory materials, as aluminum oxide, beryllium oxide and zirconium dioxide showed that graphite and carbon based materials are the only ones capable of resisting temperatures in excess of 1,370°C [28].

Other interesting characteristics of these materials include : a high chemical resistance to the attack of aggresive substances such as acids and corrosive alkalies, low coefficients of friction, low wear, and the remarkable property of auto-running-in.

Friction and wear of graphite and carbon based materials are largely influenced by the material making up the pair of rubbing surfaces. Thus it was found that the best results are obtained with chromed cast iron and with very hard steels, but for stainless steels the results are far less satisfactory.

A large range of materials can be used as lubricants : mineral oils, alcohols, petrol, water, etc. and their lubricating properties are improved by their use.

Graphite and carbon based materials are used in numerous applications ;   bearings to which no lubricant can be supplied, bearings working under conditions of severe temperature or exposed to corrosion, etc. These situations are often found in the food industry, oven and furnace mechanisms, conveyors in mines, etc. These materials can also be successfully used for seals in steam turbines, petrol pumps, and so on.

Graphite rings are widely used in oxygen, chlorine and hydrogen compressors.

Submerged electric motors can be equipped with radial and axial bearings of graphite, with water lubrication.

By combining graphite with tar, plastographite is obtained, which has a better thermal conductivity and a high ductility ; this material can be used for low loads (up to 10 kgf/cm²) without lubricant [23].

At present colloidal graphite is used in numerous applications since it is a good thermal and electric conductor, inert to chemical attacks, supports radiation and is effective at extreme temperatures. Introduced into conventional oils it acts as an antiwear additive, aids running-in and improves lubrication at high temperatures. It can be used in fluid lubricants in colloidal form, or sprayed onto the sliding surfaces. Finally, it can be deposited by immersing the parts in a plastographite bath [29]. Colloidal graphite can be used in many ways, among which the most interesting are the lubrication of some parts of power generating units, dies in the metal-working industry, etc.

6.3.3.3. *Sintered Metallic Materials and Glass.* Advances in the technology of sintered materials have made possible the production of new bearing materials capable of fulfilling unusual specifications.

One of the sintered materials with a variety of applications is graphited bronze. The sintering is performed at 815°C, in order to improve mechanical properties by reducing porosity. The process includes impregnation with oil taking 4 to 6 hours. The oil is absorbed in the pores of the bronze and the weight of the material increases by 2—4%. In combination with graphite this type of bearing construction reduces oil consumption by 10—15 times compared with that of bearings made of solid materials.

In the same way bearings can be made from sintered graphited iron (97% iron powder and 3% graphite). The technological process is the same as for graphited bronze, but the porosity of the material is higher (20—25%). This material is used successfully in slow, silent electric motors.

Pyroceramic materials with finely sized particles can be obtained from glass; they present superior mechanical qualities (redoubled elasticity and strength as compared with solid glass) and can be successfully used as bearing material for high temperatures. Their coefficient of friction lies between 0.2 and 0.6 at 800—900°C, [11].

Finally, glass and Teflon (or nylon) bearing materials must be mentioned. The external surface of this material is a fine texture of Teflon and glass fibres impregnated with a Teflon-based resin (fig. 6—10).

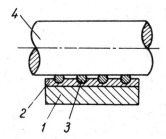

Fig. 6.10. — Glass fibre and Teflon bearing bushing; 1 — bearing housing; 2 — glass fibre backing; 3 — Teflon fibres; 4 —bearing shaft.

This material stiffens with rising pressure and temperature, and a sliding surface of only Teflon is obtained on the glass backing. The Teflon fibres surrounded by glass fibres sustain practically none of the strain under load. Such bearings can work with no lubricant, at low and medium loads [30].

6.3.4. High-Temperature Lubrication

Gas turbines, high speed engines, rockets and many everyday mechanisms are expected to work under conditions of extreme temperature, and the bearings they include present a considerable design problem if they are to be efficient and economic. Because of the breadth of this problem it is worthwhile first gathering the details of material performance outlined in the preceding sections under this heading.

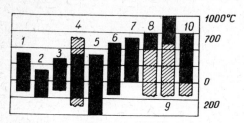

Fig. 6.11. — General view on the temperature range of utilization of lubricants : 1 — organic fluids ; 2 — greases ; 3—special greases ; 4 — dry lubricant films ; 5 — Teflon, fluorocarbons, resins, lead, porous bronze ; 6 — gases ; 7 — liquid metals ; 8 — vermiculite (hydrated silicates of altered mica).

A classification of these materials from the point of view of their thermal behaviour is provided in Fig. 6—11 where the temperature ranges in which they can be used are compared.

The hatched areas, represent the regions in which the material performance is not yet fully explored.

The problem of high-temperature lubrication has three distinct aspects : a) special lubricants (fluids, solids, powders); b) new bearing materials (ferrous and non-ferrous alloys, other metallic or ceramic materials, etc.); c) special lubrication methods (with fluid lubricants, mist, fog, vapours, etc.).

6.3.4.1. *High-Temperature Lubricants.* It has been seen that some synthetic lubricants (silicones, diesters, etc.) exhibit good thermal stability and can be used in high-temperature applications.

Solid lubricants present particular interest in such applications; they can be used as adherent coatings on the sliding surfaces, sprayed air or gas suspensions, or included in the bearing material.

Fig. 6—12 presents a review of the properties of solid lubricants used in high-temperature applications, [31].

The use of bonded coatings presents some inherent disadvantages : they have a finite life and the bonding material usually limits working temperatures ; this is the case for resin-bonded coatings, for instance. Considerable success has been obtained, on the other hand, with a sodium-silicate-bonded MoS_2 coating containing a small percentage of graphite ; this coating behaves satisfactorily up to temperatures of 350°C.

Fused coatings and coatings using ceramic bonding have particularly good high-temperature properties ; they can be used up to temperatures of 900°C, but when the temperature is under 500°C, the sliding velocity must not fall under 300 m/min. Besides the coatings of this type specified in Fig. 6—12 (fused calcium fluoride, barium fluoride, lead monoxide plus tetralead silicate and ceramic-bonded calcium-fluoride) there

are other inorganic binders that can be used successfully : potassium silicate, sodium metaborate, beryllium fluoride, sodium hexa-metaphos-
phate, and low-melting glass compositions.

   Another way of using solid lubricants which eliminates the problem
of finding an efficient binding medium, consists of supplying a number of
built-in reservoirs in the bearing to contain the solid lubricant. This is
performed by punching a number of cone-shaped depressions in the load

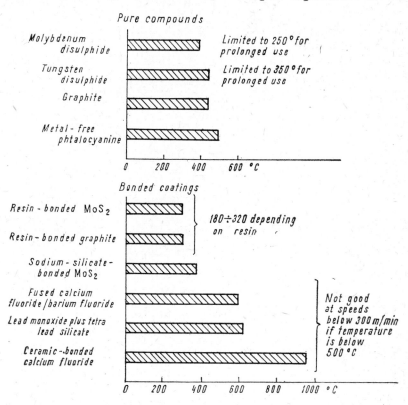

Fig. 6.12. — Useful temperature range of solid lubricants, [31].

bearing surfaces. To incorporate more solid lubricant into the bearing
retainer, machined slots can be used, instead of punched depressions. It
has been possible with this method to run bearings at 10,000 rpm
and 350°C, for as long as 50 hours.

   At the same time, an efficient solution to high-temperature problems
is to introduce dry powdered lubricants into the bearing by a carrier gas.
Bearings used in the most recent high-speed experiments with gas-
entrained solid lubricants were made of superalloys or titanium carbide
cermet ; among the lubricants evaluated were molybdenum sulphide or
metafree phtalocyanine in a nitrogen environment and lead monoxide or

cadmium oxide plus graphite in air. The most successful combination was achieved with molybdenum disulphide which remained effective up to 550°C. A critical problem in applying this method is the tendency of dry powders to agglomerate; it is then necessary to use a special dry powder feed system, consisting of a gear wheel which picks up the agitated dry-powder lubricant and feeds it into the air or gas stream which supplies the bearings.

The inclusion of a solid lubricant in the bulk of the bearing material is also a practical method; sintered metals such as nickel, copper or silver, impregnated with polytetrafluoroethylene fluorocarbon resins and with a solid lubricant such as MoS_2 have proved very efficient. Other successful composites include PTFE and molybdenum diselenide ($MoSe_2$) in sintered copper or silver; they can be used as self-lubricating materials in ball-bearing retainers, sleeve bearings and gears. Finally, PTFE-glass-fibre-MoS_2 and nickel alloys with MoS_2 are also to be found. The metal-matrix composites can work at higher temperatures than those containing polymers such as PTFE resin which deteriorates above 250°C [31].

6.3.4.2. *Bearing Materials for High-Temperatures.* In the case of antifriction bearings, the materials for races and rolling elements must be sufficiently hard to avoid brinelling, and must also possess a high corrosion resistance and dimensional stability; the required level is determined by the bearing load.

It is generally accepted that even for very lightly loaded antifriction bearings the minimum hardness of the races and rolling-elements must be about 55 Rockwell C, while for normally loaded bearings a hardness of at least 58 Rockwell C is necessary.

The hardness of all known materials diminishes with temperature, so that for high-temperature applications it has been necessary to develop new bearing materials.

Fig. 6—13 represents the maximum working temperature for several classes of materials, [31].

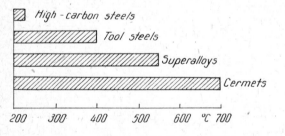

Fig. 6.13. — Useful temperature range for special bearing materials [31].

As can be observed, the working temperatures of steel are deceptively low; even the tool steels are not useful above a maximum of 400°C. For higher temperatures the ferrous alloys must be replaced by other materials, and usually superalloys (nickel or cobalt based) are used. These superalloys are suitable up to 525°C; above this limit sintered carbides (sometimes called cermets) must be used.

Sintered carbides generally contain tungsten carbide, titanium carbide, and sometimes small amounts of chromium or columbium carbide with a nickel or cobalt binder.

The ductility of these materials is rather low, so that bearings made of these materials must not be exposed to shock.

6.3.4.3. *Lubricant Supply Systems for High Temperatures.* Some special methods have been developed for these particular circumstances ; recirculating systems with organic liquids, or non-recirculating oil-air mist systems.

The recirculating systems contain a sump, possibly incorporating a scavenge pump, filters, and if necessary an oil cooler. Since the main function of the lubricant is to cool, the flow rates through the bearings are very high.

The best organic lubricant can be used in these systems up to 300°C in the presence of oxygen, and in inert atmospheres up to 370°C. Reasonable temperatures can be maintained in bearings with the help of these recirculating systems, but they have the disadvantages of requiring a considerable amount of complicated ancillary equipment and of creating significant churning power losses at the very high flow rates involved.

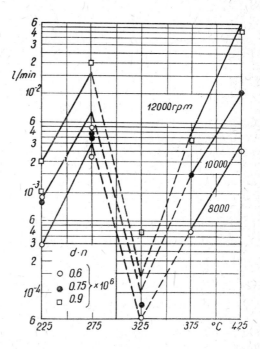

Total loss systems are naturally economically unattractive, but permit satisfactory lubrication up to 450°C; these "oncethrough" systems can be made economically acceptable by utilizing the lubricant in mist form.

However, ultra high speed bearings (50,000 — 100,000 rpm) can be successfully lubricated with an oil-air mist, as already specified in § 5.2.2. The basic peculiarities of the oil-mist systems have been discussed in § 3.2.3. Fig. 6—14 shows the effect of temperature on the minimum required oil flow for various speeds and bearing diameters [31]. The oil used in these experiments was a highly refined naphtenic mineral oil. A remarkable fact is that the minimum values of oil flow at about 300°C, are due to the

Fig. 6.14. — Minimum required oil flow in rolling bearings as a function of temperature, speed and bearing diameter, [31].

beneficial effect on friction caused by the decomposition products of the oil. In the case of recirculating systems these deposits are positively harmful.

The small quantity of oil necessary for oil-mist systems should be particularly noted, since this is the explanation for their low cost even in total loss systems.

Another method of high-temperature lubrication is vapour feed. Thus, for example, a mixture of carbon dioxide and P—4 jet engine fuel vapour has been used to blanket a high-temperature bearing and to provide a reducing atmosphere; oxidation is thus inhibited, but considerable accumulation of soot was observed in the tests.

Again, a blanketing gas with an air-fuel ratio of 7 to 10 was found to provide the necessary reducing atmosphere to inhibit abrasive wear and the addition of sulphur- or phosphorous-containing extreme pressure lubricants yielded adequate boundary lubrication of the sliding surfaces.

Several combinations of reducing atmospheres and extreme-pressure lubricants were tried on ball bearings running between 7,000 and 20,000 rpm, at temperatures of up to 500°C. The results indicated considerable promise for the high-temperature application of these systems [31].

6.3.5. Lubrication with Porous Surfaces

The use of porous metal bearings is currently experiencing a spectacular increase, due to considerable improvements in their quality and partly to a clearer appreciation of the fundamental principles involved in the operation of these bearing materials.

6.3.5.1. *Manufacture of Porous Metal Bearings.* Porous metal antifriction materials can be obtained by sintering metallic powders or by metal spraying.

The best known sintered bearing materials are porous bronzes, obtained from copper and tin powders with or without graphite, and porous iron. To the iron powder a 2—10% copper powder is added to give a liquid phase in sintering, which improves the mechanical strength. Duplex materials, of iron with 20—50% copper or bronze, are also frequently used.

In the case of metal spraying, the so-called "pseudoalloys" are obtained, aluminum-lead alloys being examples with very good operating characteristics. It is also possible to have a hard housing and to spray a layer of antifriction material on the shaft [32].

All porous materials no matter how they are produced, are finally impregnated with oil. The pores of the matrix, which constitute some 30% of the total volume of material, absorb the oil, which serves as a lubricant throughout the life of the bearing.

6.3.5.2. *Operating Characteristics of Porous Bearings.* Their main feature, their porosity, can vary between very large limits $(10-40\%)$ as a function of the manner in which they are produced. The higher the porosity, the higher the oil retaining capacity, but the lower the mechanical strength. Usually the porosity is of about 30%, which has been found to be a good compromise between the oil absorption capacity and the mechanical strength, over a wide range of application.

For a given porosity, the permeability will vary according to the size of the pores, which in turn will depend upon the size distribution of the original powder, and the degree of sintering. Sintering in the presence of a liquid phase causes a substantial increase in the permeability. It was found that a wide range of pore sizes is a significant factor in the mechanism of self-lubrication [33]. The permeability can be reduced towards the ends of the bearing and increased towards the centre, since the compaction of the metal powders usually takes place in cylindrical dies, with pressure applied along the axis of the component. For bearings with a high length to diameter ratio, this effect can be a serious consideration in the design of porous metal bearings, especially when the wall thickness is small.

It is practically possible to impregnate with oil only about 90% of the theoretical porosity, since there are usually a small number of "blind" pores in the matrix. The amount of this non-available porosity increases as the porosity and permeability decrease. However, since there are pores not filled with oil, an equilibrium is established between the surface tension forces and the sum of the forces responsible for side leakage.

The process of oil circulation in porous bearings takes place in the unloaded regions of the geometry, a corresponding quantity of oil being drawn out of the impregnated pores to compensate for the side leakage losses. These were the conclusions reached after experiments with a porous bearing impregnated with a dyed oil and placed in a felt ring with uncoloured oil [33].

Until recently it was supposed that porous bearing lubrication is not hydrodynamic, but boundary. The theoretical and experimental works of several authors (A. Cameron, V. T. Morgan, N. Tipei) have demonstrated the hydrodynamic behaviour of these bearings, under certain conditions.

Thus, if the shaft attains a certain speed, or more precisely the bearing attains a certain value of the load-carrying capacity coefficient $\zeta = \dfrac{p \psi^2}{\eta \omega}$ (where p is the mean pressure, $\psi = \dfrac{c}{r}$ the clearance ratio, η the viscosity and ω the angular speed) equivalent to the Sommerfeld reciprocal, there is a sufficient flow of oil round the bearing to ensure that not all the oil is bled through the pores before $\theta = \pi$, and in this way hydrodynamic effects can appear [34], [35]. At this critical point the eccentricity ratio ε is assumed unity, that is to say the shaft is rubbing on the surface of the bearing. Above the critical value ζ the film thickness grows rapidly and the eccentricity ratio ε drops. The eccentricity ratio is usually limited to 0.97 even below the critical value, and this is an important observation since it suggest the existence of a lubricant film, which can be explained by the supposition that "microtapered land" bearings are formed between the pores [34], [35].

For practical design purpose, the important operating parameters are the coefficient of friction and the time necessary to expell all the lubricant from the bearing.

Fig. 6—15 shows the values of the coefficient of friction f in the form of the product $f \dfrac{r}{c}$ (r is the radius of the bearing and c the radial clearance) as a function of Sommerfeld reciprocal

$$\frac{1}{S} = \frac{\mu V l}{W \psi^2} \qquad\qquad (6-1)$$

where μ is the dynamic viscosity, V the periphereal velocity, l the bearing width; for the infinitely short bearing $\lambda = \dfrac{l}{d} \to 0$, [34].

Fig. 6—15 b gives the correction factor for various $\dfrac{l}{d}$ ratios and eccentricity ratios ε.

The oil loss rates for porous matter bearings are given in Fig. 6—16, as a function of the Sommerfeld number S and a design variable $\varphi = \dfrac{\Phi \Delta}{c^3}$, where Φ is the permeability (mm²), Δ the thickness of the bearing wall (mm) and c is the clearance (also in mm) [36].

It is seen from Fig. 6—16 that the potential life of porous bearings can be, even without a supplementary oil supply, of the order of a few years. For heavy duty bearings, recharging may be necessary every 1,000 hours but this could represent several years in the life of an appliance.

The re-charging period (t) is given approximately by the relation

$$t = \frac{\pi^2 d^2}{2 \Phi S n} \qquad\qquad (6-2)$$

where n is the shaft-speed in r p m, S the Sommerfeld number, d the mean diameter of the bearing.

In order to increase the quantity of oil stored in a porous bearing (that is to say to lengthen its life), an oil-soaked pad can be fitted in contact with the outside surface of the bearing. The bearing is thus capable of recharging itself from this pad, as the oil content of the porous material is reduced. The positioning of the pad must be considered relative to the pressure wedge extent, being placed, for the best effect, close to the end

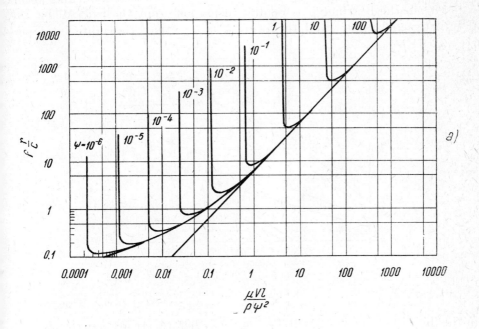

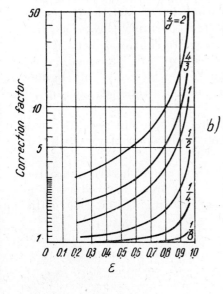

Fig. 6.15. — Variation of friction in porous bearings as a function of the operating conditions, [34] : a) infinitely short bearing ; b) correction factor with eccentricity, for various values of the length/diameter ratio.

of the loaded film. In such a system equilibrium is set up between the contained oil in the pad and the oil in the bearing. Since the porous metal bearing has, in general, a greater capillarity than the pad, and as oil is lost from the bearing, it is readily recharged from the pad. When the flow between the pad and the bearing is less than the lubricant losses

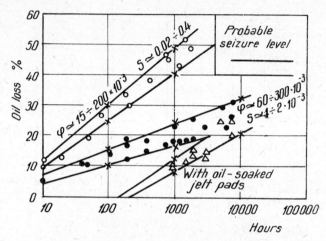

Fig. 6.16. — Oil loss rates of porous metal bearings, [36].

in the bearing, the pad will be emptied before steady conditions are reached. In Fig. 6—16 it can be seen that in the particular examples considered, about 200 hours were required to empty the reservoir.

   The capacity of porous metal bearings to run for a very long time without lubricant supply, when subjected to low and medium loads, makes their use a convenient solution to a wide range of engineering problems : bearings of industrial mechanisms, electromotor bearings, bearings in domestic appliances, etc.

   Temperature constitutes a limitation to the life of this type of bearing, since the oil can be completely lost when its viscosity drops below a certain value.

   Fig. 6—17 shows the relationship between the running temperature t_2 above the ambient temperature t_1, and the product of mean pressure in the bearing p, the peripheral velocity V and the coefficient of friction f [36].

   Naturally, a family of such curves exists depending on the thermal dissipation properties of the bearing so that the temperature rise can be written

$$t_2 - t_1 = K p V f. \qquad\qquad (6-3)$$

If a reliable value of K is obtainable, and the value of f is deduced from Fig. 6—15, information regarding the running temperature of the bearing can be found. However, since both K and f depend upon a multitude of working and design parameters, equation (6—3) can have only a limited application to the design of porous bearings.

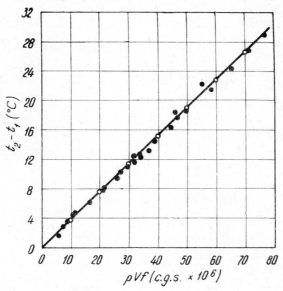

Fig. 6.17. — Variation of temperature rise as a function
of the operating conditions, [36]·

6.4. Lubricants and Lubrication Methods in Metal Processing

The wide variety of metal processing methods has led to the development of numerous lubricants, cooling fluids, and methods of lubrication. It is thus necessary to have a systematic view of the whole field ; cutting fluids and the lubrication of high-temperature processes present particular interest, so that particular attention will be given to these aspects.

Many solutions already treated in the previous sections can be usefully applied to metal processing : the utilization of solid lubricants, extreme pressure lubricants, thin metallic layers as lubricants, etc.

6.4.1. Cutting Fluids and Metal-Working Lubricants

In metal cutting operations, the fluids have a double role : as coolants and as lubricants. Efficient lubrication of the friction surfaces (worked parts tool and tool chip) together with efficient heat dissipation, can result in high quality finish of the worked surfaces, the possibility of increasing the cutting speed, reduced wear of cutting tools and less power consumption.

The cooling of steel cutting tools is of a particular importance, since the drop in hardness due to temperature rise is very steep between 600 and 800°C, as can be seen in Fig. 6—18 [37].

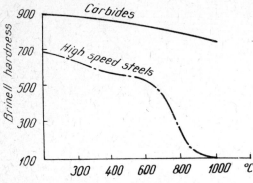

Fig. 6.18. — Hardness variation of tool materials with temperature, [37].

From the same diagram it is clear that carbide tools can be used dry, since their hardness is only slightly influenced by the working temperature.

The selection and development of metal-working fluids present many problems due to the large number of variables present in the forming processes: composition, hardness, heat treatment and grain size of the work material; composition, hardness and cutting angle of the tool; the working parameters: feed, speed and depth of cut; the method of supplying the fluid: flow rates, pressure, direction of flow.

It has been demonstrated that a careful analysis of the cutting process, and of the possible influences of the characteristics of the fluid, can lead to significant improvement in performance. In the same way, maintenance and disposal of cutting fluids and the design of cutting fluid supply systems must be attentively studied in a workshop if efficiency with minimum capital expenditure is to be obtained [37], [38].

The particularly stringent working conditions of these fluids (high temperatures and pressures, stressed metallic surfaces without oxides or impurities) means that they must fulfil the following conditions:

a) possess a very good extreme pressure resistance;
b) prevent welding of the surfaces in contact;
c) possess good boundary lubrication characteristics;
d) possess a high heat transfer capacity;
e) prevent corrosion.

The fluids used in metal-working processes can be divided into two classes: non-soluble and soluble. The first are compounds of mineral oils with other liquids, and, since they are not soluble in water they cannot be used in the form of emulsions.

Besides the mineral oils, the insoluble cutting fluids include fatty substances or other materials with pronounced oiliness. Additives can be also used.

The main combinations of non-soluble fluids are the following [37]:

a) Mineral oils: straight, sulphurized, chlorinated and sulpho--chlorinated.

b) Other lubricating fluids : fatty oils (straight, sulphurized, chlorinated, sulpho-chlorinated), synthetic oils.

c) Extreme pressure compounds containing sulphur, chlorine, phosphorus, etc.

Sometimes combinations of these fluids are used, and a large variety of cutting fluids can thus be obtained.

Typical soluble fluids include the following [37] :

a) Conventional soluble oils : emulsifiers with mineral oils.

b) Heavy duty soluble oils : emulsifiers in mineral oils plus additives for anti-weld and oiliness characteristics.

c) Various water-soluble fluids : water solutions of soaps, inorganic salts, rust inhibitors, etc.

In general, soluble fluids are used for high cutting speeds, where cooling is more important than lubrication.

For these applications, water-containing fluids are preferable, due to their greater heat capacity.

It is obvious that due to the high pressures and temperatures in metal cutting, conditions of boundary lubrication are obtained rather than those of hydrodynamic lubrication. There are several theories explaining how the cutting fluid is introduced into the high pressure areas.

One of these theories considers that the underside of the chip is sufficiently rough to provide a large number of capillaries through which cutting fluid reaches the high pressure area on the tool face.

The extreme pressure additives are obviously necessary items in the synthesis of cutting fluids. Sulphur and/or chlorine compounds forming heat and pressure resistant films, prevent metal to metal contact. Since their shear strength is lower than that of iron, the friction between tool and work-piece is reduced. Sulphur compounds are more efficient than chlorides for heavy duty operations such as threading or broaching, due to their higher melting points. Chlorine compounds, on the other hand, are more efficient in reducing friction and are useful in high speed, relatively high duty operations, such as high speed turning, forming and drilling.

Table 6—9 shows the temperature resistance and the shear strength of the above mentioned compounds in comparison with pure iron [37].

Table 6—9, [37]

Material	Melting point (°C)	Shear strength (%)
Iron	1,500	100
Iron chlorides	275/650	20
Iron sulphides	1,000/1,100	50

Fatty oils and synthetic oiliness additives form iron soaps with low shear strengths, but their melting points are lower than those of the chlorides and sulphides, so that they are not as efficient for heavy duty use.

There is no definite experimental method of evaluating the efficiency of these various additives. It is thus believed that the higher the total sulphur content of a product, the more effective it is for machining operations; recently it has been demonstrated that the active sulphur content is of far greater importance than the total quantity present in the additive. No acceptable test has yet been developed for measuring the active chlorine-content of cutting fluids.

A number of extreme pressure machines, such as those of Almen, Falex and Timken have also been used to compare cutting fluid additives. Bench tests can reproduce to some degree the conditions of high temperature, high pressure and stressed metal, but the newly formed "nascent" metallic surfaces can be obtained only in the process of metal cutting, so that for accurate evaluation, the actual metal cutting operation itself is the only available means of comparison.

Although engineering laboratories have worked many years on the problem of cutting tool life and the effect of cutting fluids, and some standard tests have been published, expensive drilling and turning work is still necessary and the tests are subject to considerable error and variation.

The use of radioactive tools has provided the first successful method of short cutting these lengthy and expensive procedures, without loosing applicability to the conditions existing in the cutting zone. This method consists of activating the tool tip and measuring the radioactivity of the chips, since the wear products of the tools adhere mainly to the chips. It has been established that the life of the tool is a direct function of the wear determined by this method.

It is thus possible to determine the optimum working parameters, the influence of the various additives and the efficiency of the fluids, for every cutting operation [38].

An interesting apparatus for determining the anti-wear properties of oils and materials, employing radioactive tracers, consists of an activated cylindrical bush sliding on a non-activated plate of hardened steel [39]. This permits very high specific pressures, eliminating completely the possibility of hydrodynamic lubrication, and by the observation of short duration phenomena the influence of oils and additives on wear of friction materials is evaluated.

The use of cutting fluids raises problems regarding hygiene. Apart from the moral responsabilities of suppliers and users of these materials, a real brake on productivity can result from dermatitis and infection. The subject will not be discussed in detail here, but the medical problem of bacteria in water/oil emulsions is of interest. Thus, experiments performed to evaluate the influence of the type of coupling agent on survival ability of bacteria have shown clearly that cresylic-coupled soluble oils are greatly superior to the noncresylic types in this respect [38]. The former can rid themselves of the infecting organisms in an hour or less, while the latter may remain infected for several days.

6.4.2. Lubrication for High-Temperature Metal Processing

Correct lubrication of high-temperature metal-working processes provides several advantages : reduction of motive power due to lower friction ; improved tool life ; increased yield of processed metal ; improvement in quality of processed surfaces ; improved tolerances for the finished product ; improved material flow allowing machining and forming of "difficult" metals ; increased deformation in a single operation ; increased deformation rates. A decrease in the cost of the product results, in spite of the cost of the lubricant and the supplementary operations involved [40].

Another advantage is the insulating effect of the lubricants : the loss of heat from the workpiece during processing is thus limited so that the temperature gradient and subsequent thermal stresses are reduced.

6.4.2.1. *Conditions of Lubricant Application.* The method of applying lubricants in high-temperature processing must be studied in order to obtain these desired effects. For example, metals (especially steel) cannot be properly lubricated during hot working if high temperatures cause scale formation, in which case they must be descaled before lubricant is applied. This is to avoid embedding scale in the metal, which causes defects in the finished product and shortens the life of the dies.

At the same time, it must be remembered that in some common metalworking processes, friction between tool and work piece forms part of the forming process, and the use of a lubricant would be contrary to the operating principle. Thus, milling, blooming, slabbing, and rolling of plate, sheet and strip necessitate friction between workpiece and rolls.

There are also processes in which friction is necessary in one part of the operation but not in another. For example in a conventional tube mill the workpiece is rotated and moved forward by rolls which force it against the piercing plug ; friction is necessary between the workpiece and the rolls, but detrimental between the workpiece and the plug.

When the workpiece is deformed in a closed space, the resulting friction between the piece and the tool is sometimes so high that these operations cannot be accomplished without lubrication.

In processes like forging, stamping, spinning and deep drawing, the use of lubricants while offering advantages, introduces at the same time certain disadvantages, so that compromise has to be made.

6.4.2.2. *Methods of Lubrication and Lubricants.* Most lubricating methods for hot metal working are based on lubrication of the tools. Since the workpiece is very hot, when the tool is cold, the lubricant must fulfil contradictory conditions : good wetting properties both for the hot workpiece and the cold tool, a wide range of viscosity, and must adhere to the tool and resist very high temperatures.

It must also be capable of repeatedly spreading over a large area while remaining a continuous film.

It is very hard, if not impossible, to find a single substance to meet all these requirements. Consequently, the use of lubricants in high temperature metal processing is now currently confined to heat insulation and gas generation at high temperatures. In fact these gases also insulate the tool from the hot workpiece, prolonging tool life. If certain salts are applied (barium chloride, sodium chloride, etc.) between the tool and workpiece, heat is removed from the latter and a liquid providing the necessary lubrication is produced.

The quantity of heat necessary to change the physical state of the lubricants (solid into liquid, liquid into gas) is large; if this heat is obtained from the workpiece, chilling of the surfaces can result, but if this heat is taken from the tool, the results are beneficial. It is thus necessary to choose the lubricating materials from those of low thermal conductivity.

Since lubrication of the tool is a difficult process to control, it is necessary to trap the lubricant in recesses in the tool and force it to the tool surface either under pressure, or by the movement of the workpiece.

A more modern approach is to lubricate the workpiece rather than the tool. In this case it must be observed that the heat lost from the workpiece chills its surface and the tool surface may be deformed under the increased loads, especially if they become too hot.

Lubricants applied to a workpiece must have the following characteristics [40]:

  a) be very good thermal insulators;
  b) form protective coatings to minimize oxidation;
  c) produce a low coefficient of friction so that most of the applied force is used in deforming the workpiece, and not be dissipated in surface friction heat;
  d) the viscosity at the temperature of the workpiece must be sufficient to permit the formation of a thin film;
  e) sufficient viscosity and oiliness to resist the tool pressures;
  f) good wetting properties;
  g) chemically inert with respect to the workpiece material;
  h) chemically stable at the opreating temperature and pressure;
  i) easy to apply and to remove;
  j) inexpensive.

Glass or glass-like materials satisfy most of these conditions. From the many possible combinations of borates, phosphates and silicates, having the properties of glass, it should be possible to find the necessary combinations for the specific problems under considerations.

For the moment, common window glass is a convenient lubricant for steel processing at about 1,200°C. Indeed, glass is one of the best thermal insulators and can be applied to the workpiece immediately it comes from the furnace to protect it against oxidation. The coefficient of friction of glass around 1,200°C is very low, and the viscosity at this temperature is sufficient to form a film which will withstand the high pressures acting on the workpiece. Glass is also chemically inert with steel and is cheap [40]. It can be applied in powder form, the application being simple and its removal only slightly more expensive than for conventional lubricants.

The glass-like materials used for metalworking above 1,000°C, are generally silicates. For intermediate temperatures some mixtures are used, among which the borates are predominant, while the phosphates are better at low temperatures.

The use of glass in bar mill or sheet mill operation, has not been successful because high friction is necessary between the rolls and the workpiece.

It has been found very satisfactory in draw bench operations, in the piercing operation in tube mills, and for coating billets in extrusion processes. In this latter example the billet is completely coated with glass and the lubricant film is supplied from a solid reservoir of glass placed against the die.

It is also used successfully in the hot drawing of tubes, hot piercing in closed containers and forging operations, but it appears to be uneconomical for hot stamping [40].

References

1. P. H. MOLYNEUX, *Application of Additives to Industrial Lubricants.* Sci. Lubr., **15**, *3*, 1963.
2. C. J. BONER, *Gear and Transmission Lubricants.* Reinhold Publishing Corporation, New York, 1964.
3. V. OAKES, *A Laboratory Evaluation of Extreme Pressure Additives.* Sci. Lubr., **11**, *12*, 1959.
4. E. J. COBRICK, *Rust Preventives.* Lubr. Eng., **14**, *8*, 1958.
5. H. H. ZUIDEMA, *The Performance of Lubricating Oils.* Reinhold Publishing Corporation, New York, 1959.
6. O. MANOLESCU, *Lubrifiere şi lubrifianţi* (Lubrication and Lubricants), in Romanian. Revista Căilor Ferate, **4**, *4*, 1956.
7. N. TIPEI, V. N. CONSTANTINESCU, AL. NICA, O. BIŢĂ, *Lagăre cu alunecare* (Sliding Bearings), in Romanian. Editura Academiei R.P.R., Bucharest, 1961.
8. E. G. ELLIS, *Lubricant Additives Today.* Sci. Lubr., **14**, *1* and *2*, 1962.
9. R. G. BICKERTON, *Some Aspects of Synthetic Lubricants.* Sci. Lubr., **15**, *3*, 1963.
10. R. C. GUNDERSON, A. W. HART, *Synthetic Lubricants.* Reinhold Publishing Corporation, New York, 1962.
11. AL. NICA, *Sisteme noi de ungere a utilajelor industriale* (New Lubrication Systems for Industrial Equipment), in Romanian. I.D.T., Bucharest, 1960.
12. — *Lubricants without Additives.* Sci. Lubr., **10**, *4*, 1958.
13. F. S. CALHOUN, G. P. MURPHY, *Effects of Additives upon Greases.* Sci. Lubr., **15**, *3*, 1963.
14. Y. A. BELL, *Inorganic Microgel Grease Performance in Industrial Applications.* Lubr. Eng., **13**, *9*, 1957.
15. R. Y. ROSSCUP, D. R. OBERLINK, W. L. HAYNE, *A New Thickener for Multipurpose Lubricating Greases.* Lubr. Eng., **14**, *1*, 1958.
16. B. C. STUPP, *Molybdenum Disulphide and Related Solid-Lubricants.* Lubr. Eng., **14**, *4*, 1958.
17. M. T. LAVIK, G. E. GROSS, G. E. VAUGHN, *Investigations on the Mechanism of Tungsten Disulphide Lubrication in Vacuum.* Lubr. Eng., **15**, *6*, 1959.
18. R. L. JOHNSON, M. E. SLINEY, *High Temperature Friction and Wear Properties of Bonded Solid Lubricant Films Containing Lead Monoxide.* Lubr. Eng., **15**, *12*, 1959.
19. R. B. CAMPBELL, *Sulphur as an Extreme Pressure Lubricant.* Proceedings of the Conference on Lubrication and Wear, Paper 61, London, 1957.

20. J. W. MIDGLEY, H. WILMAN, *The Nature of the Wear Protection of Mild Steel Caused by Phosphating*. Proceedings of the Conference on Lubrication and Wear, Paper 84, London, 1957.

21. D. ISĂCESCU, GH. VASILCA, AL. NICA, V. CALCAN, *Unele proprietăţi funcţionale ale unui material plastic pe bază de furfurol-fenol ca material pentru lagăre* (Some Operating Characteristics of an Antifriction Phurphurol-Phenol Based Plastic Material), in Romanian. St. Cercet. Mec. Apl., **9**, *4*, Bucharest, 1958.

22. FR. NUHLICEK, *Lagăre cu alunecare din materiale plastice* (Sliding Bearings from Plastic Materials), in Romanian. I.D.T., Bucharest, 1961.

23. I. IA. ALŞIŢ, *O primenenii plastmass dlia podşipnikov skolijenia*, in Russian. Vestnik Maşinostroenia, **39**, 7, 1959.

24. P. A. MIHAILOV, P. N. MALIŞEV, I. V. DUPLENKO, *Nekatorie opîtnie dannie ob antifricţionîh svoistvah kaprona*, in Russian. Vestnik Maşinostroenia, **39**, *2*, 1959.

25. A. J. G. ALLAN, *Plastics as Solid Lubricants and Bearings*. Lubr. Eng., **14**, *5*, 1958.

26. S. B. TWISS, P. J. WILSON, E. J. SYDOR, *Friction of Polytetrafluoroethylene Dry Bearings*. Lubr. Eng., **14**, *6*, 1958.

27. D. C. MITCHELL, D. A. STARKEY, *Properties and Applications of "DU" Unlubricated PTFE-Type Bearings*. Engineer's Digest, **19**, *4*, 1958.

28. I. V. TEMKIN, *Primenenie sovremenîh materialov na osnove uglia i grafita*, in Russian. Vestnik Maşinostroenia, **38**, *1*, 1958.

29.   —   *New Uses for Colloidal Graphite*. Mech. World Eng. Record, **139**, *3480*, 1959.

30.   —   *Ceramics Made from Glass Promise Dry Bearings and High Strength*, Engineering, **188**, *4869*, 1959.

31. W. J. ANDERSON, *High-Temperature Bearings*. Machine Design, vol. 36, no. 26, 1964.

32. V. MARCU, *Metalizarea prin pulverizare* (Metal Spraying). Editura Academiei R.P.R. Bucharest, 1963.

33. V. T. MORGAN, A. CAMERON, *Mechanism of Lubrication in Porous Metal Bearings*. Proceedings of the Conference on Lubrication and Wear, Paper 89, London, 1957.

34. A. CAMERON, V. T. MORGAN, A. E. STAINSBY, *Critical Conditions for Hydrodynamic Lubrication of Porous Metal Bearings*. Proc. Inst. Mech. Eng., **176**, *28*, 1962.

35. A CAMERON, *Principles of Lubrication*. Longmans, London, 1966.

36. V. T. MORGAN, *Study of the Design Criteria for Porous Metal Bearings*. Proceedings of the Conference on Lubrication and Wear, Paper 88, London, 1957.

37. L. H. SUDHOLZ, *Cutting Fluids : Fundamentals and Laboratory Evaluation*. Lubr. Eng., **13**, *9*, 1957.

38. P. DRIVER, C. J. TAYLOR, *Some Aspects of Development and Application of Cutting Fluids*. Sci. Lubr., **15**, *4*, 1963.

39. D. PAVELESCU, I. ILIUC, *Apparatus for Determining the Anti-Wear Properties of Oils and Materials*. Wear, **8**, *2*, 1965.

40. J. SEJOURNET, *Lubrication for High-Temperature Metal Processing*. Lubr. Eng., **18**, *7*, 1962.

CHAPTER VII

Special Lubrication Systems

7.1. Gas Lubrication

The utilisation of air, or of other gases, as lubricants, was considered even in the 19th century (G. Hirn was apparently the first to mention it in 1854, [1]) but the practical application of the idea has only been accomplished recently, after many associated theoretical and practical problems have been overcome.

The main advantages and disadvantages of gas lubrication are listed in table 7—1.

Table 7—1

Advantages	Disadvantages
1. Very low friction and heating. Low wear.	Low load-carrying capacity.
2. Great thermal resistance; capability of working at extreme temperatures. Insensitive to radiation.	Dry friction at starting and stopping.
3. Vibration damper; very smooth running when the stability requirements are fulfilled.	Very sensitive to instability phenomena; special solutions must be applied.
4. Environmental medium itself is the lubricant; in the case of self-acting bearings no supply-system is needed.	Very precise machining of the sliding surfaces is essential.

The operating parameters and environments for which gas bearings are most suitable include high speeds, low loads and low friction at any temperature, in corrosive or radioactive surroundings. The technical problems best solved by the use of gas bearings occur in space technology, the aviation industry, high precision instruments, high speed grinding machines and drills, and such like.

The details of design approached from a theoretical point of view, due mainly to Ausman, Tipei, Sternlicht, Gross, Constantinescu, Hays *et al.*, are presented very completely in certain works on the subject [1], [2]. The problem of bearing supply is within the scope of this book, but a full development of the principles of gas bearing operation is largely irrelevant to the design of their ancillary equipment.

For instance, self-acting gas bearings under conditions of steady state require no lubricant supply system, but draw directly from the surroundings. However, the starting and stopping periods can give rise to excessive wear if there is no provision made for supporting the bearing loads when the surface speeds are too low to generate a continuous film of lubricant. Hence self-acting bearings are generally pressurized on starting and stopping, with a limited number of supply-holes placed in the load-carrying regions. These supply-grooves have been known to improve the starting and stopping performance of a self-acting bearing, even without an external supply of pressurized gas.

For the transient operation of self-acting bearings and the continuous operation of externally pressurized bearings, a source of clean pressurized gas must be delivered to the working regions of the bearing geometry, through the now familiar circuits of pipes, valves, and filters, from some sort of compressor.

Shop-air is normally supplied at pressures of about 6 kgf/cm² (80 psi) and can be used to provide bearings with an effective load-carrying capacity of 3 kgf/cm² (40 psi). If higher mean pressures are required, it is usual to supply the gas from a separate compressor.

However the specific load is limited both by the difficult task of supplying really high pressure gas, and that of limiting the gas flow by high precision surface finishing and assembly.

The lubrication system parameters are clearly determined by the characteristics of the bearing itself and for an externally pressurized journal bearing we must first introduce their important construction and operating parameters. The aspect ratio $\lambda = \dfrac{b}{2r}$ (the ratio of the bearing width to its diameter) is generally kept below 2, to limit load-carrying losses [2]. As λ increases so should the number of rows of supply-holes. The clearance ratio $\psi = \dfrac{c}{r}$ is usually very small, lying between $0.3 - 0.5\,^0/_{00}$, which illustrates the importance of precision in constructing the bearing. The eccentricity ratio, $\varepsilon = \dfrac{e}{c}$ must be kept below 0.5, or rather the applied load should be restricted to 30% of the maximum theoretical load capacity of the bearing [2].

The determination of the supply-hole diameters and their positioning is an extremely complex problem; it is sufficient to say that for convenient flow rates and satisfactory bearing stability the supply-hole diameter should lie between 0.2−0.5 mm. If capillary restrictors are used, their diameter must not exceed 1 mm.

For every design problem there are various available solutions and the selection of the optimum solution is not an easy task. However, some general principles can be outlined. For instance, if high bearing stability is an important feature, the supply of air or gas under pressure to the loaded surfaces must be effected through a large number of small diameter orifices; if a high load-carrying capacity is the main requirement, then the provision of supply-grooves is obligatory. Recently, a number of extremely useful books have been published on the construction of gas bearings (self-acting or externally pressurized) which demonstrate solutions for a wide range of applications [3], [4], [5].

In the following only a few typical industrial applications of gas bearings will be presented. Thus, Fig. 7−1 shows the compressed air supply-system for the bearings of an electric motor (Graneek and Kerr, [3]).

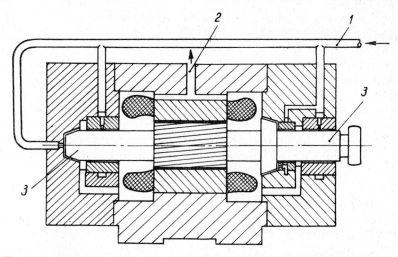

Fig. 7.1. — Electric motor with externally pressurized air-bearings [3] : 1 — air admission; 2 − air exhaust; 3 − air bearings.

The pressure pipes, the symmetrical arrangement of the admission holes for the journal bearings, and the supply arrangement for the conical thrust bearings, are the main features of the system. A point of special interest is the method in which the axial load is supported : the air is admitted through the end of the bearing, and the thrust bearing. When the axial load increases, the gap between the conical surfaces is reduced and the increase in leakage resistance leads to the formation of a higher pressure at the end of the spindle, so that the axial load is progressively resisted. In the same way, most of the exhaust air from the bearings is passed over the stator laminations for cooling purposes, before being released to atmosphere.

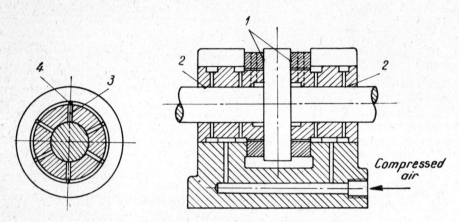

Fig. 7.2. — Externally pressurized air bearings for a grinding machine, [2] : 1 — thrust bearings; 2 — journal bearings; 3 — supply-orifices for journal bearings; 4 — supply-orifices for thrust bearings.

The motor was continuously run for 3 hours at 60,000 rpm, and the maximum temperature rise was found to be only 26°C. After 10,000 hours of operation, including several non-stop runs of 1000 hours each at 40,000 rpm, the bearings showed no sign of wear, [3].

Fig. 7—2 represents the pressurized air supply-system to the bearings of a grinding machine. This machine operates between 30,000 and 150,000 rpm, [2].

The thrust bearings are no longer conical, but plane, fed through several admission holes.

7.2. Magnetohydrodynamic Lubrication

There are occasions when lubrication with lubricants such as liquid metals can provide a satisfactory solution to the problems posed by very high temperature environments. In these situations the load-carrying capacity can be improved, or the bearing clearances enlarged if use is also made of a magnetic field to support some of the load by its interaction with a current flowing through the lubricant.

7.2.1. Generalities

It has been found that the application of a magnetic field alone (under open circuit conditions) results in no appreciable increase in the load-carrying capacity of a liquid metal bearing, except for extremely high, impractical, field strengths. Whereas, if an external magnetic field is applied, in conjunction with an external current source, a significant increase in the hydrodynamic pressures follows.

These results were obtained from the direct application of MHD concepts to lubrication problems, and studies of various types of bearings have been made by many investigators. In the following, a brief review of the results obtained in this field will be presented, after W. F. Hughes [6], and D. C. Kuzma [7].

The equations of fluid motion are the same as those of conventional lubrication, except that the electromagnetic body force $\bar{J} \times \bar{B}$ must be included; the electric forces are negligible as well as the effects due to the striction or inhomogeneities in the magnetic field, since liquid metals are in general nonmagnetic.

By neglecting inertia forces, the equation of motion takes the form

$$- \nabla p + \mu \nabla^2 \bar{v} + \bar{J} \times \bar{B} = 0 \qquad (7-1)$$

while the continuity equation keeps the usual form

$$\nabla \bar{v} = 0. \qquad (7-2)$$

In the above equations, p is the pressure in the lubricant film, μ the viscosity, J the current density, B the magnetic induction field, and v the velocity.

For steady state conditions, Maxwell's equations can be written

$$\left. \begin{array}{l} \nabla \cdot \bar{B} = 0 \\ \nabla \times \bar{H} = \bar{J} \\ \nabla \times \bar{E} = 0 \\ \nabla \cdot \bar{J} = 0 \end{array} \right\} \qquad (7-3)$$

where H and E are the magnetic and electric fields. If σ is the electrical conductivity, Ohm's law takes the form

$$\bar{J}' = \bar{J} = \sigma \bar{E}' = \sigma(\bar{E} + \bar{v} \times \bar{B}) \qquad (7-4)$$

The primes refer to a coordinate system within the fluid, while the unprimed quantities refer to those measured with respect to an arbitrary frame of reference, which is usually determined by the particular slider or bearing geometry. The velocity v is the velocity of the fluid with respect to the arbitrary frame of reference. At low velocities compared to that of light, $\overline{J} = \overline{J}'$, and $\overline{E}' = (\overline{E} + \overline{v} \times \overline{B})$.

To specify the problem completely, one more equation is necessary, that is the constitutive equation relating $\overline{B}$ and $\overline{H}$; since the fluid is non-magnetic $(\overline{B} = \overline{B}')$, it can be written, in any frame of reference

$$\overline{B} = \mu_0 \overline{H} \qquad\qquad (7-5)$$

where μ_0 is the magnetic permeability in free space.

Examination of equation $(7-1)$ shows that under certain conditions the $\overline{J} \times \overline{B}$ force can increase the pressurization of the bearing. To solve the problem numerically, relations $(7-1)$ and $(7-2)$ must be solved in the same time, using Maxwell's equations $(7-3)$ and Ohm's equation $(7-4)$, by considering a set of boundary conditions imposed by the external current circuitry and the magnetic field. The external circuitry and field geometry are extremely important, and the pressures can be increased or decreased by supplying or absorbing power in the external circuit.

The coupling between the equations can be simplified by assuming a strong external magnetic field B_0, which will enable the induced magnetic field to be neglected, so that $\overline{J} \times \overline{B}$ will be

$$\overline{J} \times \overline{B} = \sigma(\overline{E} + \overline{v} \times \overline{B}_0) \times \overline{B}_0. \qquad\qquad (7-6)$$

In this way coupling occurs only through the velocity, in a linear fashion; this simplification can be generally made, since in order to obtain an appreciable pressurization it is necessary to employ a significant external magnetic field.

7.2.2. Applications

The possibility of improving the load-carrying capacity of various types of bearing, by applying the concepts of MHD presents a certain practical interest.

7.2.2.1. Hydrostatic MHD Thrust Bearings. The effective pressurization of hydrostatic thrust bearings can be achieved by providing an external magnetic field, and circulating an electrical current through the lubricant. Several electrode and field geometries are possible. Two convenient configurations are presented in Fig. $7-3$ (an axial magnetic field with a radial current) and in Fig. $7-4$ (a radial magnetic field with an axial current), [6].

In the first case the electrodes consist of two concentric annular rings attached to the stator (flush with the surface) and in the second case they are the stator and rotor surfaces themselves, or annular portions of these surfaces. The stator is considered in the analysis to be the stationary frame with respect to which the field parameters are measured.

For the axial magnetic field the equations of motion can be written in polar coordinates as

$$-\frac{\partial p}{\partial r} + \mu \frac{\partial^2 V}{\partial z^2} + J_\theta \, B_\theta = 0$$

$$\mu \frac{\partial^2 v}{\partial z^2} - J_r \, B_0 = 0 \qquad\qquad\qquad (7-7)$$

$$\frac{\partial p}{\partial z} = 0$$

where V is the slider velocity and B_0 the external magnetic field.

The integration of the equations of motion leads to the following value for the flow rate Q [6]

$$Q = 3 \, Q_0 \left[\frac{\mathbf{M} - \tanh \mathbf{M}}{\mathbf{M}^3} \right] = \frac{4\pi \, h^3 (p_0 - p_e)}{\mu \ln \dfrac{b}{a}} \left[\frac{\mathbf{M} - \tanh \mathbf{M}}{\mathbf{M}^3} \right] \quad (7-8)$$

where Q_0 is the flow rate for zero Hartmann number $\mathbf{M}$, defined as

$$\mathbf{M} = \sqrt{\frac{\sigma \, h^2 \, B_0^2}{\mu}}. \qquad\qquad (7-9)$$

As specified, σ is the electrical conductivity, a, b and h are geometrical data evident from Figs. 7—3 and 7—4, p_0 is the pressure at $r = 0$, and p_e is the exit pressure.

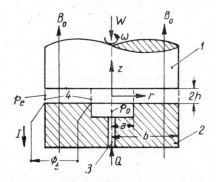

Fig. 7.3. — Hydrostatic thrust bearing with an axial magnetic field and a radial current [6]: 1 — rotor; 2 — stator; 3 — pressurized lubricant; 4 — electrodes.

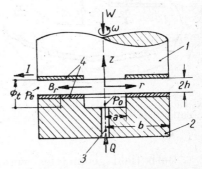

Fig. 7.4. — Hydrostatic thrust bearing with a radial magnetic field and an axial current, [6]: 1 — rotor; 2 — stator; 3 — pressurized lubricant; 4 — electrodes.

The pressure distribution is found to be

$$p - p_0 = \frac{(p_e - p_0) \ln \dfrac{r}{a}}{\ln \dfrac{b}{a}}. \qquad (7-10)$$

For the radial magnetic field the equations of motion become

$$\left.\begin{array}{c} -\dfrac{\partial p}{\partial r} + \mu\,\dfrac{\partial^2 V}{\partial z^2} - J_z\,B_\theta = 0, \\[2ex] \mu\,\dfrac{\partial^2 v}{\partial z^2} + J_z\,B_r = 0, \\[2ex] \dfrac{\partial p}{\partial z} = 0. \end{array}\right\} \qquad (7-11)$$

The main interaction $J_z B_r$ does not affect the pressure generation, while the term $J_z B_\theta$ gives rise to a pinch pressure of relatively small effect, and thus it can be concluded that only at extremely high, essentially unattainable, current densities and loads, will the purely magnetic pressurization become important in this type of bearing.

7.2.2.2. *Finite MHD Slider Bearings*. The layout of a finite MHD step slider is presented in Fig. 7—5 with a tangentially applied field and in Fig. 7—6 with a transversely applied field.

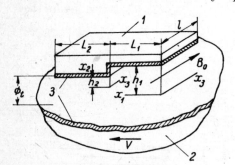
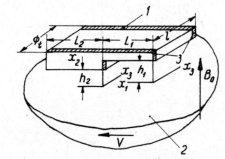

Fig. 7.5. — Slider step bearing with a tangential field [6]: 1 — slider; 2 — bearing; 3 — electrodes.

Fig. 7.6. — Slider step bearing with a transverse field [6]: 1 — slider; 2 — bearing; 3 — electrodes.

Both field geometries were investigated by Hughes [6] and yield simple solutions. Neglecting induced effects, the differential equations are

$$\frac{12}{12 + \mathbf{M}^2} \cdot \frac{\partial^2 p}{\partial x_1^2} + \frac{\partial^2 p}{\partial x_3^2} = 0 \qquad (7-12)$$

for the tangentially applied magnetic field and

$$\frac{12(M \sinh M + 2 - 2 \cosh M)}{M^3 \sinh M} \cdot \frac{\partial^2 p}{\partial x_1^2} + \frac{\partial^2 p}{\partial x_3^2} = 0 \qquad (7-13)$$

for the transversely applied magnetic field.

The general results of these equations are represented graphically in Fig. 7—7, in the form of a load-carrying capacity coefficient ζ

$$\zeta = \frac{W h_1^2}{48 \mu V l^3} \qquad (7-14)$$

for both cases, versus Hartmann number M_1 based on h_1 (see Fig. 7—5; 7—6), [6].

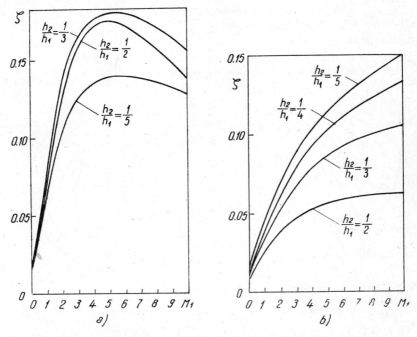

Fig. 7.7. — Variation of load-carrying coefficient M_1 as a function of Hartmann number M_1, for various thickness ratios [6]: a) bearing with tangential field, $I^* = +100$; b) bearing with transverse field, $I' = -10$.

Naturally, the results can only be considered as representative of the performance of these particular bearings, since in both cases the total dimensionless current was held constant at a fixed specified value. Thus, for the tangentially applied field, the total dimensionless current

$$I^* = \frac{I h_1}{V l^2 \mu \sqrt{\sigma}},$$ and for the transversely applied field the dimensionless

current $I' = \dfrac{I}{Vl\sqrt{\mu\sigma}}$. In both situations the pads were rectangular, so that $\dfrac{L_1}{l} = \dfrac{L_2}{l} = 1$.

It can be concluded however that : a) for the tangentially applied field the pressure generation is negative if the electrical loop is open or short circuited ; b) for the transversely applied case, only a slight increase in pressurization can be effected on open circuit, and when short circuited the magnetic field is detrimental to the generation of pressure.

On the other hand, significant increases in load capacity can be achieved by supplying power from an external source : the direction of the current is important and there exists an optimum step size and location.

7.2.2.3. *MHD Journal Bearings.* MHD journal bearings have been analysed by Elco and Hughes with axial fields [6] and by Kuzma with radial magnetic fields [7].

Fig. 7—8 shows the journal bearing with an axially applied field and Fig. 7—9 with a radial magnetic field.

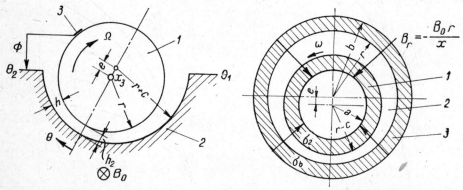

Fig. 7.8. — MHD journal bearing with an axial field [6] : 1 — shaft ; 2 — bearing ; 3 — slip ring.

Fig. 7.9. — MHD journal bearing with a radial field [7] : 1 — journal ; 2 — clearance between journal and bearing ; 3 — bearing.

In the first case the bearing and journal surfaces are the electrodes, the journal being provided with a slip ring. The variation of the film thickness is assumed to take the usual form

$$h = c(1 - \varepsilon \cos \theta). \qquad (7-15)$$

The bearing is considered infinitely long, and the Reynold's boundary conditions are used, that is $p = p_0$ when $\dfrac{\partial p}{\partial \theta} = 0$.

The equation of motion for the axially applied field is [6]

$$-\frac{1}{r} \cdot \frac{\partial p}{\partial \theta} + \mu \frac{\partial^2 V}{\partial x_2^2} - J_{x_2} B_0 = 0 \qquad (7-16)$$

and the pressure distribution

$$\overline{p} = 6 A_2 - 12 \, \overline{Q} \, A_3 - \gamma \, A_1 \qquad (7-17)$$

where

$$\left.\begin{array}{l}
\overline{p} = \dfrac{p \, c^2}{\mu \, V \, r} \, ; \quad \gamma = \mathbf{M}^2 (\overline{\Phi} - \overline{Q}) = \dfrac{\overline{I} \, \mathbf{M}^2}{A_1 \, \theta_c} \\[3mm]
A_1 = \displaystyle\int_{\theta_1}^{\theta} \dfrac{d\theta}{(1 - \varepsilon \cos \theta)} \, ; \quad A_2 = \displaystyle\int_{\theta_1}^{\theta} \dfrac{d\theta}{(1 - \varepsilon \cos \theta)^2} \\[3mm]
A_3 = \displaystyle\int_{\theta_1}^{\theta} \dfrac{d\theta}{(1 - \varepsilon \cos \theta)^3} \, ; \quad \overline{\Phi} = \dfrac{\Phi}{V \, c \, B_0} \\[3mm]
\overline{I} = \dfrac{I}{r \, V \, \sigma \, B_0} \, ; \quad \mathbf{M} = \sqrt{\dfrac{B_0^2 \, c^2 \, \sigma}{\mu}} \, ; \quad \overline{Q} = \dfrac{Q}{V c} \, .
\end{array}\right\} \qquad (7-18)$$

In these relations $\overline{I}$ is the dimensionless current, $\overline{\Phi}$ the dimensionless terminal potential, γ an interaction parameter, $\overline{Q}$ the dimensionless flow rate and c the radial clearance.

If the inlet and exit angles θ_1 and θ_2 are set, and the angle at which the film ends θ_c is known or can be found iteratively, equations $(7-17)$, $(7-18)$ can be solved in the usual manner.

Fig. $7-10$ shows a typical set of data, for a $180°$ partial journal with an eccentricity ratio $\varepsilon = 0.8$ and the minimum film thickness h_2 assumed to occur at $120°$ from the inlet (see Fig. $7-8$).

It is found that the load can be greatly increased in comparison with the nonelectromagnetic bearing, as the current is increased.

For the journal bearing with a radial magnetic field, the total load can be expressed in the form [7]

$$W = \mu \, r \, \omega \, l \, \frac{1}{\psi^2} \left\{ \frac{2 \, \pi \, \mathbf{M}}{\varepsilon} - \frac{4 \pi}{\varepsilon} \cdot \frac{1}{(1 - \varepsilon)^{1/2} - \left[\left(\dfrac{\mathbf{M} - 2}{\mathbf{M}} \right)^2 - \varepsilon^2 \right]^{1/2}} \right\}, \qquad (7-19)$$

where $\mathbf{M}$ is the Hartmann number, l the bearing width, ψ the clearance ratio and ε the eccentricity ratio.

The ratio of the magnetohydrodynamic load to the ordinary hydrodynamic load, is represented in Fig. 7—11, as a function of the Hartmann number with a constant eccentricity ratio of 0.8.

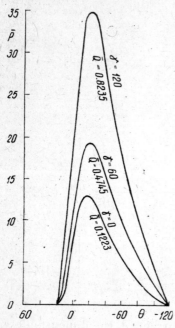

Fig. 7.10. — Variation of normalized pressure $\bar{p}$ for a 180° partial journal bearing as a function of the electric parameters, with $\varepsilon = 0.8$ and the minimum film thickness at 120° [6].

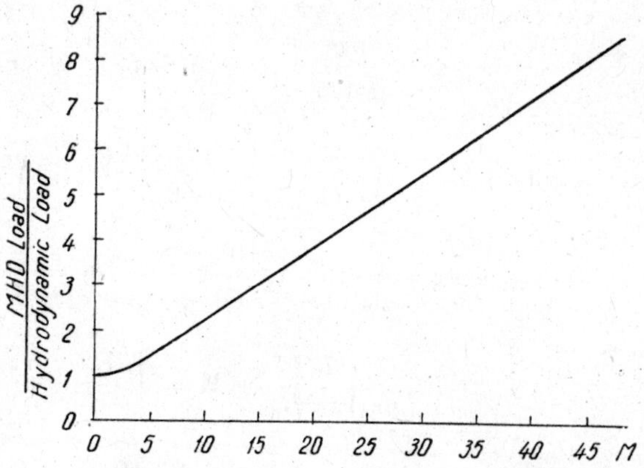

Fig. 7.11. — Load ratio between MHD and hydrodynamic loads as a function of Hartmann number, with $\varepsilon = 0.8$ [7].

It can be seen that at low Hartmann numbers the effect is significant, if not spectacular, but it is difficult to obtain large values of Hartmann number ($\mathbf{M} > 5$), for important increases in the load carrying-capacity. One solution would be the utilization of superconducting electromagnets capable of generating field strengths of 50,000 Gauss.

However, there are many technical problems in constructing a practical device of this type, so that the field of research in this direction is open to further development.

7.2.3. Magnetogasodynamic Lubrication

The insufficient load-carrying capacity of gas bearings, and the demonstration of the beneficial effects of magnetic fields applied to bearings with conducting lubricants, has led to the development of a theory of magnetogasodynamic (MGD) lubrication.

For this purpose it is necessary for the gaseous lubricant to be made electrically conducting, usually by ionization. Since a stable plasma can be obtained only at very high temperatures, it is necessary to develop methods of obtaining cold ionization of the gas lubricant film. The experience obtained in developing magnetogasodynamic generators is likely to be useful in the future in solving this problem.

At present the film can be partially ionised by radiation, or by electrical discharge through the film, using gases, or small quantities of gas, that ease this procedure.

In this way, Hartmann numbers of unity can be evaluated, which are sufficient to make the MGD bearing a practical proposition, for nuclear applications, and in the uprating of existing gas bearing applications (gyroscopes, etc.).

Theoretical analysis of the problem has shown that a transverse electrical current and a tangential magnetic field produce better results than those obtained by alternative methods [8].

The application of external magnetic and electrical fields can also improve the performance of static bearings.

A transverse magnetic field and its associated orthogonal electric current is capable of restricting the gas flow rate, which can be important in some cases. A tangential magnetic field combination however, can generate additional fluid pressure directly, much in the way that converging moving surfaces are effective.

In Fig. 7—12, the variation of pressure between externally pressurized parallel plates is presented as a function of the magnetic bearing number Λ_M [8]

$$\Lambda_M = \frac{\sigma \, B \, x_{30} \, \Phi x_2 \, l}{p_0 \, h} \qquad (7-20)$$

in which σ is the electrical conductibility, $B x_{30}$ the magnetic flux density, Φx_2 the potential after x_2 axis (perpendicular to the sliding surfaces), l the bearing length after x_3, p_0 the atmospheric pressure and h the film thickness.

In Fig. 7—12 the supply pressure ratio p_i/p_0, is assumed equal to 4. It can be seen that for positive values of Λ_M the load carrying-capacity is improved, while for negative values it is diminished.

Another interesting feature of MGD lubrication lies in the possibility of reducing the frictional drag forces by finding a suitable configuration for the external electromagnetic fields. In this way important improvements may be attained in the performance of ultra high-speed bearings, where the aim is to reduce the frictional forces as much as possible.

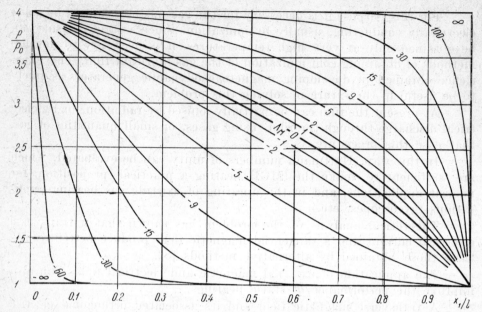

Fig. 7.12 — Influence of the magnetic bearing number Λ_M on the pressure distribution between externally pressurized parallel plates $\left(\dfrac{p_i}{p_0} = 4\right)$, [8].

7.3. Electrostatic and Magnetic Bearings

Bearings relying on forces of magnetism and electrostatics completely eliminate the need of lubricants, reduce friction and wear, and are operational in vacuum and at extreme temperatures. They are the only possible solution under certain extraordinary working conditions.

7.3.1. Generalities

Mechanical force without physical contact can be practically derived from three types of field forces: magnetic, electrostatic and electromagnetic. The first field is due to the action of permanent magnets, the second exists between electrostatically charged objects and the third depends on the magnetic field created by a current-carrying conductor. The last field source can be used in two basic ways: either by employing the force of attraction between a magnetic material and the field of an electromagnet, or through the interaction between the magnetic fields of two current-carrying conductors.

The main problem in producing bearings of these types is their stability, since the surfaces must not come into contact due to slight disturbances or alterations in the forces. Electrostatic and magnetic bearings are stable in any two directions, but unstable in the third, due to the inverse-square relationship between forces and distance. This applies to both electrostatic and static magnetic fields, but it does not apply to time-dependent fields or to magnetic materials which have relative permeabilities less than unity, (termed diamagnetic materials) these materials being repelled by a magnetic field. In contrast, paramagnetic or ferromagnetic materials are attracted by a magnetic field. A servosystem is needed for the three-dimensional stability of bearings using either electrostatic charges or magnets with ferromagnetic materials, which constitutes an additional complication to their practicability.

7.3.2. Design Variants

7.3.2.1. *Electrostatic Bearings*. The ability of electrostatically charged bodies to support loads is very small; magnetic systems have a capacity 200 times larger. The upper limit for electrostatic bearings is set by the breakdown of the dielectric medium between the bearing surfaces and is generally less than 0.1 kgf/cm^2 [9]. For magnetic bearings the limit is set by the flux saturation of the material. To achieve the load carrying-capacity of this order with electrostatic bearings the potential difference would have to be very high (about 30,000 V for 1 mm distance between the surfaces).

The single advantage of electrostatic bearings is their reduced weight compared with that of magnetic bearings.

7.3.2.2. *Diamagnetic and Superconducting Bearings*. A solution that avoids the necessity of a stabilizing servosystem can be constructed using permanent magnets in conjunction with diamagnetic materials. In such systems three-dimensional stability is theoretically attainable without external control (a completely passive system). For a maximum stability the diamagnetic material must have a permeability of much less than unity.

This condition is very hard to fulfil, since the best diamagnetic materials (bismuth and graphite) have a permeability very close to unity; a perfectly diamagnetic material (zero relative permeability) would yield a load carrying capability 10,000 times that of bismuth or graphite [9].

A superconductor by definition, loses its electrical resistivity as its temperature approaches absolute zero. Up to the present time about 20 metals and many alloys and compounds have been discovered to exhibit superconducting properties; they become resistive however, when exposed to magnetic fields in excess of a critical value.

Fig. 7—13 shows how a superconducting bearing operates. The eddy currents induced in the superconducting surface are not damped out by the resistivity of material, and hence oppose the electromagnetic field produced by the current carrying conductor, and give rise to mechanical forces which can reach specific values of 0.3 kgf/cm^2 (4 psi).

A current application of this, whose principle is shown in Fig. 7—14 [9] uses a niobium ball to produce a frictionless bearing in a cryogenic gyroscope.

In such cases the complete elimination of friction compensates for the complication involved in creating the extremely low temperature environment required.

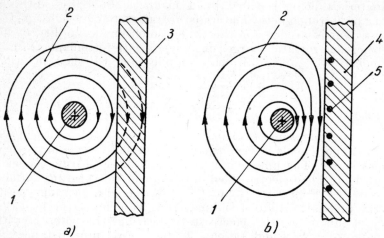

a)   *b)*

Fig. 7.13.—Principle of superconducting bearings [9] : a) non-superconductive plate next to current carrying conductor ; b) superconductive plate next to current-carrying conductor ; 1 — current-carrying conductor ; 2 — magnetic field ; 3 — non-superconductive plate ; 4 — superconductive plate ; 5 — induced eddy currents.

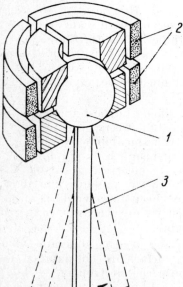

Fig. 7.14. — Superconducting spherical bearing [9] : 1 — spherical superconductor ; 2 — electroconductor ; 3 — successive positions of the moving part of the bearing.

7.3.2.3. *Magnetic Bearings.* Because of their inherent instability these bearings can only be called upon to support loads in a given direction. Thus it is usual to supplement a magnetic bearing system with some other form of support in at least one direction. This supplementary system may be arranged to provide merely location for the efficient operation of the magnetic system. Fig. 7—15 shows an example

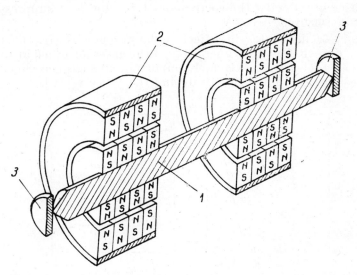

Fig. 7.15. — Radial magnetic bearing with mechanical guides for thrust forces [9]: 1 — shaft; 2— permanent magnets; 3 — mechanical guides.

which uses mechanical means to prevent the shaft moving to a lower energy position in the axial direction while the radial loads are supported magnetically [9].

The mechanical location of the shaft may have other means of constraint. For instance it is quite possible, though technologically complicated, to replace the cylindrical magnets in Fig. 7—15 with opposed conical magnetic bearings and to remove the mechanical restraints. This can be achieved in other ways [9], such as controlling the shaft position automatically. In this system the mechanical axial constraints in Fig. 7—15 are replaced by electromagnets whose current supply is controlled by an axial displacement transducer.

It is necessary to point out that the absence of a lubricant film or of direct contact does not eliminate friction *ipso facto*, since eddy currents or/and hysteresis can impede relative motion just as much as conventional friction. Great care is therefore necessary in designing these bearings in order to keep the apparent friction to a minimum.

7.4 Lubrication in High Vacuum

This general heading effectively covers the lubrication problems encountered in space, and in experimental research.

In 1939, Bowden and Hughes investigated the peculiarities of dry friction in vacuum, demonstrating the importance of adsorbed, or chemisorbed gases in reducing the coefficient of friction and suppressing cold welding and seizure.

Fig. 7—16 illustrates this effect by showing how the friction increases with time, due to the slow liberation of the gases adsorbed at the sliding surfaces. This is clearly an extremely important effect, since the coefficient of dry friction is amplified by 10 during the process [10].

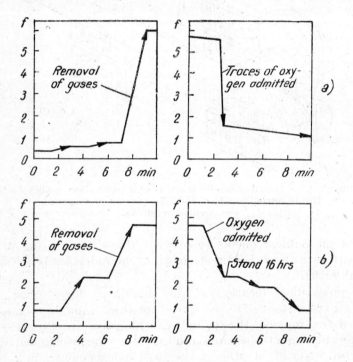

Fig. 7.16. — Effects of surface films on friction [10] : a) nickel on tungsten ; b) copper on copper.

Experiments on oil lubricated ball-bearings in vacuum, showed a similarly exaggerated deterioration in their performance at low pressures [10].

More recent experiments carried out on rolling bearings in high vacuum (10^{-8} torr) have led to the formation of a more complete picture of the mechanism by which effective lubrication is destroyed [10]. In these experiments the bearing was supplied with various lubricants, and failure was shown to be due to the evaporation of the lubricant and its subsequent blockage with wear debris.

The lubricants with the shortest effective life were found to be the polyphenyl ethers, while high V. I. silicones, were the most efficient, allowing a bearing life of up to two years.

Greases proved less efficient than oils, and again silicone based lithium soap combinations were proved more effective, yielding a bearing life of up to one year. In these cases failure was found due to the evaporation of oil from the grease thickener, which then clogs the bearing.

The results with bonded molybdenum disulphide films proved difficult to reproduce and this was attributed to the use of stainless steels in the construction of the test bearings. The method of applying the MoS_2 films proved to be of fundamental importance. The best results were obtained with MoS_2 films bonded with sodium silicate. It seems therefore that MoS_2 films may be efficient at moderate temperatures, while at high temperatures the utilization of tungsten bisulphide films (WS_2) would appear to offer more hope of success.

Another aspect investigated in these particular tests was the influence of the retainer material on the performance of antifriction bearings in vacuum. Reinforced plastics and powder metal composites were tried, some self-lubricating and others impregnated with oil. It was found that the behaviour of impregnated materials was not satisfactory, due to the tendency of the oil to evaporate. The longest life was obtained from a material named "Duroid" which is a composition of 60% polytetrafluoroethylene and 40% glass fibres impregnated with molybdenum disulphide[10].

Besides the influence of very high vacuum, lubricants and antifriction materials for space applications must resist the extremes of temperature, radiation and other unorthodox environmental conditions (zero gravity, micrometeorite bombardment, and so on).

The temperatures may vary from very high values (linked with the combustion processes) to the very low values associated with cryogenic fuels and oxidizers, and with the surrounding medium, since in the regions hidden from the sun, temperatures as low as $-130°C$ may be encountered. The oils and greases selected for use in these circumstances must therefore not freeze or become too viscous at low service temperatures, and at the same time must not become too thin or volatile at high temperatures.

The absence of gravity reduces bearing loads by eliminating the static structural forces, but retaining the inertial loads associated with dynamic forces. Gravity-fed lubrication systems are clearly inappropiate, so that pressure must be applied to the lubricant reservoir through bladders or pistons. It is generally desirable to employ lubricant supply systems capable of operating for the lifetime of the mechanism, to avoid the bulk and power losses caused by pumps and recirculating lubrication systems. The hydrodynamic lubrication of bearings is also affected by zero gravity conditions, since instabilities can occur.

The probability of damage from meteorites and micrometeorites is very small, so that no special precautions are required to combat this in the lubrication of spacecraft. On the other hand, various sources of radiation must be taken into account : cosmic rays, Van Allen belts (geomagnetically trapped corpuscular radiation), auroral radiation and solar radiation. The estimation and addition of these sources of radiation has shown that the amount is not sufficient to alter the performance of most lubricants. Thus, even at the heart of the inner Van Allen belt (at an altitude of 3,200 km) a satellite would be exposed to a radiation dose of about 10^5 roentgens (**R**) per year, while the oils most sensitive to radiation (silicones) can support 10^6 **R**/year and mineral oils are stable up to 5×10^8 **R**/year, [10].

If nuclear propulsion is to be used for space craft, the reactor will probably have to be unshielded and this will give rise to significant radiation doses (an unshielded 1000 kw reactor produces a radiation dose of 10^6 **R**/hour at a distance of 30 m).

However, at present the main influence on bearings working in space environments, remains that of the reduced pressure : 10^{-10} torr at 800 km and 10^{-12} torr at 1600 km. Over and above the evaporation of fluid lubricants, and the destruction of absorbed surface films, the rarefied atmosphere causes further problems.

Heat transfer can only be affected by radiation in a high vacuum, because the processes of conduction and convection rely on the molecular density of the ambient atmosphere. Hence the temperature of bearings can reach prohibitive values due to friction, or other exothermic phenomena (hysteresis and eddy currents in electric motors for instance).

In conclusion, lubrication is rendered much more difficult in high vacua than at ordinary pressures, and the consequences of inadequate lubrication can be more serious.

7.5. Lubrication in Radioactive Environments

The increasing use of nuclear power has meant that for design purposes the behaviour of lubricants used in association with such equipment must be understood. The use of radioactive isotopes in wear experiments has also benefited from research into this new field of lubrication.

7.5.1. Influence of Radiation on Lubricant Properties

Powerful irradiation of lubricant media is unavoidable in many nuclear installations, especially in the moving parts within the body of the reactor itself. In many cases the effect of the environment is even further complicated by high temperatures, and the possibility of chemical action with the heat exchange fluids.

7.5.1.1. *Mineral Oils.* It was discovered that the structure of a mineral oil could be so altered by exposure to neutron radiation within an atomic pile, that it could in fact be turned solid. Between dosages of 10^{12} and 1.8×10^{18} neutrons/cm² the viscosity of a mineral oil is increased dramatically with a parallel darkening and intensifying of its colour. Fig. 7—17 illustrates this effect for three different oils [11]:

a) a paraffinic bright stock of relatively high initial viscosity (543 cSt at 100°F);

b) a paraffinic distillate of lower viscosity and molecular weight (35 cSt at 100°F);

c) an aromatic distilate (24 cSt at 100°F).

As the figure demonstrates, the viscosity variation is enormous and the aromatic oil is by far the most resistant to such changes.

An interesting observation is the linear relationship between the ratio of final and initial viscosities and the neutron dosage. This relationship is maintained over a wide viscosity range, and only ceases to apply when the viscosity change is very high (about 5000 % at 100°F), at which point the oil is approaching gelation or solidification.

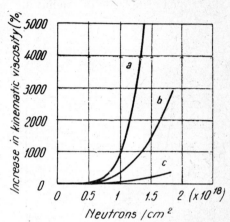

Fig. 7.17. — Increase in kinematic viscosity as a function of neutron dosage for three mineral oils [11]: a) paraffinic solvent-extracted bright stock of relatively high viscosity; b) paraffinic distillate of lower viscosity; c) distillate containing a high proportion of aromatic compounds.

The refractive index of the oil is also found to increase linearly with the radiation dose, but the mechanism of this phenomenon is not yet fully understood.

The oxidation effects are very small, so that in these experiments it was not thought necessary to evaluate the irradiation stability of hydrocarbon mineral oils in the absence of oxygen.

The various factors likely to be responsible for the resistance of certain oils to radiation have been investigated in detail.

The influence of aromatic compound content is shown in Fig. 7—18, and it is seen that an increase in aromatic content leads to a significant decrease in the viscosity change during irradiation [11].

Another factor that has been studied in some detail is the influence of molecular weight on the resistance to radiation. It was found (Fig. 7—19) that the higher the initial molecular weight and viscosity of the oil, the lower their resistance to the same dose of neutron irradiation [11].

The effect of additives has also been investigated and it has been shown that additions of $1 - 2\%$ of aromatic additives (naphthalene, phenanthrene, phenyl-α-naphtylamine) are beneficial, although their influence is of far less importance than the structure of the base oil itself. It is not possible to use higher concentrations of these additives due to their limited solubility in mineral oils.

Antioxidants (2 : 6 di-tert-butyl 4-methyl phenol, for instance) have no effect on the radiation resistance, the additive being immediately destroyed and the oil behaving as an uninhibited base material [11].

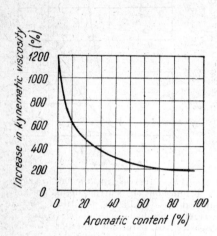

Fig. 7.18. — Increase in kinematic viscosity as a function of the aromatic content for a dosage of 1.27×10^{18} neutrons/cm^2 [11].

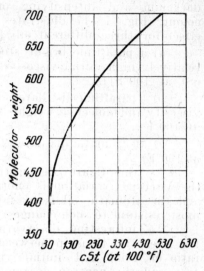

Fig. 7.19. — Variation of the kinematic viscosity as a function of the molecular weight for a dosage of 0.97×10^{18} neutrons/cm^2 [11].

Investigations have also been extended to cover the effect of electron and gamma radiation. For both gamma- and electron-irradiated samples, a linear relationship between the refractive index and radiation dose was found, as in the case of neutron radiation, with a similar increase in viscosity [11].

In order to correlate the results given by these various types of radiation, the energy levels of each system can be calculated and it is possible thus to compare the results for equivalent energy levels; no important difference exists between the effects of the three forms of radiation. The mechanism of viscosity increase with radiation dose has been suggested to be that of cross-linking the molecules, which can also be achieved chemically through the action of a peroxide to produce exactly the same macroscopic oil properties.

7.5.1.2. *Effect of Radiation on Synthetic Fluids.* Several synthetic lubricants of interest (tritolyl phosphate, silicone oils, di (2-ethyl hexyl) sebacate, tetra (2-ethylhexyl) silicate, etc.), have been tested for radiation resistance [11], [12].

In general, synthetic fluids exhibit a lower resistance to radiation than mineral oils, since at a dose of $1.6-1.8 \times 10^{18}$ neutrons/cm^2 all the synthetic fluids tested became solid, with the exception of tritolyl phosphate which suffered, however, a large increase in viscosity.

On the other hand, it must be remarked that the extension of all the results obtained with mineral oils to synthetic fluids is not always possible. Ethers of the poly (propylene oxide) type have been found to behave satisfactorily under pile irradiation, but not under gamma rays. The explanation is that in the pile, oxidation reactions yield decomposition products of low molecular weight and viscosity, capable of balancing the increase in viscosity from radiation-induced cross-linking processes, while in the case of gamma radiations these decomposition phenomena no longer take place.

At least one of the silicone group of lubricants possesses reasonable radiation resistance (siloxanes with a high aromatic content [12]) but in general they are inferior to mineral oils in this respect (Fig. 7—20), [13].

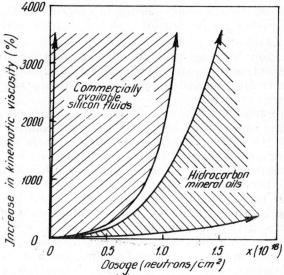

Fig. 7.20. — Comparison of relative stability to radiation of silicone, fluids (commercially available) and mineral oils [13].

7.5.1.3. *Effect of Radiation on Greases.* Sodium and lithium soap greases with various base oils (mineral and synthetic) have been examined [11], [12]. At radiation doses of 0.56×10^{18} neutrons/cm² (lower than radiation levels used for mineral oils) marked deterioration occurs.

The sodium soap-mineral oil greases become fluid even at doses as low as 0.36×10^{18} neutrons / cm². Similar greases based on silicone fluids vary in their behaviour, becoming tacky or hard, depending on their aromatic content. The lithium soap greases turn fluid.

It can thus be concluded that the radiation resistance of greases is in general lower than that of mineral oils.

However, it must be pointed out that greases prepared with a particular class of silicones (the siloxane fluids with high aromatic content, cited in § 7.5.1.2), and suitable fillers (copper, phthalocyanine for instance) can be used as high temperature radiation stable materials [12].

7.5.2. Systems of Lubrication for Irradiated Environments

The data above concerning resistance of oils and greases to radiation demonstrate the possibility of using some high aromatic content oils and specially prepared greases in irradiated media. The radiation level can in most cases be kept below the critical level with the help of suitable shielding. However, when the bearings belong to mechanisms actually within the reactor, or to the turbines of the newly projected nuclear-electric plants in which the reactor coolant is to be circulated to the turbine directly, some radically new solutions are needed in view of the high temperatures and radiation levels : gas lubrication, solid lubricants, melted metals, etc.

7.5.2.1. *Lubrication of Antifriction Bearings in Irradiated Environments.* Antifriction bearings used in nuclear reactors cannot be lubricated by conventional means. When the radiation level exceeds the limits of the best oils and greases available, it is necessary to use a solid film, or no lubricant at all.

There are many situations (charge tubes and certain charge/discharge operating mechanism for carbon-dioxide-cooled, graphite-moderated reactors) where the operating speeds and loads are so low that it is possible to obtain satisfactory bearing performance by the correct design and choice of materials, without using even a solid lubricant [14].

On the other hand, experiments with solid lubricants have shown that at present there is no entirely satisfactory solid lubricant available for antifriction bearings. However, bonded solid lubricants give the best results. Bearings fitted with machined steel cages, with a hard coating of MoS_2 and dipped in a suspension of MoS_2 after assembly, are also effective. Bonded solid graphite lubricating films are used with bearings in CO_2 cooled reactors, since the maximum operating temperature of graphite is higher than that of MoS_2.

Recently some greases (see above) have reached a sufficient level of development to be employed as antifriction bearing lubricants in some reactors.

7.5.2.2. *Special Systems of Lubrication for Irradiated Environments.* In certain atomic power plants liquid sodium is used as a heat exchange medium and it has been found possible to use this fluid to lubricate the bearings of the pumps with which it is circulated throughout the installation. The most difficult problem associated with the use of this fluid is that of sealing it from its surroundings.

These installations must also function for years without attention, so that wear must be kept to an absolute minimum. The conventional bearing materials, normally containing high proportions of tin, antimony or lead cannot be used in these bearings, due to their low resistance to the corrosive action of liquid sodium. This is why austenitic stainless steel with 18% chromium and 8% nickel was used as bearing material [15].

The low viscosity and high thermal conductivity of liquid sodium do not permit the direct application of the principles of conventional lubrication to the design of bearings with which it is to be used.

It is however possible to design bearings using liquid sodium to operate hydrodynamically in the steady state. It is therefore necessary to establish the boundary lubricating properties of liquid sodium, and the best materials and surface finishes to be used with it, since the starting and stopping of the parent machine will remain the major sources of wear.

Experiments have therefore been carried out on a special machine in which the wear surfaces consist of two flat concentric rings sliding upon each other in a controlled atmosphere. The surface finish of the rings was varied from roughnesses of 10 μin to grooves of 0.00025/0.0005 in deep and a pitch of 0.0075 in [15].

It was found that the wear rate did not decrease with surface finish but on the contrary, improved when the rubbing surfaces were grooved. The explanation lies perhaps in the hydrodynamic effect of the liquid sodium trapped in the grooves. Similar experiments with water or mineral oils did not give the same results, and this is perhaps due to their much lower thermal conductivity.

In conclusion, stainless-steel bearing surfaces with liquid sodium lubrication can be expected to withstand moderate loads within the temperature range of 100—200°C, with moderate rates of wear and without the danger of catastrophic failure. The average rate of wear can be as little as 5 mg/cm² per day, which is very low when compared with the 600 mg/cm² per day obtained from the same surfaces lubricated with a medium-grade mineral oil [15].

There are several ways of avoiding direct contact between the bearings of the liquid metal circulating pumps and the high temperature irradiated fluid. This can be effected with electromagnetic pumps without bearings, or canned rotor pumps where the bearings are isolated from the pumped fluid. Freeze-seal pumps place the shaft bearings outside the shielding of the installation so that they are also isolated from the radiation flux [16].

The reactor control-rod drive mechanisms pose a difficult lubrication problem, and can be divided into classes [16]:

a) Mechanisms operating totally immersed in the primary coolant; in this case the bearings are lubricated by the surrounding fluid (the case of liquid sodium has been discussed in detail). Stellite ball-bearings lubricated by the coolant have also been found efficient in these cases.

b) Mechanisms only partially immersed, where some of the bearings are lubricated by the coolant, the rest being lubricated with radiation-resistant oils and greases.

c) Gas-immersed mechanisms which constitute the most trouble-some category from the lubrication point of view, due to their contact with high-temperature gases. When CO_2 is the coolant, soap-thickened greases are not recommended; greases with inorganic thickeners can be successfully utilized, or antifriction bearings constructed from corrosion resistant materials, running dry [17].

References

1. W. A. Gross, *Gas Film Lubrication*. John Wiley and Sons, Inc., New York, 1962.
2. V. N. Constantinescu, *Gas Lubrication*. Scripta Tehnica, Washington, D.C., 1968.
3. — *Proceedings of the First International Symposium on Gas-Lubricated Bearings*. Office of Naval Research, Washington, D.C., 1959.
4. N. S. Grassam, J. W. Powell, *Gas Lubricated Bearings*. Butterworths, London, 1964.
5. V. N. Constantinescu, *Aplicații industriale ale lagărelor cu gaze* (Industrial Applications of Gas Bearings), in Romanian. Editura Academiei, Bucharest, 1968.
6. W. F. Hughes, *Magnetohydrodynamic Lubrication and Application to Liquid Metals*. Sci. Lubr., **15**, *3*, 1963.
7. D. C. Kuzma, *The Magnetohydrodynamic Journal Bearing*. Trans. ASME, Journ. Basic, Eng., **85**, *3*, 1963.
8. V. N. Constantinescu, *On the Possibilities of the Magnetogasodynamic Lubrication*. Trans. ASME, Journ. Lubr. Techn., **89**, *3*, 1967.
9. J. D. McHugh, *Possibilities and Problems of the Magnetic and Electrostatic Bearings*. Machine Design, **36**, *26*, 1964.
10. F. J. Clauss, *Lubrication Under Space/Vacuum Conditions*. Sci. Lubr., **15**, *3*, 1963.
11. V. W. David, R. Irving, *Effects of Nuclear Radiation on Hydrocarbon Oils, Greases, and Some Synthetic Fluids*. Proceedings of the Conference on Lubrication and Wear, Paper 70, London, 1957.
12. D. J. Fischer, J. F. Zack, E. L. Warrick, *Radiation Stability of Silicone Greases*. Lubr. Eng., **15**, *10*, 1959.
13. C. G. Williams, *Lubrication in the Nuclear Age*. Sci. Lubr., **10**, *11*, 1958.
14. A. J. Marles, *The Lubrication of Anti-Friction Bearings in a Nuclear Power Station*. Sci. Lubr., **10**, November (Special Extra Issue), 1958.
15. R. B. Campbell, *Liquid Sodium as a Lubricant*. Proceedings of the Conference on Lubrication and Wear, Paper 56, London, 1957.
16. E. H. Okrent, *The Lubrication Requirement of Nuclear Powered Surface Vessels*. Lubr. Eng., **17**, *5*, 1961.
17. Al. Nica, *Sisteme noi de ungere a utilajelor industriale* (New Lubrication Systems for Industrial Equipment), in Rumanian. I.D.T., Bucharest, 1962.

Author index

Subject index

A

Absolute viscosity, 47
Adhesion (and friction), 8—15
Additives
    for mineral oils, 159—165
    for synthetic oils, 173—174
    for greases, 175—179
Adsorption (of gases and vapours), 39, 42—43, 228
Allen, Van (belt), 230
Amonton's law, 14, 45
Antiemulsion and antifoam additives, 164
Antifreeze additives, 164—165
Antifriction bearings (lubrication of), 150—153, 234
Antioxidant additives, 162, 175—177
Antiwear additives, 163, 177—178
Area
    of contact, 11, 14, 20
    of groove in the softer metal, 12
    supporting load area, 29
Aromatic compounds (resistance to radiation), 231—232
Automatic systems of lubrication
    with double line, 79—80
    with single line, 78—79

B

Bearing materials
    cermets, 196—197
    plastics, 188—191
    sintered metals, 193
    superalloys, 196
Borate esters, 169—170
Boundary conditions, 119—124
Boundary lubrication
    applications, 32—34
    generalities, 27—28
    mechanism of, 28—32
    transition to hydrodynamic lubrication, 34—35

C

Calculation
    of hydraulic seals, 96—99
    of lubrication systems with fluid lubricants, 48—62
    of lubrication systems with semifluid lubricants, 70—72
    of MHD bearings, 215—222
    of oil coolers, 110—115
    of oil flows, 119—128, 141, 144—146
    of spray lubricating systems, 85—86
Carbon (antifriction materials), 191—193
Cellulube fluids, 168
Centralized lubricating systems, 80—83
Centrifugal separators, 106—108
Chloride films, 160—161
Chlorofluorocarbon polymers, 171—172, 179
Coatings (antifriction), 184—187
Coefficient of friction
    in boundary lubrication, 30—31
    of dry surfaces, 8, 11, 13—14, 38
    in high vacuum, 228
    of lamellar solids, 43
Cold-welding, 9, 26,
Colloidal graphite, 192—193
Colour (of oils), 116
Consistency (greases), 68, 69
Contact lubrication, 40—41
Cooling devices, 115—116
Copper films, 44
Cordovolocnite (antifriction material), 188
Corrosion (fretting), 178—179
Cutting of metals
    lubrication in, 203—209
    wear of tools, 205—206

D

Deformation
    elastic, 8
    plastic, 11—12, 13—15

PRINTED IN RUMANIA